Pelican Books

Human Identity in the U

Gwen Bell is Associate Professor of Urban Affairs at the Graduate
School of Public and International Affairs at Pittsburgh University.
Through three academic degrees, a Fulbright Scholarship to
Australia, and five years of graduate teaching, she has pursued
her interest in the interrelationship of the natural and man-made
environments and their effect on human behaviour. In addition to
her teaching activities, Dr Bell is Associate Editor of the monthly
journal *Ekistics*, published at the Athens Ekistics Centre.

Jaqueline Tyrwhitt studied at the Architectural Association, the
London School of Economics, and the Technical Institute in Berlin.
She practised briefly as a landscape architect and then qualified in
Town and Country· Planning from A. E. E. Rowse's School of
Planning for National Development – an offshoot from the
Architectural Association. During the war, she took Mr Rowse's
place as Research Director of the Association for Planning and
Regional Development, organized a Correspondence Course in
Planning for servicemen and (immediately after the war) a crash
course for ex-servicemen, which created 177 new professional
members of the Town Planning Institute. From 1948 to 1955 she
was Visiting Professor at the New School of Social Research, Yale
University, and the University of Toronto, and from 1955 to 1969
Associate Professor at Harvard University. She met C. A. Doxiadis
when on a United Nations Mission to India, and in 1955 they jointly
founded the monthly journal *Ekistics* – an international review of the
problems and science of human settlements. Jaqueline Tyrwhitt's
publications include *Patrick Geddes in India* (1947), *Trees for Town
and Country* (with B. Colvin, 1949), *The Face of the Metropolis*
(with M. Meyerson, 1963), and the English translations of the works
of Sigfried Giedion.

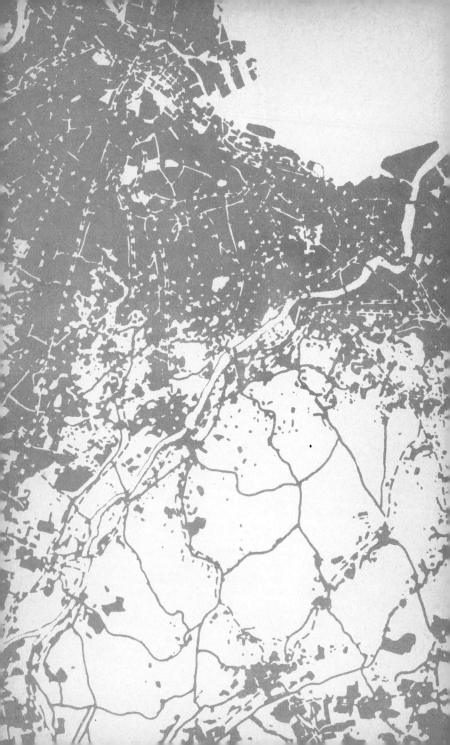

Human Identity in the Urban Environment

EDITED BY GWEN BELL
AND JAQUELINE TYRWHITT

PENGUIN BOOKS

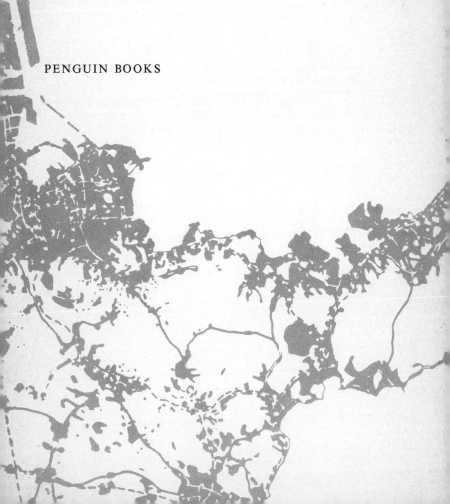

Penguin Books Ltd, Harmondsworth, Middlesex, England
Penguin Books Inc., 7110 Ambassador Road, Baltimore, Maryland 21207, U.S.A.
Penguin Books Australia Ltd, Ringwood, Victoria, Australia

First published 1972
Copyright © Gwen Bell and Jaqueline Tyrwhitt, 1972

Made and printed in Great Britain by
Butler & Tanner Ltd, Frome and London
Set in Lumitype Times

Contents

6 *Contents*

8   *Contents*

Acknowledgements and
List of Sources

PART ONE

1. Eugene P. Odum, 'The Strategy of Ecosystem Development', from *Science*, Vol. 164, No. 3877, pp. 262–70; *Ekistics* 173, pp. 234–8.

2. C. H. Waddington, 'Biology and Human Environment', from *Ekistics* 123, pp. 90–94; *Ekistics* 133, pp. 402–5.

3. Howard W. Mattson, 'Food for the World', from *International Science and Technology*, No. 48, 1965, pp. 28–39; *Ekistics* 132, pp. 332–6.

4. Arnold Toynbee, 'Has Man's Metropolitan Environment Any Precedents?', from *Ekistics* 133, pp. 385–7.

5. Luna B. Leopold, 'Landscape Aesthetics', from *Natural History*, October 1969, pp. 37–44; *Ekistics* 173, pp. 271–7.

6. M. G. Ionides, 'Piped Water Supplies for Ecumenopolis', from *Ekistics* 123, pp. 136–40; *Ekistics* 152, pp. 21–31.

7. B. T. Bower, G. P. Larson, A. Michaels, and W. M. Phillips, 'Waste Management', from New York Regional Plan Association Inc., *Bulletin*, No. 107; *Ekistics* 156, pp. 438–50.

8. John McHale, 'Global Ecology: Towards the Planetary Society', from *American Behavioral Scientist*, Vol. XI, No. 6, 1968, pp. 29–33; *Ekistics* 160, pp. 155–60.

PART TWO

9. C. A. Doxiadis, 'Anthropocosmos: The World of Man', from an address delivered upon the presentation of the third Aspen Award, Aspen Institute for Humanistic Studies, Aspen, Colorado, 29 July 1966; *Ekistics* 132, pp. 311–18.

10. Bertrand de Jouvenel, 'Utopia for Practical Purposes', from *Daedalus*, Vol. 94, No. 2, Spring 1965, pp. 437–53; *Ekistics* 115, pp. 325–9.

11. W. H. Auden, 'Culture and Leisure', from a lecture delivered at the Catholic University of America, 26 February 1966; *Ekistics* 144, pp. 418–20.

Planning Council of New York, Inc.; *Ekistics* 74, pp. 383–92; Part 2 from a background paper for the Third Session, United Nations Committee on Housing, Building, and Planning, New York, September 1965; *Ekistics* 121, pp. 325–39.

27. John Turner, 'Architecture That Works': Part 1 from *Ekistics* 112, pp. 152–5; Part 2 from *Architectural Design*, Vol. 38, August 1968, pp. 355–60; *Ekistics* 158, pp. 40–44.

28. Brent C. Brolin and John Zeisel, 'Mass Housing: Social Research and Design', extracted from their article 'Mass Housing: Social Research and Design' in the July/August 1968 issue of *Architectural Forum* (copyright © 1968 Whitney Publications, Inc.); *Ekistics* 158, pp. 51–5.

29. Team 10, 'The Role of the Architect in Community Building', from *Architectural Design*, December 1962, pp. 559–602; *Ekistics* 91, pp. 349–60. Also published in *Team 10 Primer*, ed. Alison Smithson, Architectural Press, London (undated).

30. N. Kurokawa, 'Architecture of the Road', translated by H. Oribe and Y. Sasaki from *Kenchiku Bunka*, January 1963; *Ekistics* 96, pp. 288–93.

31. Christopher Alexander, 'A City Is Not a Tree', from *Design*, No. 206, February 1966; *Ekistics* 139, pp. 344–8.

PART FIVE

32. Northeastern Illinois Planning Commission, 'The Plan Study: Methodology', from *Ekistics* 165, pp. 119–39.

33. Doxiadis Associates, 'The IDEA Method for Regional Planning', from *Ekistics* 153, pp. 185–95.

34. Donald G. Janelle, 'Spatial Reorganization: A Model and a Concept', from *Annals of the Association of American Geographers*, Vol. 59, No. 2, 1969, pp. 348–64; *Ekistics* 170, pp. 39–46.

35. Jean Gottmann, 'Urban Centrality and the Interweaving of Quaternary Activities', from *Ekistics* 174, pp. 322–31.

36. Delos Four, 'Need for More Balance in the Flow of Communications', from *Ekistics* 131, pp. 273–9. Buckminster Fuller extracts from Vision 65 Summary Lecture given at the International Center for the Communication Arts and Sciences, Southern Illinois University, October 1965, and published in *The American Scholar*, Vol. 35, No. 2, pp. 206–18; *Ekistics* 131, pp. 279–84. Marshall McLuhan extract from Delos One, *Ekistics* 95, p. 257.

PART SIX

37. C. Nagashima, 'Megalopolis in Japan', from *Ekistics* 140, pp. 6–14; *Ekistics* 152, pp. 83–95.

38. Richard L. Meier, 'Notes on the Creation of an Efficient Megalopolis: Tokyo', from *Ekistics* 138, pp. 294–307.

39. Richard L. Meier and Ikumi Hoshino, 'Cultural Growth and Urban Development: Inner Tokyo 1951–68', from *Ekistics* 155, pp. 390–94.

40. J. M. Richards, *Lessons from the Japanese Jungle*, from the *Listener*, 13 March 1969, pp. 339–40; *Ekistics* 165, pp. 75–7.

41. Jaqueline Tyrwhitt, 'The Pedestrian in Megalopolis: Tokyo', from *Ekistics* 147, pp. 73–9.

42. Koji Taira, 'Urban Poverty, Rag-Pickers, and the "Ants' Villa" in Tokyo', from *Economic Development and Cultural Change*, Vol. 17, No. 2, January 1969, pp. 155–77; *Ekistics* 166, pp. 163–7.

43. Masao Yamada, 'Approaches to the Twenty-First Century: A Development Policy for the Tokyo Metropolitan Region', from *Ekistics* 129, pp. 114–22.

44. R. Kakumoto, 'A Case for Satellite Cities of 300,000 in Japan', from *Chuo-Koron*, January 1966; *Ekistics* 146, pp. 17–24.

45. Kenzo Tange, 'Images of the Future Urban Environment', from *Ekistics* 150, pp. 289–91.

Introduction

In 1850 there were four cities of the world with more than one million people. In 1950 there were about a hundred cities with a million or more population. By 2000 − less than three decades away − there will be over 1,000 cities of this magnitude.

As these cities continue to grow they will coalesce into larger cities, called megalopolises. It is evident that the population of cities, just like the population of the world, will not suddenly stop growing. Indeed, the urban population is growing much faster than any other segment of the world. The question that must be faced is how these myriad cities can continue to develop at an accelerating rate without destroying all that we believe makes life worth living.

Although one might hope that there is an escape from the city, the web of urbanization already encompasses the globe. We, the editors, were confronted directly with this fact when we sought some escape to concentrate on the preparation of this book. We retired to the solitude of the rock-perched monastery of Kastriani, joined only by a narrow thread to the sparsely settled Aegean island of Kea. Here we seemed to have found refuge from all the effects of urbanization. The sky was the clearest blue, the air fresh with the scent of aromatic bushes. Then one day we clambered down the bluff to enjoy a swim. Great black globs of greasy oil scum fouled the shore. The residue of urbanization lay at our feet.

Already the island of Kea had been absorbed into the network of megalopolises. We needed no clearer evidence that a system must be found, and found soon, that can comprehensively and comprehendingly encompass the multi-interactions of man's environment. Only through such a system would man be able to find a personally satisfying life within the bounds of our urbanizing planet.

How had Kea, a small settlement of 5,000 people, become

enmeshed with megalopolis? First, it has been caught in the industrialized web of cities that stretches from the oil-rich nations of the
Middle East to Athens and across Europe to North America. There
is a second reason. One of the major industries of Kea is the manufacture of Christmas-tree decorations. Plastic is imported from Germany,
formed into decorations in Kea, and shipped to the United States for
sale. Thus, the welfare of this small island is tied to the production of
plastic in the West European megalopolis and to the demand for
Christmas decorations in the United States.

Hence, in Kea as in other settlements of the world, the human need
for solitude and the enjoyment of natural surroundings is competing
with the needs of industrialization. This web of interactions has two
dimensions; the interrelationships of settlements of all sizes; and the
interrelationships of all the components for maintaining urban life.

Thus, the world finds itself in the midst of a dilemma. Despite all
its technological advancement, its teeming warehouses of knowledge,
and its increasing mastery of outer space, can it indeed produce an
intra-space solution to population location and environmental
harmony?

There are substantial grounds for hope. Several dominant figures of
the first half of the twentieth century have emphasized the need for
the understanding of population characteristics, planning for future
growth, and the creation of programs for present action, and three of
them have provided tools which can make it possible to maintain
human identity throughout the urbanization process.

The larger question becomes: will such tools be used or simply
allowed to rust?

Around the turn of the century, Patrick Geddes, a Scottish botanist
better known as the 'father of town planning', developed the first
matrix for urban analysis. The second was the C.I.A.M. grid, invented
a generation later by Le Corbusier, a French architect and urbanist
who practised throughout the world. Then, in the mid 1950s, C. A.
Doxiadis conceived both 'Ekistics', the science of human settlements,
and its representation on a grid.

Symbolically, each of these matrices encompasses the totality for
analysis of urban problems and also sets the framework for new
developments. Such grids display any component within two dimen-

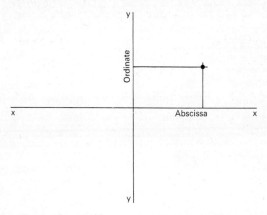

Figure 1. Coordinates for a grid.

sions at a point of intersection of abscissa and ordinate (Figure 1).

There are common traits in the three grids. The first two were totally unconnected, but both (the first certainly and the second probably) were derived from the work of the Frenchman Frederick Le Play (1806–82) who, although trained as a mining engineer, did pioneer work in the methodology of social research, particularly in the study of family budgets. Le Play emphasized the relationship between the family, its physical environment and its work patterns. *Lieu, Travail,* and *Famille* were cited as the three dominating forces of society.

This trilogy was directly taken over by Geddes as Place, Work, and Folk. The connection is less direct in Le Corbusier's four functions of land use: *Habiter, Travailler, Cultiver le corps et l'esprit,* and *Circuler.*

The Le Corbusier grid was first used as the standard key to a comparative analysis of thirty-three cities prepared by delegates from eighteen countries for the fourth C.I.A.M. (Congrès Internationeaux d'Architecture Moderne) held in 1934. This Congress produced the *Charte d'Athènes,* a series of statements and recommendations, in which the same four functions were used as the main heads. Among the audience at the final session of this Congress in Athens was a young Greek architect, C. A. Doxiadis. He was greatly impressed by the ideas put forward on this occasion, and twenty years later he developed the five ekistic elements: Nature, Man, Society, Shell, and Networks.

Thus the ordinates of the three grids are very similar:

Geddes	*Le Corbusier*	*Doxiadis*
Place	Recreation	Nature and Shell
Work	Working	Society
Folk	Living	Man
—	Transportation	Networks

It is the abscissa that differ.

Geddes's Diagrams

Patrick Geddes, who called his grids 'diagrams', operated them as true matrices: ordinate and abscissa were identical and the resulting nine squares represented the various relationships between the three concepts (Figure 2). For example, 'place work' represents natural resources, 'place folk' natives or neighbours, and 'work folk' the working population. The total represented a synthesis of interaction in one town.[1]

To Geddes, his diagrams were 'thinking machines' – means for checking that everything relevant had been taken into consideration. But Geddes was supremely interested in the improvement of the environment of towns. And from thinking he moved to action.

Geddes devised a way of organizing a four-fold diagram that

Figure 2. Patrick Geddes's basic diagram.

PLACE	Place Work	Place Folk
Work Place	WORK	Work Folk
Folk Place	Folk Work	FOLK

pointed the way to constructive action (Figure 3). Each quadrant of the diagram expresses an explicit component of the planning process. The first quadrant represents the present urban structure, and he called it 'acts'. The quadrant below it is the survey phase of planning, when the collection of data and its analysis are translated into 'facts'. The third moves to the area of reflective 'dreams', where policies and plans are evolved. Finally, the fourth emerges into executive 'deeds': operative programs for development. These would reappear as 'acts' in the first quadrant at the start of the following planning cycle. The key terminology changes for each phase, but remains parallel:

1	2	3	4
Acts	*Facts*	*Dreams*	*Deeds*
Place	Sense	Imagery	Achievement
Work	Experience	Ideation	Synergy
Folk	Feeling	Emotion	Ethnopolity

Thus, this 'thinking machine' became a tool to express the evolution of cities. Inherent within it was the notion of feedback: that every planned action would effect the following stage in the development of a city.

The C.I.A.M. Grid

Le Corbusier had a completely different goal for his C.I.A.M. grid, which he expressed when he first introduced it:

I am going to talk to you about a sort of poetry – the poetry of classification. . . . Mountains of paper impede the work of the urbanist. They are his enemy number one. . . . I determined to find some visual way to do away with these mountains of paper; for though the eye can register exceedingly quickly, the reading of reports is an extremely slow job. The problem was to create a tool. But though a tool can simplify the work, it can make no fine plans of itself. It can help one set down one's thought more rapidly or with greater precision, but it can never make fools intelligent. . . . All we ask of the C.I.A.M. grid is that it shall bring the intelligent points of a scheme immediately before the eyes, and that foolishness shall be as quickly apparent.[2]

Operative Acts : The Town — Executive Deeds : Utopia

PLACE	Place Work	Place Folk	Achieved Polity	Achieved Synergy	ACHIEVEMENT
Work Place	WORK	Work Folk	Synergized Polity	SYNERGY	Synergized Achievement
Folk Place	Folk Work	FOLK	ETHNOPOLITY (Love)	Politized Synergy (Wisdom)	Politized Achievement
Feeling Sense (Home)	Feeling Experience (Mastery)	FEELING	EMOTION (Mysticism)	Emotioned Ideation (Philosophy)	Emotioned Imagery (Poetry)
Experienced Sense	EXPERIENCE	Experienced Feeling (Folkways)	Ideated Emotion (Doctrine)	IDEATION (Science)	Ideated Imagery (Design)
SENSE	Sensed Experience	Sensed Feeling	Imaged Emotion (Symbol)	Imaged Ideation (Mathematics)	IMAGERY (Imagination)

Directive Facts : The School — Reflective Dreams : The Studio

Figure 3. Patrick Geddes's diagram.

Although Le Corbusier deliberately disassociated the C.I.A.M. grid from the processes of synthesis and design, he and his staff did use the grid as a tool in their work. The grid (Figure 4) was drawn up on the wall in Le Corbusier's Paris office and its spaces were used for displays of relevant aspects of his work on particular projects – such as the new capital city of the Punjab, Chandigarh. Along the abscissa, there is a sequence of headings intended to act as a check list for the practising architect-planner. The numbers listed beside each heading represent a simple code by which information could be recorded and retrieved.

In contrast to the complete feedback loop of Geddes's ever-spiralling thinking machine, the C.I.A.M. grid categorized feedback in its last two columns. Both of these efforts added new dimensions to the understanding of urban processes in the development of cities. And both had shortcomings. Both Geddes's diagrams and the C.I.A.M. grid were for individual places or projects without a clear way of transferring analysis between elements.

The Ekistic Grid

A major contribution of the ekistic grid[3] is that it incorporates a complete spectrum of the range of human settlements – from the single man to the world-encompassing ecumenopolis. This makes it a more powerful tool for urban analysis than the Geddes diagrams (which Geddes used as personal thinking machines) or the C.I.A.M. grid (which Le Corbusier used to classify the work of his architectural and planning practice). Both these grids could be used to analyse different aspects of a single particular settlement, but the ekistic grid can set this single settlement into the matrix of its total urban system, which probably includes both larger and smaller settlements. This overview enables a number of problems to be seen in a more meaningful context.

The first three of the fifteen 'ekistic units' that occupy the abscissa of the ekistic grid have a simple and obvious relationship, and have been assigned arbitrary population figures: man (1 person), room

	10 Environment Physical, Historic and Demographic Data	11 Land Use Rural and Urban, Existing and Projected	12 Building Volume 3-Dimensional City Structure	13 Community Facilities	14 Ethics and Aesthetics	15 Economic and Social Aspects
Living						
Working						
Recreation						
Transportation						
Miscellaneous						

	16 Legislation	17 Finance	18 Stages of Realization	19 Miscellaneous	20 Rational Reaction Client, Public, and Authorities	21 Emotional Reaction Client, Public, and Authorities
Living						
Working						
Recreation						
Transportation						
Miscellaneous						

Figure 4. The C.I.A.M. grid.

Community Scale	I	II	III	I	II	III	IV	V	VI	VII	VIII	IX	X	XI	XII
	1	2	3	4	5	6	7	8	9	10	11	12	13	14	15
Ekistic Units	Man	Room	Dwelling	Dwelling Group	Small Neighbourhood	Neighbourhood	Small Town	Town	Large City	Metropolis	Conurbation	Megalopolis	Urban Region	Urbanized Continent	Ecumenopolis
Nature															
Man															
Society															
Shells															
Networks															
Synthesis															
Population t (Thousands) m (Millions)	1	2	4	40	250	1.5t	7t	50t	300t	2m	14m	100m	700m	5,000m	30,000m

(left side label: Elements)

Ekistic Logarithmic Scale

Figure 5. The ekistic grid.

(2 persons), dwelling (4 persons). The average population figures given for the following twelve units start from 40 for the dwelling group and rise to 2,000,000 for the average metropolis and 14,000,000 for the conurbation. These are not unfamiliar scales of magnitude, but the next three columns denote the urban agglomerations that are now emerging: the megalopolis (100,000,000 people), the urbanized region, the urbanized continent and, finally, ecumenopolis, the world city of about 30,000 million people which is expected to represent the condition of the world in the twenty-first century (assuming we escape a totally catastrophic breakdown into barbarism).

The units increase in logarithmic progression by multiples of six or seven (see Table 1). This mathematical relationship of urban settlements was first noted by the central place theorists and particularly developed by Walter Christaller.[4] Christaller's field of study was south Germany, but a comparable study carried out a generation later in the Middle West of the U.S.A. showed a similar range of relationships.[5]

TABLE ONE

Average Population	Ratio	Log. 6	Ekistic Unit
1			Man
2	1 : 2	0·387	Room
4	1 : 2	0·387	Dwelling
40	1 : 10	1·286	Dwelling Group
250	1 : 6·25	1·023	Small Neighbourhood
1,500	1 : 6	1·000	Neighbourhood
7,000	1 : 6	1·000	Small Town (9,000?)
50,000	1 : 5·55	0·952	Town
300,000	1 : 6	1·000	Large City
2,000,000	1 : 6·66	1·059	Metropolis
14,000,000	1 : 7	1·086	Conurbation
100,000,000	1 : 7·14	1·097	Megalopolis
700,000,000	1 : 7	1·086	Urbanized Region
5,000,000,000	1 : 7·14	1·097	Urbanized Continent
30,000,000,000	1 : 6	1·000	Ecumenopolis

The names given to the ekistic units are oriented towards a western urbanized culture. None the less their relationships hold true even if one is considering a much more rural constellation of settlements. It is just that the names must be changed, not their positions in the scale. For instance, the urban dwelling group becomes a rural hamlet; the small neighbourhood becomes a small village; the characteristic urban neighbourhood a large village. In this context, the names describe free-standing settlements that form part of a geographically separated system of settlements, whereas in an urban setting they are the physically juxtaposed sub-units of a major settlement. One can liken the comparison to pulling the units apart, as though they were linked to one another by elastic bands. Even when the world reaches the stage of ecumenopolis, its components are likely to be identifiable at the scales of megalopolises, metropolises, and urban neighbourhoods.

The abscissa of ekistic units remains constant in all uses of the ekistic grid, and the most usual ordinate consists of the five ekistic elements, Nature, Man, Society, Shell, and Networks, with a sixth line denoting their synthesis. As this book is organized on the basis of these ekistic elements, they require some more detailed descriptions.

Nature, the first element, represents the ecosystem within which cities must exist. It involves a number of component processes including the hydrologic cycle, biosystems, airsheds, climatic zones, etc. Archaeological studies show that even primitive man with limited tools made profound changes in natural systems. Over-cultivation in the Thar desert of the Indian subcontinent and over-grazing in the Middle East are two examples of how early cultivations weighted the natural balance and tipped it towards an uninhabitable landscape. If such significant changes in the natural system could be brought about by such limited numbers of men, it seems logical to suppose that to-day's 3,600 million persons must have far greater effectiveness in fouling the planet. And, if the earth is to support 30,000 million people in the future, the interrelationships and ranges of adaptability of human settlements and natural processes must be very clearly understood and observed, for neither can survive without the other. At another level we cannot forget man's psychological and physical needs for contact with the world of nature.

Man himself is also constantly adapting and changing. The medical profession in its move from 'barbarism' to concepts of the constitution of the healthy individual, can contribute many important inputs to the better organization of urban life. Studies have shown that certain physical and psychological diseases are directly associated with urbanization. These include obesity, respiratory ailments, and alienation (anomie). This gives rise to many questions, such as whether it is possible for mankind to adapt to a completely urban world with no rural escapes; what urban densities 'are tolerable'; and how the city may be made a satisfactory environment for the growing child. Thus, just as forward-looking medical and public health schools find a need to study the city, city builders must turn to study man.

The realm of *society* comprises all those aspects of the urban scene that are commonly dealt with by sociologists, economists, and administrators: population trends, social customs, income and occupations, and the systems of urban government. In the context of *Human Identity in the Urban Environment*, the most urgent aspect of society seems to be the problem of the retention, or reorganization, of values inherent in independent small communities after these have become incorporated in megalopolis – in other words, the place of the neighbourhood in megalopolis.

Shell, or the built environment, is the traditional domain of the architectural and engineering professions. The aspect that comes to the forefront in this book is the problem of how mass-produced, anonymous housing can cater for the needs of very diverse individuals and family groupings. Where can man make his own mark? Where can he leave the touch of his own hand?

Networks provide the glue for all systems of urbanization. Their changes profoundly affect urban patterns and urban scale. We have only to think of the effect of the advent of the railroads, or of piped water supplies, or of the telephone, upon the extent, the texture, and the densities of human settlements. The increasingly rapid developments of all types of networks – coupled with population pressures – have been the most potent heralds of megalopolis. The enormous growth in the uses of energy for the communication of ideas has whetted man's appetite for participating in all sorts of things that were formerly outside his ken. The television screen has stimulated desires both to participate in new sports – skiing, etc. – and to participate in debates – political representation, etc. To respond to man's demands, transportation, communication, and utility networks must all expand even faster than the anticipated growth of settlements.

Synthesis arises from a consideration of the interactions of all the ekistic elements in terms of a single ekistic unit: for example, in this book the interactions of Nature, Man, Society, Shell, and Networks are considered in terms of megalopolis. Or synthesis can comprise a single ekistic element in terms of the whole range of ekistic units: for example, the effect of certain aspects of society (changes in the birth rate) or networks (advent of the automobile) upon all scales of human settlements. Again synthesis can arise from synergetic associations with the total result having positive benefits greater than the individual inputs; for example, a health facilities program and air pollution control in conjunction may lead to lower mortality rates than predicted by each of the independent programs.

But the ekistic elements are not the only items that can occupy the ordinate of the ekistic grid. Sometimes it is illuminating to relate the ekistic units with historic time (past, present, and future). This immediately points up the spectacular recent growth of megalopolises. Another time it may be helpful to use the traditional academic disciplinary fields (sociology, economics, political science, technology, the arts). Or the ordinate may be used for percentage ratings of a special factor, such as population types, housing types, etc. Experimentation can lead to many new and useful examples, and an ekistic grid with a blank ordinate is provided in Figure 6 for the reader to experiment with. Use of the ekistic grid in this way can serve as a means of opening up many insights into the processes of urbanization.

In summary, the two dimensions of the ekistic grid can encompass the developed and the undeveloped, the individual and the mass, the natural and the man-made, the spontaneous and the planned. In the use of the grid, comparison may relate local problems of a community to the range of ekistic problems found in similar sized settlements, or to similar problems as evidenced by settlements of other sizes. In this process universal issues may be distinguished from

Figure 6. Ekistic grid with blank ordinate for reader to experiment with.

Community Scale	I	II	III	I	II	III	IV	V	VI	VII	VIII	IX	X	XI	XII
	1	2	3	4	5	6	7	8	9	10	11	12	13	14	15
	Man	Room	Dwelling	Dwelling Group	Small Neighbourhood	Neighbourhood	Small Town	Town	Large City	Metropolis	Conurbation	Megalopolis	Urban Region	Urbanized Continent	Ecumenopolis
Population	1	2	4	40	250	1.5t	7t	50t	300t	2m	14m	100m	700m	5,000m	30,000m

t (Thousands)
m (Millions)

Ekistic Logarithmic Scale

parochial ones. Similarly, those actions which might have the most far-flung effects may be sorted from those that are most limited.

Ekistics and Urban Planning

The term Ekistics is derived from the ancient Greek adjective *Οἰκιστική*, which meant contributing to settling down in a dwelling or a city. Ekistics denotes both a specific settlement orientation and at the same time a wide field of interest, encompassing all those processes which have served to form settlements throughout history.

'Town and Country Planning', 'City Planning', or 'Regional Planning', as they are practised throughout the world, usually focus on predetermining those aspects of the city and region that can in fact be planned: the location of industrial zones, major public buildings, and public open spaces; the networks – highways, streets, and utilities; the sizes of land parcels; building regulations of residential areas; etc.

The technique of planning emphasizes a rational process which can lead to specific physical results. Theorists spell out this process as: identification of the problems; determination of policies for solution; consideration of priorities; and designation of action. The physical planner is trained to look ahead so that his proposals can deal with new problems at the moment they rise over the horizon and thus prevent them from developing into storms above our heads.

Urban planning became a profession with its own established standards and qualifications early in the present century, but physical planning is but one of a number of processes to be considered when arriving at an ekistic synthesis. Urban studies proceeded to penetrate into a number of other fields. The work of Christaller in Germany in geography and the work of Louis Wirth in Chicago[6] in sociology led to an urban orientation being included in these disciplines. As the problems of an ever-increasing urbanization became more acute, other professions followed, and urban studies are now included, for instance, in economics and law, anthropology and public health.

The Growth of Urbanization

Prior to the Industrial Revolution, rapid population growth inevitably resulted in the foundation of new settlements. Man was dependent upon food grown near at hand, and an overly large city exhausted local food supplies. Increase in population preceded the numerous Greek colonial settlements that were established all around the Mediterranean, the Roman settlements set up along the trade routes they opened across Europe, and the many new medieval towns of the eleventh and twelfth centuries (prior to the Black Death), as well as the colonization of the New World.

However, the Industrial Revolution was but one of three major coincidental revolutions. It was accompanied by equally dramatic revolutions in agricultural production and in transportation. This meant that the entire picture was changed. People were no longer forced out of the parent city. On the contrary, new populations could flock into them, following the pied piper of higher paid employment, and still be fed.

Yet the cities of the nineteenth century were totally unprepared for this great influx and Engels's descriptions of the living conditions in Manchester in 1844[7] depict problems as deplorable as those in Calcutta more than a century later.

First the idealists and the 'reformers', and then businessmen themselves recognized the need for powerful controls of land use if reasonable standards of living space were to be maintained for the population. But except for a few important experiments, action in the nineteenth century was confined to regulation of street widths and housing conditions. It was not until the twentieth century, after the first impetus of the Industrial Revolution had spent its force in Europe and immigration to the New World had subsided, that the first town-planning acts started to come on to the statute books of the western countries.

These were timid affairs mainly designed for the prevention of worse abuses than those that had already occurred, and for preservation of the health, safety, and welfare of the urban population. They were born from fear and anxiety, and bore little or no relation to the major problems posed by new technologies or to new population expansions in the immediate future.

A summary of the sequence of concepts and action in Britain may be used to illustrate this general trend. New small-scale, self-contained industrial settlements had been advocated in Britain from the time of Robert Owen, 1816, onward: the notion gradually becoming more formalized following several pioneering experiments. Then, four generations later, in 1946, the New Towns Act gave official sanction to the realization of a concept that was by then obsolete in terms of its scale and its ideology in relation to the actual problems of the country at that moment in time.

In 1913 Patrick Geddes had written his major work, *Cities in Evolution* (published in 1915), in which he referred to the growth of conurbations – groupings of metropolises ranging from 10 to 20 million people. About a generation later, a growing consensus of informed opinion had come to the conclusion that 'garden cities' of 25,000–50,000 population could not provide an urban milieu able to respond to contemporary economic and social needs. The figures suggested generally hovered around the 250,000 mark. But these voices were unheard. It was only after the mid century, when a number of the small-sized 'mark one' new towns had been built, that these ideas began to attract public attention; and the 1960s saw several plans (still on paper) for new 'counter-magnet' cities of 250,000–500,000.

But the rate of change is still accelerating. All indications point to an era of 'megalopolitan' growth before the world can – hopefully – steady itself at a new level of several times its present population: i.e. ecumenopolis. A handful of new counter-magnet cities of half a million are likely to make no more impact upon this rapid urban expansion than the early garden cities exerted upon the square miles of inter-war suburban sprawl.

Our desperate need for the last decades of this century is to establish some easily understandable and implementable techniques for handling very large-scale developments of industrially produced housing, educational facilities, and entertainment centres; dangerous and noise-producing transportation routes; and large tracts of industrial plants. Necessarily, this means acceptance of a long-term integrated approach

– an ekistic approach – that is considerably broader than the traditional approach of the planning profession.

Definitions of Megalopolis

As already noted, the early growth of metropolises during the first half of the nineteenth century was directly related to developments of modes of transportation – particularly railways – which made it possible to supply the needs of their many new inhabitants. Obviously, megalopolis demands a much more intricate and far-flung transportation system. A metropolis of 2,000,000 people may have a radius of ten miles and a throughway or transit system that can enable access to the centre from the periphery in less than half an hour. However, the megalopolis may have ten times as many people and its length may be ten times the radius of the metropolis, even though its width may only be ten to twenty miles. Associated with it are new developments in mass transportation which can already traverse the length of a megalopolis in less than half a day: examples include the Tokaido Express, a train that traverses the length of the Japanese megalopolis in four to five hours, and the frequent aeroplane shuttle services between the major centres of the eastern megalopolis of the United States.

The Tokaido megalopolis of Japan, which already contains over 50,000,000 people, is the largest megalopolis in the world, although the megalopolis that runs along the eastern seaboard of the United States was the first to be identified and described. It was in 1961 that the French geographer, Jean Gottmann, used the word 'megalopolis' – 'as a geographical place name for the unique cluster of metropolitan areas of the Northeastern seaboard of the United States'.[8]

However, the use of the term 'megalopolis' was not entirely new. During the three years, 371–69 B.C., the Arcadians of ancient Greece built a new capital in the central Peloponnese which they called Ἡ μεγάλη πόλις (the large city). When this city was later conquered by the Romans it became known as 'Megalopolis'. The lavishness of its layout and its frequent vicissitudes caused it to be referred to in a Greek comedy as 'Megalopolis, the large city is a large solitude' (quoted by Strabo, 8.8.1). Today this Megalopolis is a small town of 2,000 inhabitants.

Prior to 1960 several writers, for example H. G. Wells, Patrick Geddes, and Lewis Mumford, had predicted the development of huge, composite settlements. Thus, Gottmann's definitions and description of a modern megalopolis led others to apply his parameters in identifying this phenomenon elsewhere in the world.

Gottmann described two variables which set off megalopolis from smaller settlements: density and interconnections. He delimited the area of study as having over 100 people per square mile and being adjacent to existing metropolitan centres of over 1,000,000 inhabitants. Thus, the area which he identified as megalopolis was a rather narrow belt of high urbanization, stretching from south of Washington to north of Boston, with tentacles reaching further south towards Portsmouth, Virginia, and further north towards Portland, Maine.

Gottmann did not quantify his second parameter of interconnections. But he considered them essential for the understanding of the phenomenon of megalopolis, stating: 'the key to most of the questions involved in this study of megalopolis lies in the interrelationships between the forces and processes at work within the area'.[9]

A few years later, John Papaioannou of the Athens Centre of Ekistics devised a formula that took account of both Gottmann's parameters.* Using this formula and data applicable to about 1960, he delimited thirteen true megalopolises (Table 2). Three of these already had more than 35,000,000 people in 1966: the Japanese megalopolis, including Tokyo, Nagoya, Osaka, and Kitakyushu;

---

* Definition of a megalopolis: a megalopolitan grouping is called a true megalopolis if the strength (S) in any one of its links is equal or larger than 4·00, according to the following formula:

$$D = 100 \cdot {}^2P \cdot ({}^22)^{4-S} \cdot ({}^42)^{N+T}$$
$$P = {}^2P_1P_2$$

when D represents the distance between two centres; P their population; N is a factor depending on the number of units between the two centres; T is the transportation factor. See J. Papaioannou, 'Megalopolis, a First Definition', A.C.E. Research Report, No. 2, 1967; *Ekistics*, No. 152, July 1968.

TABLE TWO

Megalopolises in 1966

Megalopolises	Popula-tion (in millions)	Area (in 1,000 sq. km.)	Density (persons per hectare)	Number of Centres
(a) More than two centres				
1. Japan: Tokyo–Yahata, 1966 Tokyo, Nagoya, Osaka, *Kitakyushu*.	69·2	76·0	9·10	4
2. Rhine: *Randstadt*, *Ruhr*, *Frankfurt*, *Mannheim*, Stuttgart, Hamburg, Berlin, *Leipzig*, Brussels, *Lille*, Paris, (Hanover, 1973).	60·5	79·37	7·63	11
3. U.S.A.: Eastern Seaboard Boston, New York, Philadelphia, Baltimore, Washington.	37·0	138·6	2·67	5
4. English: London, Birmingham, *Manchester*, *Newcastle*.	30·0	29·8	10·05	4
5. U.S.A.: Great Lakes, 1965 Milwaukee, Chicago, Detroit, Cleveland, Pittsburgh.	24·5	91·6	2·67	5
(b) Two centres only				
6. China: Yang Tse Shanghai, Nanking.	20·1	49·6	4·05	2
7. China: Peking Peking, Tientsin.	12·7	15·95	7·96	2
8. China: Manchuria Shenyang, (Anshan), Dairen.	12·0	19·0	6.32	2
9. U.S.A.: Californian Los Angeles, San Diego.	8·6	14·8	5·81	2
10. Egypt: Nile Cairo, Alexandria.	7·8	12·2	6·39	2
11. Hong Kong: Hong Kong, Canton.	7·0	13·0	5·39	2
12. Javanese: Djakarta, Bandoeng.	6·5	9·75	6·66	2
13. North Italian: Milan, Turin.	4·6	6·18	7·44	2

Notes:
1. Undated megalopolises, 1960 figures.
2. Future centres (in brackets) excluded from calculations.
3. Composite settlements in italics = a group of settlements centring on the one named.

Figure 7. Megalopolises A.D. 1966–2000.

Manchurian MG

Japanese MG

Hong Kong MG

Peking MG

Yang Tse MG

Javanese MG

Nile MG

Rhine MG

English MG

Italian MG

Great Lakes MG

Eastern Seaboard MG

Californian MG

1956   Megalopolis
1970
1980
2000   Probable
2000   Doubtful

the Rhine megalopolis spreading from Paris to Hamburg and Stuttgart to Rotterdam; and the U.S. eastern seaboard megalopolis which was described by Gottmann.

How to Use This Book

It is probably apparent by now that a major problem of the last third of this century will be how to ease the transition to a megalopolitan way of life for many millions of people throughout the world. As we noted in the opening paragraphs of this Introduction, the advent of megalopolis has repercussions that affect all scales of settlements, down to small hamlets on seemingly remote islands. No one, nowhere, can remain immune. The fear is that such large increases in the numbers of people and in the sizes of settlements may lead to a more regimented form of human existence. This is why Parts One to Five of this book place great emphasis upon 'the human community'. This represents the scale of the traditional 'small town' on the ekistic grid and the repeating component of any large urban complex. It is an area in which man-without-the-machine can be master. No part of the human community is beyond easy walking distance, yet it is large enough to meet the daily needs of the 'shut-ins', whether they be small children and their mother, or the aged or invalids.

The two themes of the megalopolitan scale and the dignity of the individual weave in and out of the first five parts of this book, which are composed of an anthology of articles selected from the annals of the journal of *Ekistics*. The five parts follow the headings of the five ekistic elements: Nature, Man, Society, Shell, and Networks. They are designed to be read in this order, starting with 'Nature' – the earliest and most fundamental feature of the planet – and ending with 'Networks' – the most technological and complex of man's large-scale manipulations of nature. Articles in both these sections focus mainly on megalopolis, rather than on human identity. Between them come the three human-oriented sections – Man, Society, and Shell.

But although the articles grouped under each of these five headings compose a fairly consecutive story in themselves, many articles also refer across to one or more of the other sections. Thus if, for instance, a reader is particularly interested in the societal aspects of human identity in megalopolis, he will turn to the section on Society, and its introduction will also draw his attention to several additional articles that appear under other headings.

In Part Six of the book, which is devoted to Synthesis, a different approach has been taken. The phenomenon of megalopolis is so new that the editors were faced with the alternative of assembling a number of theoretic statements, or of attempting to illustrate the process of arriving at a synthesis in a single megalopolis. They chose the latter, and as a case study they selected the largest of the existing megalopolises: the Tokaido megalopolis of Japan. With its ancient culture and singularly rapid technological development, the Tokaido megalopolis provides a unique bridge between the developed and the developing worlds, rural and urban economies, and the Oriental and Occidental ways of life. In several respects it may be symbolic of the more distant urban future of ecumenopolis, when all parts of the globe will become linked to a single interlocking urban system, within which each individual can achieve his own identity.

NOTES

1. Patrick Geddes, *Cities in Evolution*, London, 1915; revised edition 1948; original reprinted 1968.

2. Le Corbusier, 'Description of the C.I.A.M. Grid, Bergamo 1949', in *The Heart of the City*, ed. J. Tyrwhitt, J. L. Sert, and E. N. Rogers, Lund Humphries, London, 1951.

3. C. A. Doxiadis, 'Order in the Field of Ekistics', *Ekistics* 110, January 1965, pp. 2–3; also C. A. Doxiadis, *Ekistics*, Hutchinson, London, 1968.

4. Walter Christaller, *Die zentralen Orte in Suddeutschland*, Jena, 1933; trans. Carlisle W. Baskin, *Central Places in Southern Germany*, Prentice Hall, New Jersey, 1966.

5. Brian J. L. Berry, *Geography of Market Centres and Retail Distribution*, Englewood Cliffs, N.J., 1967.

6. Louis Wirth, *On Cities and Social Life*, selected papers ed. Albert J. Reiss, Phoenix, Chicago, 1964.

7. F. Engels, *Condition of the Working Classes in England in 1844*, London (reprinted), 1952.

8. Jean Gottmann, *Megalopolis: The Urbanized Northeastern Seaboard of the United States*, M.I.T. Press, Cambridge, Mass., 1961, p. 4.

9. ibid., p. 9.

Part One. Nature: The Living Environment

Introduction

The developing megalopolises do not only mean an increasing number of people and an increasing number of buildings. They also involve an increasing encroachment on the natural environment – near-by agricultural land and forests are either built over or they become recreation areas; near-by rivers become polluted and so does the air. The megalopolises are not only polluting themselves but are also creating toxic situations which upset natural cycles in places quite remote from them. Urban encroachments upon the natural environment and urban pollution of air and water are not new phenomena in themselves, but the advent of megalopolis means they are occurring on quite a new scale: a scale that threatens the natural balance of the ecosystem. If the world is to survive as a habitable planet, then man must apply his intellect to the task of rectifying this balance.

In the second half of the twentieth century we are going through a transitional period, from a world population size that could treat nature as an exploitive environment, and still live, to a world population size that must treat nature as a system which requires constant maintenance, or expire. Professor Odum divides nature into four conceptual zones: agriculturally productive areas; protective environments; urbanized and industrial landscapes; and compromise, transitional zones. Each of these zones has a function to play, for as he says, 'the landscape is not just a supply depot but is also the *oikos* – the home – in which we must live'. Later he notes that man must be seen as 'a part of, not apart from, the environment'.

The eight articles in Part One touch on each of Odum's four divisions of nature: Waddington and Mattson consider the agricultural productive areas; Toynbee and Leopold the protective environments; Ionides and Bower the urbanized landscapes; and McHale addresses general problems of interaction and the transition from yesterday's world (in which natural resources were seemingly inexhaustible) to the world of tomorrow, when 'the resources of the planet can no more belong, by geographical chance, to any individual, corporation, country, or national group than the air we breathe'.

The Productive Environment

Professor Waddington shows why it is that so much potential productivity is lost on the path from the primary producers (plants) to the ultimate consumer (man): from the seed sown in the ground to the food we eat. He introduces us to the complicated hierarchical network of the food web, and then points out how the interrelation of animals and plants is like a spider's web, in which if you pull only one strand nothing much happens. The whole resilient, interlocking complex of the biological system has evolved with the ability to meet 'unforeseen challenges', and he suggests that this aspect merits very careful study by ekisticians.

Although man has probed into the natural environment with oil-drilling rigs, disturbed it by adding chemicals to the air, and altered it by diverting water courses, the natural structure has a built-in ability to return to a state of equilibrium. This is not a static condition but 'a definite pathway of change in time'. However, if changes are too great or happen too suddenly, the system may no longer be able to return to its 'pathway' and a sequence of unforeseen events may be put in motion.

In the sixties, signs appeared in a variety of places that this was occurring. Air polluted by industries in England was blown to timber stands in Scandinavia, causing them to deteriorate. Urban wastes dumped into estuaries reduced certain fish species in the ocean. Such examples, which could be multiplied, show the special concern which must be taken in regard to buffering the urbanized environment from the productive environment. Man must endeavour to understand the ekistic relations of the natural and man-made systems so as to identify critical thresholds that must be respected.

It is generally accepted that the growing world population will certainly run into serious difficulties in respect to supplies of food and water. The question of how the world's needs are to be met is still open. Both Waddington and Mattson discuss the relative efficiency of various sources of nourishment. For example, livestock are far less efficient producers of protein than are fish or oil seeds, since 90 per cent of everything that the livestock eat is used to keep them warm and to give them enough energy to move around. The authors consider the possibilities of developing livestock foodstuffs that do not compete with anything edible by man, as well as the possibilities of altering man's preference from animal products to more efficiently produced protein foods. However, changes in food habits normally take generations to become widespread, and Waddington predicts that man will continue to use agriculturally derived food for the next hundred years.

Howard Mattson is even more explicit about man's conservatism, and he also emphasizes that the law of diminishing returns makes it very difficult to extend the cultivated landscape much beyond its present limits. This extension is discouraged by Odum who stresses the positive value of 'waste places' or 'unproductive' landscapes as 'essential life-cycle resources, not to mention recreational and aesthetic needs'. The relative sizes of these different land areas on the surface of the globe can be seen in a chart prepared for the City of the Future project at the Athens Centre of Ekistics (Figure 1). The main

Figure 1. World land divisions.

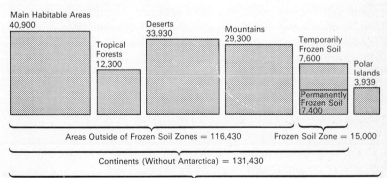

Main Habitable Areas 40,900

Tropical Forests 12,300

Deserts 33,930

Mountains 29,300

Temporarily Frozen Soil 7,600

Permanently Frozen Soil 7,400

Polar Islands 3,939

Areas Outside of Frozen Soil Zones = 116,430 Frozen Soil Zone = 15,000

Continents (Without Antarctica) = 131,430

Land (Without Antarctica) = 135,369

habitable area of 40,900 square kilometres includes urban and agriculturally productive areas; its extension into the areas of tropical
forests, deserts, mountains, tundra, ice caps, or the 350,200 square
kilometres of ocean will be extremely limited.

Mattson adds that the size of the new populations – especially in
the developing countries –precludes them from relying on food grown
elsewhere on the globe: 'ships and harbour facilities, to say nothing
of distribution facilities, couldn't handle the tonnages involved. The
bulk of the new supplies *must* be generated within the hungry nations
themselves'. This means the development of far more intensive agricultural practices upon the already demarcated arable areas of the
earth.

The Protective Environment

We turn to another aspect of nature: the protection of the so-called
'natural' environment ('so-called' because, as Waddington in particular notes, all major civilizations live in man-made landscapes).

Arnold Toynbee describes how man has always desired to escape
from the city from time to time. Before the nineteenth century cities
'too big to escape from on foot' were rare exceptions, but then, for
several decades, the urban man was trapped, for 'only a privileged
minority could afford to buy even a third-class railway ticket to a
destination in the open country'. As incomes rose and automobile
ownership became more and more common, the situation changed
but 'in conquering the countryside, the city's escaping urban prisoners
are transforming the countryside'. This unwitting destruction of the
thing they love is the dilemma that now confronts the world. How can
'town and country coexist in a mutually beneficial symbiosis' under
the conditions of tomorrow?

Luna Leopold sets forth one approach to getting down to operational details. He suggests that a rational planning approach should
be applied to the selection of specific natural areas for preservation.
Thus, he presents a method that can determine the recreational
quality of a natural area based on its physical, biological, and human
interest features.

The examples tested by Leopold were all river valleys, and indeed water, in the form of rivers, lakes, or the seaside, is one of nature's strongest attractions to the urban dweller. Fresh water is also one of the natural commodities that is going to be in increasingly short supply as megalopolises extend across the earth.

Urban-Industrial Environment

The natural watersheds of cities have in the past been the source of their fresh water supplies and the river system the deposit for their waste disposal. But with the growth of megalopolises, the water catchment areas of each of its urban components begin to overlap, thus creating water shortages. Similarly, the waste disposal capabilities of the river system begin to be taxed beyond their capacity for regeneration. This situation creates an apparent drought for the urban population, although the rainfall and actual water supply have not changed.

The problem of large-scale urban water supplies is discussed by M. G. Ionides and the parallel problem of the disposal of urban wastes is presented by the New York Regional Plan Association. Both come to the same conclusion. Megalopolises must develop closed systems re-using both their water and their waste materials. Ionides considers that present technologies are only in the equivalent of the 'hunting and mining' phase in connection with the re-use of water resources. Metropolises and megalopolises extend their tentacles farther and farther out into the countryside to capture new water supplies and find new waste disposal dumps, butchering the countryside in the process. As we come to adopt any one of the more efficient systems of water supply suggested by M. G. Ionides, these tentacles will become retracted and adequate water resources ensured both to the rural countryside (and agriculture) and to the city dwellers.

Compromise Environments

Even if a megalopolis develops a closed system of water supply and re-use of waste disposal, it can never, in itself, become a closed system. The very basis of megalopolises is an open system of communications that interconnect physically and electronically across their productive hinterlands and protective natural areas. As John McHale notes, many of their pollution problems already affect areas well beyond their bounds and − especially in the case of air pollution − can eventually affect the climatic balance of the world itself. The development of megalopolises thus demands not only their consideration and treatment as a total entity for all planning purposes, but also a responsible attitude towards their relations with the rest of the world, and a realization of the world itself as a natural system.

The days of implementing rigid plans disappeared with the small town. Now, in an era of huge and complex urban areas we must, as Professor Waddington puts it, design something in the spirit of the natural biological process: 'something which is sufficiently flexible and resistant to change and to catastrophe, to be able to make quite a good job of it, even if the world does not turn out as you thought it was going to'.

1. The Strategy of Ecosystem Development

EUGENE P. ODUM

The principles of ecological succession bear importantly on the relationships between man and nature. The framework of successional theory needs to be examined as a basis for resolving man's present environmental crisis.

As viewed here, ecological succession involves the development of ecosystems; it has many parallels in the developmental biology of organisms, and also in the development of human society. The ecosystem, or ecological system, is considered to be a unit of biological organization made up of all of the organisms in a given area (that is, 'community') interacting with the physical environment so that a flow of energy leads to characteristic trophic structure and material cycles within the system.

Definition of Succession

Ecological succession may be defined in terms of the following three parameters.[1] (1) It is an orderly process of community development that is reasonably directional and, therefore, predictable. (2) It results from modification of the physical environment by the community, that is, succession is community-controlled even though the physical environment determines the pattern, the rate of change, and often sets limits as to how far development can go. (3) It culminates in a stabilized ecosystem in which maximum biomass (or high information content) and symbiotic function between organisms are maintained per unit of available energy flow. In a word, the 'strategy' of succession as a short-term process is basically the same as the 'strategy' of

TABLE ONE

A Tabular Model of Ecological Succession: Trends to be Expected in the Development of Ecosystems

Ecosystem Attributes	Developmental Stages	Mature Stages
Community Energetics		
1. Gross production/community respiration (P/R ratio)	Greater or less than 1	Approaches 1
2. Gross production/standing crop biomass (P/B ratio)	High	Low
3. Biomass supported/unit energy flow (B/E ratio)	Low	High
4. Net community production (yield)	High	Low
5. Food chains	Linear, predominantly grazing	Weblike, predominantly detritus
Community Structure		
6. Total organic matter	Small	Large
7. Inorganic nutrients	Extrabiotic	Intrabiotic
8. Species diversity — variety component	Low	High
9. Species diversity — equitability component	Low	High
10. Biochemical diversity	Low	High
11. Stratification and spatial heterogeneity (pattern diversity)	Poorly organized	Well-organized
Life History		
12. Niche specialization	Broad	Narrow
13. Size of organism	Small	Large
14. Life cycles	Short, simple	Long, complex
Nutrient Cycling		
15. Mineral cycles	Open	Closed
16. Nutrient exchange rate, between organisms and environment	Rapid	Slow
17. Role of detritus in nutrient regeneration	Unimportant	Important

Ecosystem Attributes	Developmental Stages	Mature Stages
Selection Pressure		
18. Growth form	For rapid growth (r-selection)	For feedback control (K-selection)
19. Production	Quantity	Quality
Overall Homeostasis		
20. Internal symbiosis	Undeveloped	Developed
21. Nutrient conservation	Poor	Good
22. Stability (resistance to external perturbations)	Poor	Good
23. Entropy	High	Low
24. Information	Low	High

long-term evolutionary development of the biosphere – namely, increased control of, or homeostasis with, the physical environment in the sense of achieving maximum protection from its perturbations. The strategy of 'maximum protection' (that is, trying to achieve maximum support of a complex biomass structure) often conflicts with man's goal of 'maximum production' (trying to obtain the highest possible yield). Recognition of the ecological basis for this conflict is, I believe, a first step in establishing rational land-use policies.

Changes that occur in major structural and functional characteristics of a developing ecosystem are listed in Table 1. Twenty-four attributes of ecological systems are grouped, for convenience of discussion, under six headings. Trends are emphasized by contrasting the situation in early and late development. The degree of absolute change, the rate of change, and the time required to reach a steady state may vary not only with different climatic and physiographic situations, but also with different ecosystem attributes in the same physical environment. Where good data are available, rate-of-change curves are usually convex, with changes occurring most rapidly at the beginning, but bimodal or cyclic patterns may also occur.

Diversity and Succession

Perhaps the most controversial of the successional trends pertain to the complex and much discussed subject of diversity. It is important to distinguish between different kinds of diversity indices, since they may not follow parallel trends in the same gradient or developmental series. Four components of diversity are listed in Table 1, items 8 to 11.

While an increase in the variety of species together with reduced dominance by any one species or small group of species (that is, increased evenness) can be accepted as a general probability during succession, there are other community changes that may work against these trends. An increase in the size of organisms, an increase in the length and complexity of life histories, and an increase in interspecific competition that may result in competitive exclusion of species (Table 1, items 12 to 14) are trends that may reduce the number of species that can live in a given area.

Thus, whether or not species diversity continues to increase during succession will depend on whether the increase in potential niches resulting from increased biomass, stratification (Table 1, item 11), and other consequences of biological organization exceeds the counter-effects of increasing size and competition. No one has yet been able to catalogue all the species in any sizeable area, much less follow total species diversity in a successional series.

Species variety, equitability, and stratification are only three aspects of diversity which change during succession. Perhaps an even more important trend is an increase in the diversity of organic compounds, not only of those within the biomass but also of those excreted and secreted into the media (air, soil, water) as by-products of the increasing community metabolism.

The cause-and-effect relationship between diversity and stability is not clear and needs to be investigated from many angles. If it can be shown that biotic diversity does indeed enhance physical stability in the ecosystem, or is the result of it, then we would have an important guide for conservation practice. Preservation of hedgerows, woodlots, non-economic species, non-eutrophicated waters, and other biotic variety in man's landscape could then be justified on scientific as well as aesthetic grounds, even though such preservation often must result in some reduction in the production of food or other immediate consumer needs. In other words, is variety only the spice of life, or is it a necessity for the long life of the total ecosystem comprising man and nature?

Relevance of Ecosystem Development Theory to Human Ecology

Figure 1 depicts a basic conflict between the strategies of man and of nature. The goal of agriculture or intensive forestry, as now generally practised, is to achieve high rates of production of readily harvestable products with little standing crop left to accumulate on the landscape – in other words, a high P/B efficiency. Nature's strategy, on the other hand, as seen in the outcome of the successional process, is directed towards the reverse efficiency – a high B/P ratio. This is shown by the relationship at the right in Figure 1. Man has generally been preoccupied with obtaining as much 'production' from the landscape as possible, by developing and maintaining early successional types of ecosystems, usually monocultures. But, of course, man does not live by food and fibre alone; he also needs a balanced CO_2–O_2 atmosphere, the climatic buffer provided by oceans and masses of vegetation, and clean (that is, unproductive) water for cultural and industrial uses. Many essential life-cycle resources, not to mention recreational and aesthetic needs, are best provided for man by the less 'productive' landscapes. In other words, the landscape is not just a supply depot but is also the *oikos* – the home – in which we must live. Until recently mankind has more or less taken for granted the gas-exchange, water-purification, nutrient-cycling, and other protective functions of self-maintaining ecosystems, chiefly because neither his numbers nor his environmental manipulations have been great enough to affect regional and global balances. Now, of course, it is painfully evident that such balances are being affected, often detrimentally. The 'one problem, one solution approach' is no longer adequate and must

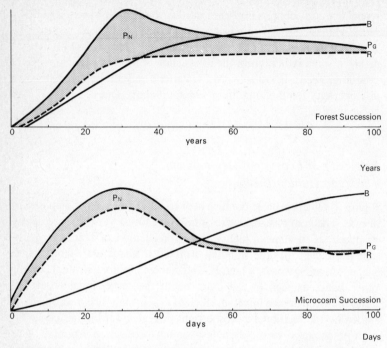

Figure 1. Comparatives of the energetics of succession in a forest and a laboratory microcosm. P_G gross production; P_N net production; R total community respiration; B total biomass.

be replaced by some form of ecosystem analysis that considers man as a part of, not apart from, the environment.

The most pleasant and certainly the safest landscape to live in is one containing a variety of crops, forests, lakes, streams, roadsides, marshes, seashores, and 'waste places' – in other words, a mixture of communities of different ecological ages. As individuals we more or less instinctively surround our houses with protective, non-edible cover (trees, shrubs, grass) at the same time that we strive to coax extra bushels from our cornfield. We all consider the cornfield a 'good thing', of course, but most of us would not want to live there, and it would certainly be suicidal to cover the whole land area of the biosphere with cornfields, since the boom and bust oscillation in such a situation would be severe.

The basic problem facing organized society boils down to determining in some objective manner when we are getting 'too much of a good thing'. This is a completely new challenge to mankind because, up until now, he has had to be concerned largely with too little rather than too much. Thus, concrete is a 'good thing', but not if half the world is covered with it. Insecticides are 'good things', but not when used, as they now are, in an indiscriminate and wholesale manner.

The general relevance of ecosystem development theory to landscape planning can, perhaps, be emphasized by the 'mini-model' of Table 2, which contrasts the characteristics of young and mature-

TABLE TWO

*Contrasting Characteristics of Young and
Mature-Type Ecosystems*

Young	Mature
Production	Protection
Growth	Stability
Quantity	Quality

type ecosystems in more general terms than those provided by Table 1. It is mathematically impossible to obtain a maximum for more than one thing at a time, so one cannot have both extremes at the same time and place. Since all six characteristics listed in Table 2 are desirable in the aggregate, two possible solutions to the dilemma immediately suggest themselves. We can compromise, so as to provide moderate quality and moderate yield on all the landscape, or we can deliberately plan to compartmentalize the landscape, so as to simultaneously maintain highly productive and predominantly protective types as separate units subject to different management strategies (strategies ranging, for example, from intensive cropping on the one hand to wilderness management on the other).

The Compartment Model

Successful though they often are, compromise systems are not suitable nor desirable for the whole landscape. More emphasis needs to be placed on compartmentalization, so that growth-type, steady-state, and intermediate-type ecosystems can be linked with urban and industrial areas for mutual benefit. Knowing the transfer coefficients that define the flow of energy and the movement of materials and organisms (including man) between compartments, it should be possible to determine, through analog-computer manipulation, rational limits for the size and capacity of each compartment. We might start, for example, with a simplified model, shown in Figure 2, consisting of four compartments of equal area, partitioned according to the basic biotic-function criterion – that is, according to whether

Figure 2. Compartment model of the basic kinds of environment required by man, partitioned according to ecosystem development and life-cycle resource criteria.

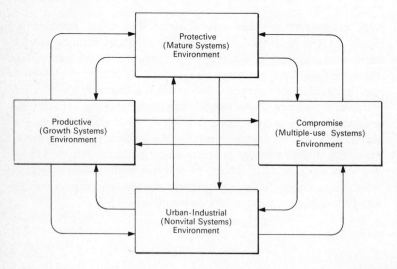

the area is: (1) productive; (2) protective; (3) a compromise between (1) and (2); or (4) urban-industrial. By continually refining the transfer coefficients on the basis of real world situations, and by increasing and decreasing the size and capacity of each compartment through computer simulation, it would be possible to determine objectively the limits that must eventually be imposed on each compartment in order to maintain regional and global balances in the exchange of vital energy and of materials. A systems-analysis procedure provides at least one approach to the solution of the basic dilemma posed by the question: 'How do we determine when we are getting too much of a good thing?' Also it provides a means of evaluating the energy drains imposed on ecosystems by pollution, radiation, harvest, and other stresses.[2]

Implementing any kind of compartmentalization plan, of course, would require procedures for zoning the landscape and restricting the use of some land and water areas. While the principle of zoning in cities is universally accepted, the procedures now followed do not work very well because zoning restrictions are too easily overturned by short-term economic and population pressures. Zoning the landscape would require a whole new order of thinking. Greater use of legal measures providing for tax relief, restrictions on use, scenic easements, and public ownership will be required if appreciable land and water areas are to be held in the 'protective' categories.

Until we can determine more precisely how far we may safely go in expanding intensive agriculture and urban sprawl at the expense of the protective landscape, it will be good insurance to hold inviolate as much of the latter as possible. Thus, the preservation of natural areas is not a peripheral luxury for society but a capital investment from which we expect to draw interest. Also, it may well be that restrictions in the use of land and water are our only practical means of avoiding overpopulation or too great an exploitation of resources, or both. Interestingly enough, restriction of land use is the analog of a natural behavioural control mechanism known as 'territoriality' by which many species of animals avoid crowding and social stress.[3]

It goes without saying that the tabular model for ecosystem development which I have presented here has many parallels in the development of human society itself. In the pioneer society, as in the pioneer ecosystem, high birth rates, rapid growth, high economic profits, and exploitation of accessible and unused resources are advantageous, but, as the saturation level is approached, these drives must be shifted to considerations of symbiosis (that is, 'civil rights', 'law and order', 'education', and 'culture'), birth control, and the recycling of resources. A balance between youth and maturity in the socio-environmental system is, therefore, the really basic goal that must be achieved if man as a species is to successfully pass through the present rapid-growth stage, to which he is clearly well adapted, to the ultimate equilibrium-density stage, of which he as yet shows little understanding and to which he now shows little tendency to adapt.

NOTES

1. E. P. Odum, *Ecology*, Holt, Rinehart & Winston, New York, 1963, Ch. 6.

2. See H. T. Odum, in *Symposium on Primary Productivity and Mineral Cycling in Natural Ecosystems*, ed. H. E. Young, University of Maine Press, Orono, 1967, p. 81; H. T. Odum, in *Pollution and Marine Ecology*, Wiley, New York, 1967, p. 99; K. E. F. Watt, *Ecology and Resource Management*, McGraw-Hill, New York, 1968.

3. R. Ardrey, *The Territorial Imperative*, Atheneum, New York, 1967.

2. Biology and Human Environment

The purely natural areas of the world's surface are exceedingly small. The city of the future, the ecumenopolis, will consist not only of the built-up areas, but of the open country in between.

We can compare the whole world's surface to a great city state which had its central built-up city and also its productive agricultural area around it. The same complex will be true of ecumenopolis. And I should remind you that man lives at present, and always has lived, on what is produced by the biological world. Recent advances have made it technically conceivable that we could synthesize all our food without the aid of plants and animals. This would need very great effort and development: probably comparable to that put into the development of the atom bomb. Nobody has yet started it and I think you can, for all intents and purposes, rule out for the next hundred years the possibility that man will give up living on biology; if he really tried hard he might get away from it towards the end of the century, but first he has to get started.

I start then from the point of view that our productive environment is man-made and that all major civilizations have lived in rather characteristic types of man-made landscape. The landscape of Britain, for instance, was entirely invented in the eighteenth century in conjunction with rotation of agricultural crops and herding of the domestic animals in enclosed fields. The whole thing is as artificial as a city: it isn't anything like the landscape of Britain would be if left to itself. Similarly, the great rice fields of China are entirely man-made landscapes. But if you fly across Africa, it is an un-man-made landscape. And one of the major tasks of today is to discover what to do with this landscape, which means understanding how it works and deciding what to do with it to make it produce better.

Agriculture is essentially a rather slow process. You plant seeds and they have to grow, and you eventually get a crop several months or possibly a year or so later. With cattle and pigs and sheep and so on you have to think in terms of two or three years. This is not always in the forefront of the minds of people who have been too much influenced by the physics and chemical science of the past few decades. Architects are really also having to deal with a process: the process of a building put up as a family mansion turning into the offices of doctors and lawyers, or of a city which is something always in a process of change. By handling relatively inert-looking things, like bricks and mortar and concrete and steel, architects may be tempted to think they're dealing with something steady; but they're really dealing with something in process of change.

I want to give you some notion of how the production system of the biological world works. About 71 per cent of the earth's surface is sea, of which only a small amount is shallow sea. Cultivated land is about 7 per cent of the earth's surface: it is reckoned that approximately double the amount as is at present cultivated *could* be cultivated. It only needs a good deal of capital outlay in irrigation and so on (Table 1).

TABLE ONE

*Land Suitable for Agriculture in Per Cent of the Earth's Land Surface**

Food crops	4·2
Feed and industrial crops	2·8
Cultivated (subtotal)	7·0
Pasture	4·0
Potentially arable (adequate rainfall, temperature and topography)	7·0
Total	18·0

* From Schmitt, 'Planetary Food Potential', in *Annals of the New York Academy of Sciences*.

Then you have forests of various kinds, deserts, the tundra, grasslands, marshes, and swamps. A simple idea of a hierarchical organization of the production of food is that you start with a lot of very simple plant plankton in the upper surface of the sea absorbing the sunlight. They get eaten by rather larger animals; shrimps and so on. The shrimps get eaten by big animals like porpoises and whales; and man – an Eskimo – eats the porpoises and whales.

The efficiency of the plants in using the incidental energy of the sun and turning it into sugar or starch is exceedingly low. The total amount produced is not only what you can reap at the end but what the crop uses to grow. If you work out how much energy would be required to make a certain amount of sugar, the total efficiency is only 1·6 per cent.

Why this terrific reduction in the total amount of solar energy on one square kilometre? It is reduced by a whole lot of factors. Part of it is absorbed by the atmosphere. Quite a bit is reflected from the plants instead of being absorbed. Then plants only grow for about half a year on the whole and they have got to use quite a lot to keep themselves alive while growing.

Even an efficiency of 1·6 per cent would make the total crop of the world's cultivated areas about forty times what it is estimated that we actually get. So we have several more factors to take into account. You can never actually cover the whole cultivatible surface of the earth with plants, because there is space needed between them. Also, some leaves are sitting on top of others and shading them so that you get an inefficiency in the utilization of the light. Finally, you lose quite a lot when taking the crop from the fields. We have thus added some more practical production factors but even this means that theoretically we should be able to grow about three times as much as we actually do (Tables 2 and 3).

But we have left out losses from all sorts of pests, apart from general inefficiency. If we now look at production on land and water we find that dry land areas produce very little unless they are irrigated. Ocean waters and deep lake waters are fairly productive, but coastal waters and other waters are much more productive, particularly if they are fertilized by pollution. Pollution by sewage, of course, is also fertilization.

Another sort of hierarchical organization can start with production by the green plants; then a first lot of animals who eat the grass, such as mice; a second lot of animals that eat the first, such as hawks; and a third lot that attack them, such as wild cats. There is a great

TABLE TWO

Loss of Solar Energy on 1 Square Kilometre*

1/2 $\pm$ 15 per cent for atmospheric absorption.
1/2 $\pm$ 20 per cent for portion of the solar spectrum utilized in photosynthesis.
9/10 $\pm$ 10 per cent for reflection from the plant cover.
1/9 $\pm$ 10 per cent for the photosynthetic efficiency of chlorophyll.
4/5 $\pm$ 10 per cent for average latitudinal effect (by) graphical integration.
1/2 $\pm$ 10 per cent for the growing season cone crop/yr.
3/5 $\pm$ 15 per cent for respiration loss.
i.e. $6 \times 10^{-3} \pm 35$ per cent (theoretical).

The 'standard error' or degree of confidence of the geometric sum is determined as the square root of the sum of the squares of the relative errors.

$2 \cdot 5 \times 10^{19}$ kcal. $\times 6 \times 10^{-3} = 1 \cdot 5 \times 10^{17}$ kcal. represents about forty times the estimated present world food energy production of $3 \cdot 6 \times 10^{15}$ kcal./yr.

TABLE THREE

Further Reductions of Solar Energy on 1 Square Kilometre*

Under actual conditions, however, further multiplicative reduction factors must be applied:

1/2 $\pm$ 30 per cent for incomplete plant cover.
1/2 $\pm$ 30 per cent for incomplete light utilization (light saturation).
1/3 $\pm$ 25 per cent for edible portion of plant.
2/3 $\pm$ 25 per cent for losses in harvesting, processing and preparation of food.
i.e. $5 \cdot 5 \times 10^{-2} \pm 55$ per cent (field conditions).

The total reduction factor thus is approximately $6 \times 10^{-3} \times 5 \cdot 5 \times 10^{-2} = 3 \cdot 3 \times 10^{-4}$ ± 65 per cent. This would permit the production of about $2 \cdot 5 \times 10^{19}$ kcal. $\times 3 \cdot 3 \times 10^{-4} = 8 \times 10^{15}$ kcal. of consumable food energy on 10,000,000 square kilometres, or about three times the present world consumption of $2 \cdot 5 \times 10^{15}$ kilocalories ($3 \cdot 6 \times 10^{15}$ kcal. production less 30 per cent losses).

* From Schmitt, 'Planetary Food Potential', in *Annals of the New York Academy of Sciences.*

reduction in numbers and an increase in size as you go from the primary producers to the second ones, up to man himself (Figure 1).

In terms of the mass of living material, very roughly speaking, you can say that you lose 90 per cent before reaching man. The net result

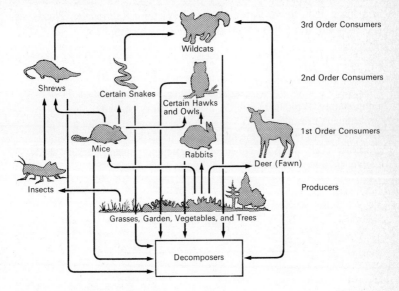

3rd Order Consumers

2nd Order Consumers

1st Order Consumers

Producers

Wildcats

Shrews

Certain Snakes

Certain Hawks and Owls

Mice

Rabbits

Deer (Fawn)

Insects

Grasses, Garden, Vegetables, and Trees

Decomposers

Figure 1. The food web.

of it is an unavoidable reduction in efficiency (Figure 2). The things we eat are, of course, at a number of different stages from the primary production. The fish we eat is about two food-links away. But a calculation of what the sea could produce shows it could be about a hundred times what we are actually getting out of it. There is undoubtedly an enormous unexploited resource in the sea.

On land the organization is very complicated. You have the primary producers of various sorts of green matter: green vegetables, trees, and so on. You have animals living off this in an elaborate network, not only rabbits which are eaten by foxes, but all sorts of cross-links so that the system makes, not a straight hierarchical organization, but a network organization (Figure 1). And, of course, you have bacteria, moulds, and all sorts of things which decompose dead bodies and bring them down to a compound to feed the vegetation. We find the same sort of picture in the sea. Things are absorbed in the floating microscopic animals and plants at the top of the sea and some drop down to the bottom by being decomposed. Then they go up again and fall back so that you have a complicated circulation network.

Figure 2. Pyramid of mass, energy, and numbers of organisms in a community. 'Producers' are the plants, primary converters of environmental resources into living material. 'Consumers' are animals. The three levels represent the hierarchy of predation in the community; consumer level 2 feeds on consumer level 1; and consumer level 1 feeds directly on the producers.

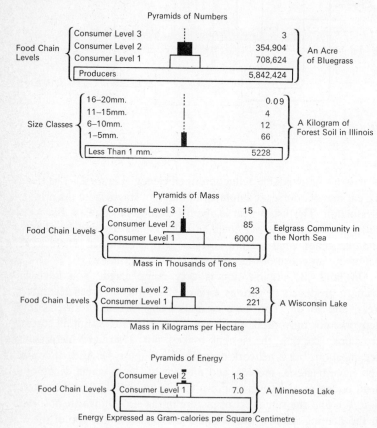

This subject of production by biological communities has been an extremely neglected part of biology in recent years. This has undoubtedly been a most exciting period in the development of analytical biology leading to an understanding of the elementary basic processes. But concentration on this has, to some extent, meant a neglect of the study of these complex networks of interrelation between complex things like rabbits or cabbages. The realization of the need is very parallel to the growth of ekistics amongst those concerned with the human habitat. The movement for a further study of production ecology by the biologists stems from exactly the same basic humanistic reasons as a realization that man is in a world which he has really got to learn to control and make a decent place to live in.

The ekisticians are concerned with the human built-up environment and the biologists are concerned with the utilization and control of the landscapes in which we are going to pass our life. Work on this is organized in an 'International Biological Program', whose objective is a study of the biological basis of productivity and of human welfare. Thus, what the biologists are doing is setting up something rather comparable to ekistics.

Biologists are finding themselves having to tackle a problem which is conceptually very difficult, and it's a problem which has at least as much application to human welfare as ekistics. Both are dealing with people, animals, things, in intimate interrelations – influencing one another in a sort of network world.

We don't know yet how to deal with these organized systems, but one or two points do emerge in biology. One is that biological systems are very often organized in such a way that the whole system is very resistant to being altered. It's like a spider's web. If you take out one link, nothing much happens: the rest gets a bit of a jolt and then settles down so that the end result is much as it was before. This property of organization in biology has been built up, roughly speaking, by trial and error. It's not an inherent property of biological systems. But natural selection has picked out those chance types of system which have this property of being resistant to outside action.

Progressive Self-Stabilizing Systems

'Homeostasis' is the word used in biology for the property of keeping something constant. For instance, if for some reason there is too much oxygen in the blood, or too much carbon dioxide, or the acidity is abnormal, the body will respond in ways which result in bringing the concentration of these substances in the blood back to the normal level. We say, therefore, that there is a homeostasis of the blood composition. Nearly all aspects of biological organisms exhibit some degree of similar homeostatic properties. The mechanism by which these homeostatic systems work go under the fashionable name of 'feedback'. This means that if you have a system that for some reason or another is pushed away from its normal situation, so that some component is increased in concentration above what it should be, this component itself acts back on the rest of the system in such a way that its concentration is brought back again to normality. It is this sort of system that is called 'negative feedback'.

However, the idea of homeostasis and negative feedback are only the very first stages in arriving at a decent understanding of biological organization. Biological organisms have another fundamental quality, which is also, I am sure, fundamental in the ekistical systems which might be considered parallel to biological organisms. This property is that of changing in time. Biological organisms are not static things; they are always developing, and if you leave out of consideration the fact of development you get only a very thin and incomplete idea of what an organism is like. Certainly if you leave it out from town planning you will obviously be overtaken by history before you have really begun. In both biology and ekistics we have to deal with organizations which change as time passes.

This is a type of change which biologists have been rather hesitant in dealing with. It complicates the issue, and many biologists are un-willing to concentrate their attention on the homeostatic properties of adult organisms which will remain much the same over fairly long periods of time without very noticeable development. However, one really has to go beyond this, and face up to the problems of development which will certainly occur eventually. Biologists have had to develop, therefore, a whole branch of science which deals with the causal processes which bring about long-range changes in time. For this branch of biology there is again a good group word, 'epigenetics', which is derived from the word *epigenesis* which was well known to Aristotle. In practice this science deals with the interactions between the hereditary potentialities which organisms inherit from their parents, and the surrounding circumstances in which they are growing up and developing.

During the gradual processes of development there is again something corresponding to the property of homeostasis which we saw as a characteristic of stationary states. Developing systems do not, of course, preserve a stationary state, but they do have a tendency to preserve a definite *pathway of change in time*. If you watch a developing system without disturbing it, it will change along a particular course of events, which one can call an epigenetic pathway. Now if in some way you push a developing biological system off its normal developmental pathway, it is most frequently observed that changes will occur which will tend to bring it back on to the pathway at some later point. Thus, the pathway is in some sense stable – not in the sense that it does not involve changes in time, but in the sense that, if the system is pushed off the path at one time, it will tend to come back to the path a bit later on. This sort of stability also has a technical name which is derived from the Greek; the word is 'homeorhesis', in which the 'rhesis' is derived from the Greek word for 'to flow'. There is also a word, again derived from Greek, for the path along which a homeorhetic system flows; this word is 'chreod', derived from '$\chi\rho\eta$', it is necessary, and '$\delta\delta\delta\varsigma$', a path. Thus, a homeorhetic system is one which develops along the given chreod, and tends to return to the chreod if it gets pushed off it by some disturbance.

Another word usage in this connection is to say that development changes are 'buffered'. One can say that the developing system is buffered against chance happenings that may occur, so that it will tend to go on developing normally even if there are influences which might have been expected to divert it.

I think that this property of homeorhesis, of following a buffered chreod in a gradual course through time, is one of the fundamental properties of biological organisms. I strongly suspect that in designing any system which will exhibit the properties of organization, one of the major questions to ask is how far you are building in properties of homeorhesis and buffering. How far is your system going to be able to retain its character in spite of the unforeseen things that are certainly going to happen to it? When you make a plan you foresee certain things that you expect to happen in the future, and design the system to deal with these, but you have to remember that many things will certainly happen that you cannot now foresee. Some technological invention will be made which throws quite unexpected stresses on the system you have designed. I think it should be possible to work out, and incorporate into the design, general systems of reaction which operate so as to buffer the system against these unforeseen disturbances.

I will just mention shortly another way of thinking about such matters. It is important to remember that any respectable organism, like an animal or a man, and certainly any organized system like a town, is fantastically complex if one tries to describe it in full detail. If you want to consider all the factors in it that may be important, you must take into consideration many hundreds of different things. In an animal these might be the different chemical constituents and their concentrations, and in a town there would be not only the geographical facts about streets, parks, location of buildings, etc., but also a great many economic and other factors. If you want to express the situation of your system in some graphical way, you would really have to make a separate graph for each of the variables, and you would need one dimension of space in which you can plot the concentration or quantity of each particular factor. If you want, for instance, to express the situation of a system containing 100 different chemicals, you can only do so properly in a space of 100 dimensions. In such a space the situation of the system at any particular time can be represented by one point. Now there is one branch of mathematics which deals with spaces of many dimensions of this kind. This is the type of mathematics known as topology. I think that in the future the most professional way of expressing the properties of developing systems, whether they are animals or towns, is going to be by use of topological notions.

If you represent your system by one point in a multi-dimensional space, you will then want to show in some way the forces which are acting within the system to bring about changes. These can be represented by a system of vectors associated with the point. One can draw such vectors in a diagram by a set of little arrows pointing in various directions. For instance, in the drawing in the upper left of Figure 3, I have indicated an embryo (or, if you like, a town plan) as a sort of map at the bottom. Associated with each point on the map, there is above it a point in the multi-dimensional function-space which

Figure 3. The upper three drawings show diagrammatically how the conditions in a complex developing system can be represented by topological structures in a multi-dimensional space. The lower part shows a still greater simplification in which the development pathways are represented as valleys along which the system moves.

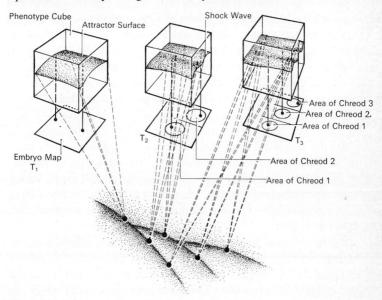

represents the condition of the system at that point in the embryo. Thus, all the points in the embryo map are represented in the functional space by a series of points, which form another surface in this multi-dimensional space. Now we are supposing that the system has homeostatic properties, and this is represented by putting in arrows representing the forces acting at the various points, and arranging these in such a way that the forces all tend to converge on to the surface. This would mean that if a few points get pushed away from the surface, the sectors represented by the arrows will tend to bring them back on to it. A system of this kind can be said to exhibit an 'attractor surface'.

Now if we go on to picture development in time, we have to express this by supposing that an attractor surface gradually changes in shape, as is shown in the upper part of the drawings in the figure. The sequence of changes undergone by the attractor surface really defines the pathway of the development change the system will undergo. The fact that the surface is always an attractor surface, so that the system tends to come back to it, means that the pathway of change will be a chreod, to which the developing system tends to return if diverted from it. Sometimes the attractor surface may get folded, as indicated in the drawings in the figure. When this is so, we get two different regions of the embryo or town which begin to follow different chreods. This is what happens in an embryo when, for instance, it develops a brain in one place, a heart in another, a liver in a third, and so on.

In some such way as this, one can use the language of topology to describe the simple features which arise within systems that are really in detail fantastically complex. Biologists are beginning to find this language useful when they want to discuss the overall simplicities in complex embryos, and possibly planners will find such ideas useful, also, in discussing the general features of their complex entities such as towns or regions.

There is one final set of ideas which I might also briefly mention. In biology we have been struggling for a long time with the problem of getting a useful definition of the 'value' of an organism in relation to the changes of evolution. There are some organisms which are extremely good at carrying out specialized particular tasks. One might at first say that they are 'good'. But very often they do one thing well and nothing else at all efficiently, and they may be eliminated from the scene if there is some change of climate or other factor which does not suit them. We need to get some general concept which will express the successfulness of the organism over a long period of time, in which many unforeseen things will occur.

As a final word I would like to say that the biological system has to be designed to meet unforeseeable challenges. Animals change by a mutation of their hereditary factors, but they don't know whether the world is going to slip into an ice age or if some horrible new virus is going to come along and kill them or else kill off their food supply. They are playing a game of chance, and any viable sort of system has got to take this into account. You cannot really tell what you are designing for, however much you investigate it. You can get some idea of the nature of the likely things you are designing for, but you have got to be able to design something which is sufficiently flexible and resistant to change and catastrophe, to be able to make quite a good job of it, even if the world does not turn out as you thought it was going to.

It seems to me that ideas which may be important in this connection are beginning to emerge from the work of people who are trying to design game-playing machines. For instance, a machine (i.e. a computer) which is programmed to play a game of chess or checkers, works by taking a given set-up on the board, calculating a number of alternative moves that can be made against it, then the alternative responses to these moves, then the alternative second moves, and so on for a sequence of three or four moves, worked out in all their possible alternatives. The limit is only in the capacity that the computer has to deal with the rapidly increasing number of alternative situations. When it has gone as far as its designer has decided is reasonable, all these moves are summarized, and the overall picture, arising from the whole set of possible alternative futures, is considered as a 'value' of the particular set-up which the computer is considering. A good chess or bridge player, of course, does something rather similar in a more or less intuitive way. It seems to me that in all those subjects which deal with the future, such as the biologist's considerations about evolution, we may find that we can get useful systems of ideas from these notions being developed by people working with game-playing machines. Ekistics and planning are, of course, an attempt to deal with the future. I suggest that when you say 'a good plan', you are using an idea similar to that which is employed when you say 'this is a good hand of cards', or 'a favourable set-up for white' on the chess board.

3. Food for the World

HOWARD W. MATTSON

It has become a cliché to say that half of the world's people suffer from poor nutrition or that half a billion are actually seriously hungry. Data and definitions are frequently fuzzy in this field, but there can be no argument that a large proportion of the world's population gets a good deal less of their 'daily bread' than they need, and most need much more protein. Worse yet, because of their rapidly increasing population, the gains in food production that *are* being made are literally being eaten up as fast as they occur. The result: actual reductions in per capita food production in many already hungry nations.

Population Control a Must

This may be a good place to state the assumptions that I will be using throughout this article.

First, we should understand at once that ultimately, the food problem is really the population problem. Without eventual control, even the most far-reaching food development programs will fail.

Second, most of the responsibility for stimulating this increased food supply will lie with the developed countries of the world, simply because they are the only ones with both the awareness and the means to do it.

Nor can the problem be solved by some 'simple' redistribution of surpluses from one region to another. Even if enough food could be grown in the developed world, ships and harbour facilities, to say nothing of distribution facilities, couldn't handle the tonnages involved. The bulk of the new supplies *must* be generated within the hungry nations themselves.

Agriculture – Tried and True

Modern practices are still mostly confined to large commercial farms, many producing for export. Until the innovator can practically guarantee the cash-poor subsistence farmer that using his product or method will yield more than it costs, the farmer will not bite. A subsistence farmer reaches his decisions on a different basis from a commercial farmer. He says 'The less I put in, the less I lose when the crop fails.'

What About Meat?

First, we should shoot down some misconceptions. There is nothing magic about milk, meat, and eggs as sources of protein. The term 'complete protein' applied to these products simply implies that they contain all eight so-called essential amino acids, those constituents of our own protein which our bodies cannot synthesize from other elements or compounds.

The big problem facing us at this point, however, is that animals are notoriously inefficient at converting feed to meat. Almost 90 per cent of what a cow or pig eats is used up simply keeping it warm and walking around; more is lost during butchering. Milk cows are somewhat better – the best can convert about 23 per cent of their forage into milk, while chickens are perhaps highest on the list. Under ideal conditions, growers can produce a three-pound broiler on six pounds of feed in less than six weeks.

How Now, Brown Chemical Factory?

There is one quite bright spot in the area of animal protein which deserves more space, yet it is fraught with its own difficulties. While most animals need the same set of essential amino acids that we do, cows and sheep are ruminants, and can manufacture amino acids much as a chemical plant does, from almost any form of carbon, hydrogen, oxygen, and nitrogen. Cows have been raised quite successfully on mixtures of ground corncobs (pure cellulose, to provide the carbon, hydrogen, and oxygen), urea (a cheap chemical source of nitrogen), and a little molasses to start bacteria working in the cow's first stomach (the rumen). While the weight gain and milk production from such diets is only about one half to two thirds that on more usual diets, it is completely 'free' in terms of competition with food for human consumption; and the milk and beef is completely normal in composition.

Another technique which leads to increased beef or milk production is fertilization of the pasture land. Much of the world's grazing land is not suitable for other crop production because of low fertility, difficult terrain, or tree cover; if such land could be made to yield larger amounts of forage or grass, more cattle per acre could be supported without competing with other crops for human consumption. Also, adequate forage must be available the year round, and this means cutting and storing forage in countries with alternate wet and dry seasons.

If you increase cattle production, however, you raise a new problem – that of utilizing the product. Milk, for example, is a perishable commodity, and the technological inputs required for its processing are high in terms of both people and equipment: processing plants are almost nonexistent in the underdeveloped world today. It is pointless to urge (or help) a farmer in such an area to increase his milk production without providing him with enough near-by facilities to handle the increase.

There Must Be Other Protein Sources

We haven't yet mentioned fish, which is an obvious oversight in a world whose surface is three quarters covered with water. Fish are perhaps our most under-utilized conventional food source; they provide only about 1 per cent of man's total food intake, although they do provide some 3 per cent of the total protein intake, and actually 10 per cent of the animal protein.

What is the potential for such increases? Most of the estimates of non-utilized fish stocks range from two and a half to four times our present catch, if you talk in terms of conventional 'hunting' operations. This is a far cry from 'untapped riches', but it is substantial. Also, any increases would come about without competition with land-based agriculture.

Mechanization projects include redesign of trawlers for greater efficiency and fuel economy and the installation of electronic gear to *find* the fish. Few of these technical inputs will remain effective without supporting repair, parts, and credit facilities, as well as a fair level of technical competence in the people.

Increased catches of fish raise the same problem as does increased milk − lack of markets and processing facilities. The stocks of fish caught are frequently so great that they cannot possibly be sold fresh − fish are too perishable for that − but processing plants to preserve the fish in what we consider traditional forms for human consumption are limited or nonexistent. Also, the typical inland housewife is generally unfamiliar with fish cookery, since she seldom sees it in her market. Most of such huge catches are thus 'reduced' to fish meal, a dried, defatted powder.

There is another approach to fishing which is growing slowly in use, and that is fish farming. Here you avoid the rigours and uncertainties of hunting by stocking a backyard pond or rice paddy with fresh or brackish water fish. Fish culture is growing in such countries as China, Japan, Uganda, and Indonesia. Large yields are possible: in Uganda, yields of 300 lb. per acre come from just stocking a pond with tilapia, a hardy little fish which grows quickly to a weight of one or two pounds without any help. If the farmer adds supplementary food, such as elephant grass and sweet potatoes, annual production can be boosted to 2,000 lb. per acre.

Actually, higher yields of protein per acre can be achieved by fish culture than by any other agricultural method known. The obvious drawback is the need for dependable water.

What About Non-Animal Protein?

Protein from all animal sources now totals about 20 million tons per year, while protein from cereal grains totals 106 million tons. There are two other sources of vegetable protein that are little used today: the legumes – various beans, peas, and lentils – and the oil seeds, such as soy beans, peanuts, and cottonseed. Present production of legumes provides only $7\frac{1}{2}$ million tons of protein; protein production from oil seeds is about equal to that from all animal products, but very little of it is used for human consumption. Legumes for some reason have never been as popular as grains as a staple food.

The possibilities of increasing their supply are quite similar to those of the other major crops we've mentioned; basically, they will respond to increased doses of fertilizer, but the economic use of additional nutrients depends on a fairly long-term program of improved breeds, practices, and other crop management procedures, as well as increasing their attractiveness to the housewife.

The situation with the oil seeds is a rather strange one. For some reason, historical or cultural, soy beans are eaten in quantity by humans only in the Orient.

Why should such good sources of needed protein go to waste? The main historic reason is that these crops have been grown for their oil; the residue from the pressing operations has always presented a disposal problem.

There are two basic hindrances to increased use of oil seeds in improved nutrition: The facilities in which the oil is pressed are generally highly unsanitary and antiquated, usually yielding a fibrous, dirty press cake, full of hulls and other scrap. Also, the protein has been seriously degraded by excess heat. Few existing processing plants could be converted to making a product fit for human consumption; new plants would have to be built.

Second, many countries resist using these materials on the ideological grounds that they are 'second-rate' foods – previously considered useful only for animal feed or manure. This resistance will have to be overcome before they will be accepted widely.

Isn't Anybody Using Them?

Fortunately, a start has been made on both problems, which deserves careful watching, although it won't provide a cure-all. This effort is by the Instituto de Nutrición de Centro America y Panama – I.N.C.A.P. for short. This organization set out some years ago to explore the idea that there were unused nutritious foodstuffs available locally in most underdeveloped countries.

Their typical approach was to take the locally accepted major staple grain – corn, in the case of Guatemala where their pilot program began – and improve it with a complementary high-protein local oil seed. They tried many combinations, and have tested nine 'Incaparina' recipes for safety and nutritional value. All use a corn base, supplemented by sesame or soy flour, torulla yeast (for vitamin B), plus vitamin A.

In Guatemala, Incaparina is used to make a traditional thin gruel drink called *atoles*, which Guatemalans relish as much as Americans do malteds. Using Incaparina has produced remarkable results in curing the effects of protein deficiency in children; it is nutritionally equivalent to milk, but costs only one fifth or one sixth as much as milk.

In countries where corn gruel beverages are not as popular as in most of Latin America, another form for its use must be found. It can be substituted for up to two thirds of the wheat flour in non-bread recipes, or used to enrich soups, puddings, and other foods.

There are a number of aspects of the Incaparina program which are instructional in terms of the future prospects for similar programs. First, while it is intended to be strictly commercial, in the sense that its production should be on a profit-making basis, the expenditure for research and development that has gone into formulation, testing, and marketing has been very large in terms of the ultimate return. This is mostly for preliminary research, needed to prove out a concept; future projects of this type will entail primarily formula modification and market development expense.

Secondly, in spite of the facts that the basic food is native to the population, that the medical profession and public-health people are on its side and that the price is kept low by volume production, it is not yet a runaway success.

Bear this in mind as we look next at some of the more exotic proposals to increase food supplies. The 'better mouse-trap' approach is not the whole answer.

The Wild Blue Yonder

Before we evaluate the potential contribution of these more or less conventional approaches to world food resources, we ought to look at the more exotic proposals which come to discussion regularly. One of the hottest is the potential of micro-organisms as food producers on such 'grazing lands' as coal, crude oil, and black liquor from paper pulp operations. The organisms themselves include bacteria, fungi, and yeasts.

Alfred Champagnat, Director of Research of Pétroles B.P. in France, has described work on the fermentation of petroleum fractions to yield yeast protein, as a counterpart to the more usual carbohydrate fermentation. A number of modifications from normal fermentation processes are necessary. First, hydrocarbons are insoluble in water, so they must be strongly stirred to ensure adequate contact with the micro-organisms. This is fairly easy to do in the laboratory, but will present formidable problems on a large scale. Second, more air must be supplied to the fermenting mixture, and the mix must be cooled.

The potential advantages of such a scheme, however, are tantalizing. Champagnat estimated that the equivalent of the total current animal protein supply could be produced from just 3 per cent of the world's annual petroleum production. The widespread existence of refineries would also reduce the problems of transportation and distribution.

There are other advantages. Micro-organism culture requires only small teams of specialists and little space; it does not compete for nutritional raw materials, and it is independent of sun, rain, and climate. It also has a very rapid growth rate: while a 1,000-lb. cow was producing 1 lb. of protein, the same amount of micro-organisms could produce 2,400 lb.

N.A.S.A. and the Bureau of Mines have put forth coal distallate, as substrate for raising micro-organisms. They have reported yields at anywhere from 7 to 44 per cent, from different fractions. Fungi (not mushrooms) have also been grown on various high-carbo-hydrate substrates, such as black-strap molasses, sugar beets, manioc roots, and citrus molasses, with high yields. Algae growing (perhaps even raised on sewage to help solve two problems at once) is a perennial favourite and extracting protein from forage crops like alfalfa, which are more efficient converters of sunlight than con-ventional grains and vegetables, comes up regularly at technical meetings.

What part can such products and processes play in meeting the rapidly growing food deficit? While some of these developments may be essential if the world's population ever goes over 8 to 10,000 million, they cannot be expected to help when we will need them the most — ·between now and 1980 or even 2000. None of these exotic sources of protein is past the pilot plant stage, and most are in the research and development stage. Few of the proponents have made more than a cursory attempt to test market acceptance; usually, this consists of carrying a bottle of the product to the technical meeting at which the paper is presented.

Will They Really Help?

Where then does the most promise lie? First, assuming that the need will be upon us far more quickly than we expected, we must con-centrate on getting the most return for our money and technical effort. This means that it is pointless to mount a *crash program* to develop exotic foods from petroleum, coal, algae, or other 'far-out' sources. Such foods are not going to play any important part in alleviating mass starvation in the next fifteen to twenty years, if for no other reason than consumer acceptance.

Second, it is almost as pointless to assume that any really different 'natural' food is going to be accepted quickly.

Certainly, work on increasing the productivity of the sea should be continued at a high pitch. The same can be said for fish culture in inland pools, and even for similar activities in restricted areas of the ocean.

The major hope, however, devolves on the soil, but even here we must be realists, if we are to avoid wasting our limited resources – limited considering the fantastic size of the job to be done. Attempts to open new lands to crops will almost always cost more than they will yield.

Where Will It Come From, Then?

The food to feed the world's rapidly increasing population will have to come from crops and animals grown on *land that is now in more or less successful production*. The methods will have to be those which have been devised in the developed world: vastly increased fertilizer application, pest control in its widest sense – including weeds, insects, and disease – introduction of improved varieties, and better management practices. This type of work must be done on the spot; we cannot simply export our temperate zone know-how to the tropics and get the same results.

Teach the Interested First

It makes little difference to the economy and nutrition of the majority of the countries if the lowest-level farmers do not increase their yields immediately.

Increasing production by agriculture in the ways outlined above is not a glamorous job. It requires great inputs of grubby, very ordinary activity, including lots of sweat. The level of technology needed is uninspiring. When we speak of educational requirements here, for example, we're not talking about Ph.D.s, but about carpenters, mechanics, and plumbers. In some communities, if a tool needs a new nut or gasket it can't be repaired. Production in some of the backward areas could be doubled simply by introducing steel hoes to replace the pointed sticks now used. In many areas of the world, even the scythe is unknown. Ploughing with draught cattle will increase production over hoes, but plough design is critical – undernourished draught cattle are not tractors. Labour-saving devices requiring large capital expenditures are not necessarily desirable, but tools to allow a better job to be done very definitely are.

4. Has Man's Metropolitan Environment Any Precedents?

ARNOLD TOYNBEE

Man's metropolitan environment is a very recent one, if we measure its age by the time-scale of the age of man himself. Hominoids of some species may have been in existence by now for a million years; *homo sapiens* has been in existence for at least 200,000 years, and perhaps for much longer than that. But man's metropolitan environment hardly began to take shape till 150 years ago; so man has lived in this environment, up to now, for only an infinitesimal fraction of the total time that he has been in existence, so far, on this planet. However, it looks today as if life in a metropolitan environment may be man's permanent destiny. It is hard to see how he can ever escape from this environment if the earth's human population is going to double or treble in size within the next generation or two, as the demographers predict.

Man's present metropolitan environment has two characteristic features. In the first place, it is an expanding environment. Since the modern type of city first made its appearance it has been growing; its growth has been accelerating, and we can foresee no limit to it short of the limits of the habitable part of the earth's surface. In the second place, the modern metropolis has consequently expanded out of all proportion to man's natural powers of locomotion. Before the nineteenth century there had been very few cities anywhere at any time that were so large that people could not get about the town on foot, or at any rate on donkeyback or on horseback. Most cities were so small that their inhabitants could walk from their home in the town right out into the open country in a few minutes. This human-size scale was the scale of eighteenth-century Frankfurt as described by Goethe, and even of nineteenth-century Dorchester as described by Thomas Hardy. A great-uncle of mine who visited Cologne in 1833 found it then still a little walled town of the antique type. Cities that were too big to escape from on foot were not, of course, entirely unknown before the nineteenth century. Rome, for instance, was on this scale while it was the political capital of the Mediterranean basin; Babylon was, too, in the sixth century B.C.; and I imagine that the successive capitals of a united China have also been of this order of magnitude. But, before the nineteenth century, cities of this size were rare exceptions, whereas, during the last century and a half, they have been becoming the rule.

A city that outdistances man's walking powers is a trap for man. It threatens to become a prison from which he cannot escape unless he has mechanical means of transport, the thoroughfares for carrying these, and the purchasing power for commanding the use of artificial means of communication.

I was born and brought up in London, and my memory of life in that city goes back to about 1894. In the last decade of the nineteenth century, the vast majority of Londoners really were prisoners of the town. At that date, one could escape from London by train only, not by road, for this was still the pre-automobile age. Only a privileged minority could afford to buy even a third-class railway ticket to a destination in the open country. As a child, I used to contribute my pennies to a beneficent institution called the Children's Country Holiday Fund. One used to hear of children, sent by this fund to enjoy a week's holiday in the country, who had never set eyes on a green field till then.

When I was a student at Oxford, we had an organization for bringing people from the East End of London to Oxford for a day's trip and entertaining them in College, during the Oxford summer term. I remember a fellow student of mine, who was my co-host on one of these occasions, opening his conversation with one of our East End guests by saying, 'I suppose town is empty now.' The student was thinking in terms of the privileged minority in the West End of London who went out of town for the summer as a matter of course. Our East End guest stared at him, quite puzzled. He could not understand his host's meaning. The East End of London was no emptier in the summer than it was at any other season. The vast majority of the East Enders never got away. Their part of London – and it was the major part – was always teeming with its population of prisoners for life. The prisoners who were released for a moment by the Children's Country Holiday Fund and by our equivalent organization at Oxford were so few that their temporary trips out of town made no noticeable difference.

In London, and in the world's other big cities too, I have lived to see a change. The means of transport have improved. The development of automobiles has brought the roads into action again, side by side with the railways, for carrying fast long-distance traffic; and most people now have the money to pay for these facilities. The father of a family who, sixty or seventy years ago, would have been too poor to buy railway tickets for his family may now be the owner of a car. Short of that, he will be likely to have the money to take his family out into the country by bus, and to pay for a country holiday for them out of his own pocket. The town dweller who, yesterday, was the prisoner of the city has become the conqueror of the countryside.

For the present-day urban majority of the human race, this is a great and good alleviation of their recent hard lot. The question is whether this alleviation can be more than temporary. This ominous question presents itself because, in conquering the countryside, the city's escaping urban prisoners are transforming the countryside. They are, in fact, annexing it to the city. This is bound to be the effect of the improvement in the means of transport, working together with the population explosion. Part of the conquered countryside is being transformed into a built-up area. There are places within a few miles of Mount Lykavittos, in Athens, which I knew first in 1911, but which I cannot recognize today because streets and houses now cover what, half a century ago, was open country. I have had the same experience in the mainland area of Hong Kong, and in Japan. Not the whole of the former open country is going to be built over; but the part that will be left still open is going to be urbanized in a subtler way. It is going to cease to be arable land or pasture land, and is going to become the city's 'green belt' – an enclave of parks and playgrounds appropriated by the town dwellers for their recreation. The fields and the pastures are going to retreat before the aggressive advance of the streets and houses, till they are driven right off *terra firma*, into the sea. This has already begun to happen in Japan, where you now find sheltered areas of the sea being broken in for the cultivation of oysters and edible seaweed.

When all the dry land on the face of our planet has been annexed to the city in the one way or the other, the city dweller is going to become, once again, the prisoner that he was in the nineteenth century; and this time there will be no escape for him by any further improvement in his means of communication. He may be able to travel to mid ocean or to outer space or to the moon, if he is rich enough to buy the tickets for voyages of these unprecedented lengths, but that will do him no good; for none of those far destinations will be able to provide the fugitive family with a country holiday camping ground. None of these inhospitable distant locations can take the place of the lost open country, and the conquest of the open country by the townsman means the eventual loss of it for countrymen and townsmen alike.

Of course, this is not the first time in history that the city has impinged upon the countryside beyond its bounds. The city has never been self-sufficing. It cannot be, because it cannot produce within its own bounds the food for feeding its own population. It has to import this food from outside, and to pay for it by exporting services or manufactured goods. The Sumerian cities in Iraq are the earliest set of cities of which we have any knowledge. By present-day standards, they were tiny. Yet the network of their trade extended in a radius of hundreds of miles from their city centres, and their trade carried cultural influence with it. All cities have always made themselves felt in the surrounding countryside, but, till now, they have not annexed the countryside, and have not assimilated it to themselves. City and countryside always traded with each other and influenced each other, but they still remained distinct; and it was the difference between them that made them complementary to each other. Both their separateness and their inseparability were symbolized in the city wall. This wall kept the rural population out, and kept the urban population in; but the insulation of the two populations from each other was only partial. The city wall was pierced by gates; these were open during daylight hours; the country people came into town to market; the townspeople peddled their manufactures in the countryside. This world in which town and country coexisted in a mutually beneficial symbiosis was still Goethe's world and Thomas Hardy's world, as I have already noted; but it is not going to be our grandchildren's world. Their world is going to be one that is all city; the countryside will have been eliminated.

Has there ever been urban life without a complementary country-side? There have in the past been cities that have lived for hundreds of years on end in something like a permanent state of siege, with an enemy almost always at their gates. I am thinking of such cities as medieval Venice and Byzantine Constantinople and the Phoenician cities. These last were perched on tiny off-shore islands or on pro-montories. Tyre and Aradus and Motya, off the west coast of Sicily, were island cities; Sidon and Carthage were on capes jutting out into the sea. These Phoenician cities were congested. At Motya the houses were six storeys high, and there was not room on the island for a cemetery. Are not these authentic examples of cities without a countryside? And did not their inhabitants manage to live without one? No; for this is not the whole story. It is true that the adjoining mainland was usually closed to these cities, but the sea was always open to them. The sea was commanded by their navies and was traversed by their merchant marines, and freedom of the seas gave them access to vast countrysides beyond the water. The world-wide ecumenopolis of the future will have no such outlets. It may learn to navigate outer space, but it will not find a habitable countryside on the far side of it.

Man, then, seems likely to relapse into his nineteenth-century plight of being the prisoner of the city, and, this time, with no possibility of escape. This is a formidable outlook for us, because the imprisoned town dwellers of the past have been apt to develop an ugly temper. The imprisoned proletariats of Athens, Alexandria, Rome, Constanti-nople, Paris, and Leningrad have each, in turn, been prone to break out into mob violence. An inescapable city cannot be a seed-bed for vegetables or cereals, but it has often been a seed-bed for riots and revolutions. This was so much in the mind of the French town planner who laid out the design for Washington D.C., that he pro-vided the political capital of the United States with the 'circles' that have, ever since, been a distinctive feature of it. The purpose of these circles was military. They were designed as emplacements for batteries that could enfilade the avenues which radiate from Washington's circles like the spokes of a wheel. Happily, Washington has never yet seen violent mobs being dispersed by 'a whiff of grape-shot' (Napoleon's counter-revolutionary phrase); and it has become customary to smile at this supposedly antiquated military precaution. This smile is no longer in place now that Washington has become a dangerous centre of racial tension.

An urban population tends to become violent when it has been excluded from the countryside or has been deprived of it. This is not surprising; for a totally and unmitigatedly urban life is surely something contrary to human nature. It may be necessary to save the countryside in order to save man himself. But can the countryside be saved under present conditions?

5. Landscape Aesthetics

LUNA B. LEOPOLD

The time has come when the argument of the environmentalist might best be presented by: (1) separating facts from emotions in relation to the environment; and (2) by providing him with a means of quantifying his arguments: using numbers to talk about the landscape. While to some of us this may be a little like using a computer to describe Shakespeare, it seems that society still has the right to have all aspects of any proposed development presented in a way that is as objective as possible.

One strategy used by environmentalists or conservationists to combat the paucity of statistical data involves an attempt to describe society's interest in landscape integrity in monetary terms, which make a region's aesthetic attributes appear to be similar to the kinds of benefits ascribed to planned development. From this has arisen the unfortunate and unsound procedure of evaluating recreation in terms of what is called the 'visitor day'. This argument is based on the idea that the average visitor to a particular place spends one dollar a day (or some other amount) there, which he would not have spent had he not visited the spot, and that the enjoyment derived therefrom is in direct proportion to the amount of time or money spent in the given area. To me, this procedure misses the whole point of recreational activity since we know, by experience, that recreational enjoyment is by no means dependent upon either of these factors. It appears more sound to develop a way of directly describing the quality of the recreational experience. A first step towards this goal is to describe objectively the landscape itself, which the recreationist visits for enjoyment without regard to expenditure of money or time.

Towards this end I began a study designed to produce a method that would quantify the aesthetic features of the environment so that the resultant data could be used in many planning and decision-making contexts. Such data could be especially useful when choices must be made among alternative courses of action. They would tend to provide a more prominent consideration of non-monetary values to society.

Three types of factors appear relevant to landscape aesthetics. These groupings of factors and their 'subfactors' are listed in Table 1. The first group involves the physical features of an area – the presence of mountains and valleys, width of valleys, height and type of mountains. The second group includes those features that have to do with the region's biology, especially – in the case of river valleys – the vegetation near the stream and on the mountain sides, and the biology within the water itself. A third class encompasses what I have called 'human interest factors'. These are often more intangible than either the physical or the biological ones, but they are nevertheless influential in determining how the landscape impresses us. For example, if one is at the point on the Delaware River where George Washington is supposed to have thrown the silver dollar, that historical incident, however apocryphal, gives that place a distinct meaning.

Another set of circumstances, also related to the human interest factors, is the presence or absence of vistas or scenic outlooks. The many travellers who pull off to the side of the road at a turnout marked 'scenic viewpoint' or 'scenic outlook' are an indication that the ability to look from some vantage point across great distances, often to mountains or into far valleys, gives the landscape some special character – whether at a mountain top or in a river bottom.

The question of access also falls within the realm of human interest. In the listing of criteria I have broken accessibility down into two parts: access to the individual, especially the hiker, and mass use, meaning availability to motorized transport.

Human interest is affected by the general level of urbanization; it can make a piece of landscape more interesting or the opposite. The view from the Berkeley hills of California, for example, across the bay to San Francisco is made attractive by the skyline of San Francisco itself. In this case, the presence of the city seen from afar seems to make the landscape more interesting. On the other hand, in certain kinds of mountain country, the presence of a great many

TABLE ONE

Factor Number and Descriptive Categories		Evaluation Numbers				
		1	2	3	4	5
Physical Factors						
1. River width (feet)	at low flow	<3	3–10	10–30	30–100	>100
2. Depth (feet)		<·5	·5–1	1–2	2–5	>5
3. Velocity (feet per second)		<·5	·5–1	1–2	3–5	>5
4. Stream depth (feet)		<1	1–2	2–4	4–8	>8
5. Flow variability		Little variation		Normal	Ephemeral or large variation	
6. River pattern		Torrent	Pool and riffle	Without riffles	Meander	Braided
7. Valley height/width		≤1	2–5	5–10	11–14	≥15
8. Stream bed material		Clay or silt	Sand	Sand and gravel	Gravel	Cobbles or larger
9. Bed slope (feet/feet)		<·0005	·0005–·001	·001–·005	·005–·01	>·01
10. Drainage area (square miles)		<1	1–10	10–100	100–1000	>1000
11. Stream order		≤2	3	4	5	≥6
12. Erosion of banks		Stable		Slumping		Eroding
13. Sediment deposition in bed		Stable				Large-scale deposition
14. Width of valley flat (feet)		<100	100–300	300–500	500–1000	>1000
Biological and Water Quality Factors						
15. Water colour		Clear colourless		Green tints		Brown
16. Turbidity (parts per million)		<25	25–150	150–1000	1000–5000	>5000
17. Floating material		None	Vegetation	Foamy	Oily	Variety

cont.

Factor Number and Descriptive Categories	Evaluation Numbers				
	1	2	3	4	5
Biological and Water Quality Factors (cont.)					
18. Water condition (general)	Poor		Good		Excellent
19. Algae: amount	Absent				Infested
20. Algae: type	Green	Blue-green	Diatom	Floating green	None
21. Larger plants: amount	Absent				Infested
22. Larger plants: kind	None	Unknown rooted	Elodea, duck weed	Water lily	Cat-tail
23. River fauna	None				Large variety
24. Pollution evidence	None				Evident
25. Land flora: valley	Open	Open with grass, trees	Brushy	Wooded	Trees and brush
26. Land flora: hillside	Open	Open with grass, trees	Brushy	Wooded	Trees and brush
27. Land flora: diversity	Small				Great
28. Land flora: condition	Good				Overused
Human Use and Interest Factors					
Trash and litter					
29. Metal ⎡number per	<2	2–5	5–10	10–50	>50
30. Paper ⎢100 feet of	<2	2–5	5–10	10–50	>50
31. Other ⎣river	<2	2–5	5–10	10–50	>50

Factor Number and Descriptive Categories	1	2	Evaluation Numbers 3	4	5
Human Use and Interest Factors (cont.)					
32. Material removable	Easily removed				Difficult removal
33. Artificial controls (dams, etc.)	Free and natural				Controlled
34. Accessibility: individual	Wilderness				Urban or paved access
35. Accessibility: mass use	Wilderness				Urban or paved access
36. Local scene	Diverse views and scenes				Closed or without diversity
37. Vistas	Vistas of far places				Closed or no vistas
38. View confinement	Open or no obstructions				Closed by hills, cliffs or trees
39. Land use	Wilderness	Grazed	Lumbering	Forest, mixed recreation	Urbanized
40. Utilities	Scene unobstructed by power lines				Scene obstructed by utilities
41. Degree of change	Original				Materially altered
42. Recovery potential	Natural recovery				Natural recovery unlikely
43. Urbanization	No buildings				Many buildings
44. Special views	None				Unusual interest
45. Historic features	None				Many
46. Misfits	None				Many

Key: < less than > greater than ⩽ less than or equal to ⩾ greater than or equal to cottages along a road may tend to detract from its inherent character, and have the opposite effect.

Within the list of human-interest criteria, I have included the term 'misfits'. Probably one of the things that makes the Swiss mountain landscape so appealing is that the type of architecture and the handling of building location seem to fit especially well into the particular environment. On the other hand, if you were to put a flashing neon sign advertising hamburgers on one of the Swiss chalets, it would be a cultural shock, and I would call it a misfit.

The first two classes of factors are less complicated than the human interest group. The physical factors are the easiest to measure in the field. Such factors as river width, river depth, and certain other characteristics, require only a recording device or an elementary observation of the river channel. Under biological factors the list includes water colour, turbidity, amount of algae, and the kind and extent of water plants, which are often indicative of stream purity or pollution. Under the three categories, a total of forty-six criteria were chosen to describe a landscape's aesthetic character.

After the factors were chosen, twelve river valleys in central Idaho, including Hell's Canyon, were chosen for evaluation. All were sites that have some potential for power development. Locations with such potential were selected in order to restrict the sites under discussion to those having something in common with Hell's Canyon. Each site was physically evaluated by standing at the edge of the river, thus providing uniformity in the way the observer looked at the environment. One could just as well have chosen evaluation sites that were part way up the valley sides, but this would have the disadvantage of putting the observer at varying distances from the river.

At each site the checklist of forty-six items was filled out. It can be seen from Table 1 that most of the physical factors could actually be evaluated with some common unit of measure. Others, however, had to be estimated in terms of categories — erosion of stream banks, for example. In all cases there were five evaluation categories specified in the checklist. During evaluation, each site was described by assigning to each factor a number from 1 to 5, according to its physical, biological, or human interest characteristics. Where physical measurements were involved, the five categories varied in their span in an unbroken progression. For example, the five categories of river width were: less than 3 feet, 3 to 10 feet, 10 to 30 feet, 30 to 100 feet, and more than 100 feet. In this way, the categorization of a given site with regard to one of the factors could always be fitted into the category quantities.

One of the purposes of the study was to eliminate personal subjectivity in landscape analysis. Accordingly, the 'evaluation numbers' for each of the forty-six factors in the checklist serve a descriptive function only; evaluation number 5, for example, is not to be interpreted as 'superior' to evaluation number 1, or vice versa. If a given site has a river width of more than 100 feet, our analysis does not rank this area above one whose river width is, let's say, less than 3 feet, but merely assigns different evaluation numbers to each of these locations.

The results of such a comparative study depend in part on the sites chosen for comparison. This being the case, another set of comparisons was made between Hell's Canyon and a series of rivers in four national parks of the United States. In this way I could find out not only whether Hell's Canyon is very different or rather like other river sites in Idaho, but also how the region compared aesthetically with some of the great beauty spots that the nation has already recognized by giving them national park status.

Any scheme for comparing landscapes must rest on some philosophical framework. The philosophy underlying the scheme I used is the following: *Landscape that is unique either in a positive or negative way is of more significance to society than one that is common.* A place of great scenic beauty is of importance because of its scenic qualities. On the other hand, one could imagine a unique site which is extraordinarily unattractive – a large, neglected, pestilential dump, for example. This also has significance for society, but in the opposite sense.

Having obtained the checklist data from twelve river valley sites in the Idaho region, the next step was to compare the sites, factor by factor, in order to determine the relative uniqueness of each factor at each site. Let us take river width, for example. Each site would be placed in one of five categories. Most of the sites had river widths falling into category 4 – somewhere between 30 and 100 feet. A small number had widths greater than 100 feet and a few fell in category 3, having a width from 10 to 30 feet.

To discover the relative uniqueness of each site's river width, we then determined how many among the twelve sites had river widths falling within each of the five categories. If it happened, for example, that there was only one river more than 100 feet wide, no other sites would share the 5 categorization, and this would determine what I call the 'uniqueness ratio' of this one river. The uniqueness ratio for the river in question is equivalent to the reciprocal of the number of sites sharing the category value. The number 1, or unity, divided by the number of sites sharing the value, in this case 1, gives a uniqueness ratio for that particular site of 1·0. If there were two sites that shared category 5 in river width, each would be assigned a uniqueness ratio for river width of unity divided by 2, or $\frac{1}{2}$ (0·50). If, for a particular factor, all twelve sites fell in the same category, each of the twelve would be assigned a uniqueness ratio of 1 divided by 12 or 0·03.

By this method, then, each site had a uniqueness ratio for each of the forty-six factors that were measured in the field. Adding uniqueness ratios for all forty-six factors for a given site yields a 'total uniqueness ratio'. In this way, the total uniqueness ratios for the twelve sites may be compared one with the other; the higher the ratio, the more unique the site. This is a way of measuring numerically the relative uniqueness of each of the sites chosen for comparison. The results of this uniqueness ratio technique, when applied to the twelve Idaho river valley sites, are given in Table 2.

There is a technical difficulty involved with the simple addition of the uniqueness ratios for the forty-six factors at a given site. By the process of addition, each of the forty-six factors is given essentially equal weight in determining the total uniqueness ratio. On further consideration of the list of forty-six factors, one may decide that some are far more important than others, and therefore, for certain purposes, selected groups of the factors can be used for other analyses. Nevertheless, the uniqueness ratios for the forty-six factors present a general means for quickly comparing a group of sites.

The uniqueness ratio technique is objective in that it does not distinguish whether a given site is uniquely aesthetic or uniquely un-aesthetic. The valley of the Little Salmon River near New Meadows (Site 7), for instance, was indeed the least attractive, most uninteresting, and unspectacular of the twelve sites surveyed. But because this site was different from the others in being a stream that was sluggish, algae-infested, murky, and slow flowing, it rated a high uniqueness ratio – the highest of all the twelve sites. It was unusual in a negative sense.

TABLE TWO

'Total uniqueness value' (see text for full explanation) is an objective measure of how different each site is from other sites studied, without regard to 'positive' or 'negative' aesthetic values.

Site Number and Location	Total Uniqueness Ratio
1. Wood River, 6 miles above Ketchum	11·07
2. Salmon River, $\frac{1}{4}$ mile above Stanley	11·00
3. Middle Fork Salmon River at Dagger Falls	11·87
4. South Fork Salmon River, near Warm Lake	13·93
5. Hell's Canyon, below Hell's Canyon Dam	16·09
6. Weiser River at Evergreen Forest Camp on Highway 95	11·17
7. Little Salmon River, 6 miles north of New Meadows	23·10
8. Little Salmon River, 4 miles south of Pollock	13·78
9. Salmon River, 2 miles below Riggins	10·25
10. Salmon River, at Carey Falls, 20 miles above Riggins	14·31
11. French Creek, 1 mile above junction with Salmon River	11·95
12. North Fork Payette River, near Smiths Ferry	10·21

As can be seen in the table, the second largest total uniqueness score is Site 5, the Snake River in Hell's Canyon. In interpreting its rank order in total uniqueness score, one can say that Hell's Canyon was different from all others in ways that made it scenically interesting and therefore unique in a positive sense. Surprisingly, then, the two highest uniqueness scores represented the two sites that might be called the two opposite ends of the scale of aesthetic interest.

A visual picture of the position of the various sites in the uniqueness scale can be obtained from the graph in Figure 1 in which the ratios of human interest and biological uniqueness form, respectively,

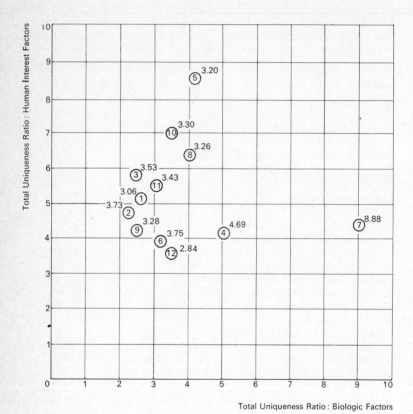

3.20   Uniqueness of Physical Factors

⑤   Site Number

Figure 1. The graph provides a measure of the relative uniqueness of each of twelve Idaho river valley sites in terms of the three groups of aesthetic factors listed in Table 1; biologic uniqueness is measured on the horizontal axis, human interest uniqueness on the vertical axis, and the physical uniqueness ratio is listed alongside each site number.

the ordinate (vertical, or y-axis) and abscissa (horizontal, or x-axis) with the physical uniqueness ratio written in numerical form next to each plotted point. It can be seen that Site 7 stands alone on the graph, primarily because of its uniqueness score on the biological scale – a result of its being the only polluted river among the sites surveyed. It can also be seen that Sites 5, 10, and 8 stand more or less alone because of low values in the biological factors and high values on the human interest scale. The graph, then, is an easy way of seeing that the total uniqueness score of Hell's Canyon, Site 5, and the polluted river, Site 7, are indeed at the opposite ends of a scale of landscape desirability.

Having demonstrated that the total uniqueness score does not involve personal preference or preference bias, one can now proceed to select combinations of factors from the checklist in order to perform additional types of analyses. In this study, checklist factors were chosen for their particular significance with regard to the impression that the site gives to the viewer. The *selection* of factors does involve personal judgement as to which ones appropriately describe the landscape characteristics; but the selected factors themselves remain independent of this judgement. Factor selection may therefore be thought of as a subdivision of the objective basic data.

In this step factors were selected from the forty-six-factor checklist for the purpose of evaluating each site in terms of two characteristics – valley character and river character. Valley character I conceived as a *combination* of the scale or grandeur of the landscape, the availability of distant vistas, and the degree of urbanization. Valley character is certainly influenced, in part, by the bigness of landscape features. The spectacular character of many of the grandest scenic views in the world comes in large part from the presence of high peaks in close proximity to the valley floor from which the viewer is seeing the landscape. Specifically, where the valley floor is narrow and the adjacent hills or mountains exceptionally high, the viewer has the concept of a large-scale landscape. Where, in contrast, the valley floor is very wide and the adjacent hills low, the impression is one of flatness – the opposite of grandeur. The Swiss Alps are so spectacular because the valleys are narrow and the mountains are near by and extremely high.

The method of obtaining a value for landscape scale for each of the twelve Idaho river valleys is dependent upon a diagram, as shown in Figure 2. For each of the sites, the height of the mountains was plotted as ordinate and the width of the adjacent valley floor plotted as abscissa on the bottom graph of the diagram. On this graph, Sites 5, 10, and 11 fall in a zone of large-scale landscapes (high mountains, narrow valleys) and other sites fall near the other end of the scale, which I call a 'subdued landscape'. To simplify the combination of height of hills and width of valley to the single value, landscape scale, the position of each plotted point in the bottom graph in Figure 2 is projected orthogonally on to a diagonal line (line A). (The projection of each point is indicated by those lines leading from the points at a 45° angle, upward and to the right, in the lower graph.) Line A now serves as the line on which the sites are ranked according to their respective landscape scales. Having a value of landscape scale for each site, this joint value can be used for the construction of a new graph, as has been done in the central portion of Figure 2, using line A as a horizontal, or *x*-axis.

At this point, it was reasoned that the impression of a landscape on the viewer is partly determined by this landscape scale, and partly by the 'degree of view confinement'. Where distant vistas are available in large-scale landscapes, one has the impression of spectacular scenery. In contrast, where the view is confined by heavy cover or by adjacent hills, the result is aesthetically ordinary from the scenic point of view. Again this is one of the reasons why the Alps give a strong impression of scenic grandeur; not only is one looking out from a narrow valley to the high mountains immediately adjacent, but one can see up and down the valleys for long distances, viewing ranges of mountains as background vistas. In contrast, when one is in the bottom of a narrow, tortuous gorge, with no distant outlooks, as in

---

Figure 2. 'Height of near-by hills' plus 'width of valley' equals 'landscape scale'. This value plus 'scenic outlook' equals 'landscape interest', which, combined with 'degree of urbanization', yields 'scale of valley character', a measure of the viewer's aesthetic impression of the landscape at each site.

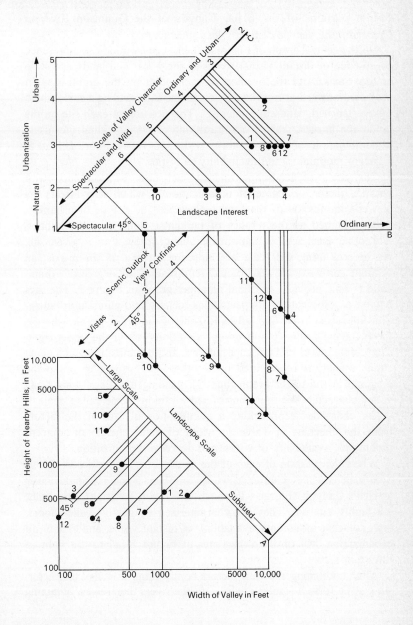

certain portions of the Black Canyon of the Gunnison River in Colorado, the view is distinctly less spectacular.

On the central graph of Figure 2, then, scenic outlook (the presence or absence of distant vistas) serves as the *y*-axis and landscape scale as the *x*-axis. And the position of each point on the graph is again projected upward at a 45° angle on to line B, providing a scale which I have labelled 'landscape interest'. The position of each site on the landscape interest scale is thus a ranking of the individual sites using a combination of three factors: width of valley floor, height of adjacent mountains, and availability of vistas.

The scale of landscape interest can now be combined with another factor − degree of urbanization − which also affects the viewer's impression of the total landscape. The degree of urbanization is defined as the totality of buildings, houses, roads, utilities, and other earmarks of man-made change present in a given site. As before, using the scale of landscape interest as the *x*-axis, an ordinate, or *y*-axis, is constructed representing the degree of urbanization. This provides the final or upper graph in Figure 2. The sites having a combination of spectacular scenery and minimal urbanization fall in the lower and left-hand zone of the upper graph, whereas those having ordinary and urban conditions fall in the upper right. The combination of landscape interest and urbanization, each given equal weight, is represented by another 45° projection on to the diagonal in the upper graph (line C), yielding a scale of what I call valley character. We thus constructed a ranking scale called 'scale of valley character' representing a combination of four of the factors from the checklist in Table 1: width of valley, height of adjacent mountains, availability of vistas, and degree of urbanization.

When the position of each of the twelve sites is considered on this final scale of valley character, we see that Sites 5 and 10, Snake River at Hell's Canyon and the wild reach of Salmon River at Carey Falls, are highly unusual. They are characterized by narrow valley floors, high adjacent mountains, availability of distant vistas, and little or no urbanization. All of the other sites in Figure 2 fall to the right of Sites 5 and 10.

After combining the four factors contributing to valley character, we can perform a similar analysis on the rivers themselves, obtaining a measure called 'scale of river character'. Experience indicates that the grandeur or majesty of a river is dependent upon a combination of its size and apparent speed. Rivers tumbling over a succession of falls tend to be more impressive or aesthetically appealing than those that appear sluggish. The latter characteristic is not so much dependent upon true velocity, which is usually poorly estimated by the untrained eye, as it is on the *appearance* of speed judged mostly by waves and surface riffles caused by rapids or falls. We therefore wish to find a combination of factors that gives the viewer the impression of the river's grandeur itself. For this we use river width, river depth, and the presence or absence of rapids, riffles, and falls, chosen from the checklist factors.

Eventually we arrive at a ranking of the sites according to river character; those rivers that are wide, deep, and have rapids, falls, and riffles rank high on this scale. In this instance, Sites 5 (Hell's Canyon) and 10 (Salmon River at Carey Falls) again outrank the other locations. As the last step in our analysis, we use a graph to compare the twelve sites according to both valley character and river character (Figure 3), and thereby obtain a final rank reflecting a total of seven of the factors chosen from among the forty-six on the initial checklist.

It can be seen that on this graph Hell's Canyon is indeed unique, for it falls in the farthest position in the upper right-hand part of the graph. Nearest to it again is Site 10, the wild reach of the Salmon River near Carey Falls. Nearly all of the other sites fall in the central cluster in the centre of the graph. Site number 7 (Little Salmon near New Meadows), the least interesting of all those surveyed, falls at the opposite end of the scale, appearing in the lower left-hand portion of the figure.

The same kinds of data that were used in the construction of the graphs just described were tabulated for Hell's Canyon in combination with four national park rivers. A similar set of graphs was derived, the results of which are shown in Figure 4. In this comparison, it can be seen that the points representing Hell's Canyon and Grand Canyon fall nearly together in the upper right-hand portion of the graph. They are comparable in the combination of valley character and river character and stand in exceptional positions. By

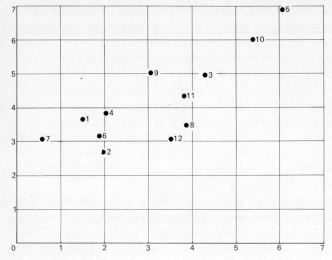

Scale of River Character

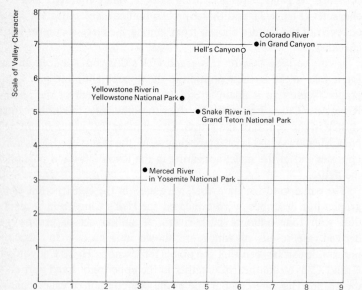

Scale of River Character

Figures 3 and 4. The viewer's aesthetic impressions of Idaho river valleys and river valleys in national parks are evaluated in terms of 'valley character' and 'river character'. Relative to other locations, numbered sites falling in the upper right-hand portion of the graphs tend to have large rapid-flowing rivers, large-scale landscapes, scenic vistas, and little urbanization. On the basis of this assessment, Hell's Canyon ranks second only to the Grand Canyon of the Colorado.

---

comparison, the Merced River in Yosemite is of a lower order of interest. Truly the Yosemite Valley as a whole is one of the great scenic beauty spots of the world, but the river within the valley is not of a special character.

The result of the data collection and analysis indicates that it is possible to set up a list of factors that influence the aesthetic nature of a given location. The factors can be considered all together, in this case by the computation of a total uniqueness ratio, or they can be selected and used in various combinations to express certain aspects of a landscape's characteristics. It is hoped that the study will indicate both the need for, and the possibilities of, an objective description of landscape.

6. Piped Water Supplies for Ecumenopolis

M. G. IONIDES

Taking a long-term look into the future, towards ecumenopolis, where will all the water come from? Already there is a sense of crisis almost everywhere in the world, and especially in the most intensely developed countries — the ones which have moved farthest towards ecumenopolis.

One thing is sure. If we want to find the whole solution we must examine the whole problem, and to do this we must start with a whole diagnosis. What has happened? Why has piped water supply become a major problem in so many countries? Why has it happened all at once, and so suddenly?

Let us look at these questions in terms of growth, along the time-scale. Figure 1 shows the three essential elements of any piped water supply system. They are a 'catchment basin', a 'storage reservoir', and a 'delivery system'. The rain falls on the catchment area; it is stored (and the flow is evened out) in the reservoir; and the water is spread out to the consumers through the delivery system.

These three essential elements are always present, whether the system is large or small, whether it is a surface catchment and a surface reservoir, or a groundwater catchment and a groundwater reservoir. (See Figures 2 and 3, which illustrate the elements in section.)

The city grows. Not only this, but the rate of consumption per head grows also: more baths, more water-borne sanitation, more dish-washing machines and laundering machines and, of course, more processing water for all kinds of industries and services. So, supply has to grow, which means that the catchment area has to grow too, because the intensity of rain is fixed and so we can only get more water by commanding a bigger catchment, and more reservoirs.

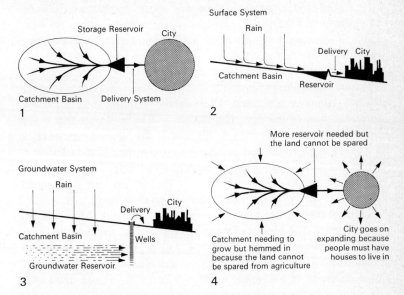

Figure 1. The three essential elements of any piped water supply system.
Figure 2. Surface catchment and surface reservoir.
Figure 3. Groundwater catchment and reservoir.
Figure 4. Problems caused by urban growth.

Now man's urban and rural interests come into real conflict. In its crude form the conflict is obvious enough; a fight between two competing forms of land use – water supply on the one side, agriculture on the other (Figure 4).

It is certain that this competition is going to sharpen, and that the agricultural side will win. The reasons can be identified precisely and trends for the future can be foretold.

As world population goes up, the total demand for food goes up also. It rises geometrically because there are two factors at work: the increase in the number of mouths to feed, and the increase in standards. Beyond a certain stage, the increase in total production can no longer be met simply by increasing the area of land under agriculture; the increase must also come from higher productivity per acre. And as time goes on, the emphasis must inescapably move towards 'vertical' development instead of 'horizontal' – intensive rather than extensive; bigger yield per acre rather than more acres; because there are no more new acres left.

This has already been happening; and one of the fundamental factors in increasing productivity is soil moisture – i.e. water – and its effective, complete utilization. There can be no doubt at all that in the future, the aim of the first-class farmer will be to ensure that every drop of water which arrives on his land in the form of rain leaves it by transpiration through a productive crop of one kind or another; and to ensure that not a single drop flows off into the valley, nor a single drop percolates down through the subsoil into the ground waters, if by any means it can be used to produce crops.

Some of the best farmers may even reach this ideal. Most will fall far short of it. The supply of water to flow into the streams and rivers and to recharge the ground waters will depend largely upon the farmers who fail. In other words, the continued utility of our traditional methods of gathering water will come to depend upon continuance of inefficient farming.

It is already going this way. In England, to quote a most cogent example, farmers are increasingly building their own dams and reservoirs to store the rain for irrigation during times of drought. Every drop they save in this way is deducted from the supply which used to go down the valley for all the other uses, including water supply for the towns and cities.

So agriculture is coming into head-on collision with water supply. First, by opposing any further inundation of agriculturally useful lands for water supply purposes, especially for reservoirs; and second, because the farmers will progressively make more efficient use of the water which falls on their lands as rain, and will thereby allow less and less of it to escape, either as surface run-off or as percolation into the subsoil and the ground waters.

Simultaneously, while the remaining sources of water are being diverted, increasingly, towards agriculture, the need for new sources of water for domestic and industrial uses is growing geometrically. It is like two trains heading for collision, each going faster and faster, and at the same time, each growing longer and heavier.

Let us suppose that the absolute ultimate stage has been reached. Wherever the earth's surface is under crops of any kind (including for present purposes forests and pastures and gardens) the rainfall will be totally used. All the surface run-off is saved and stored and used for irrigation during drought. Techniques for managing soil moisture have ensured that there is no percolation into the ground waters. Let us push the picture to its ultimate (and of course imaginary) *reductio ad absurdum* and assume that all the wells and boreholes have dried up (it is already happening in many places, so perhaps the idea is not so absurd after all) and that the quantity of water reaching the river systems is no more than is needed to maintain them as waterways, as amenities, and for fishing, but nothing left for providing supplies for waterworks. Perhaps the supplies to the canalized and controlled river valleys will then come mainly from sewage-works effluent, pure and wholesome as it can and should be, but for psychological reasons not usable for other purposes.

In these circumstances it is obvious that domestic and industrial water supplies would have to come – could only come – from the rain which falls on the roofs of buildings, on roads and on other built-over surfaces; or from the sea, by desalination. For short, we might refer to these as the 'built-up run-off' and the sea.

I put 'built-up run-off' before the sea for good reasons, despite the fact that desalination of seawater fills the newspapers while the other source is hardly mentioned and remains unstudied.

Conservation, Recirculation, and the Closed Circuit

When a city takes water from a fresh inland source, and discharges its waste water back into the river and thence to the sea or the lake, it is operating what might be called an 'open' or 'natural' circuit. This is illustrated in Figure 5a. The waste water is purified and diluted in the river and the sea, and is then vaporized into the atmosphere, returned inshore by the rain, and so re-enters the circuit. Of course, the actual particles of water are not the same each time round, but for the relevant practical purposes this makes no difference.

By means of a desalination plant, man can nowadays provide a supplementary source, if the fresh inland source is not sufficient (Figure 5b). What he has in effect done is simply to insert an artificial vaporization and condensation process into the cycle, in parallel with the natural cycle. It is a 'virtual' closed circuit because the actual particles of water which are sucked from the sea and desalinated are not the same particles that are discharged, as waste water, via the river and into the sea.

If man chooses, he can eliminate the natural or open circuit altogether and rely wholly on the virtual closed circuit, as in Figure 5c.

He can go a step further too (Figure 5d). Here, the actual waste waters are treated and then vaporized and condensed to remove the dissolved solids. A comparatively small additional 'topping-up' supply, equal to actual consumption and losses, is drawn from the sea and put into the circuit. Since the saline load in this case is far smaller than in Figure 5c, this is presumably cheaper. On the other hand, if

Figure 5. Conservation and recirculation.

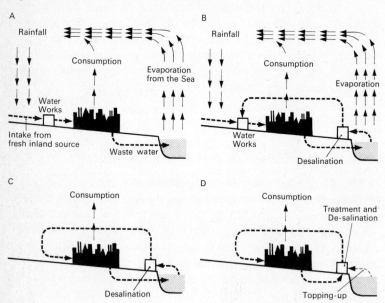

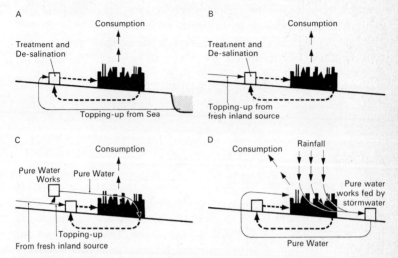

Figure 6. Circulation and the closed circuit.

this process is to be used for domestic supply as well as processing, public sentiment has to accept the recirculation of water which, though it has passed through a vaporization process, is none the less a purified sewage effluent.

Once we get to Figure 5d, an obvious question obtrudes. Why send all the waste water down to the sea, treat it, and then pump it back? Is this journey really necessary? Why not do it as in Figure 6a?

At this point, another idea comes up. In the arrangement of the alternative in Figure 6a, the supply from the sea is only a small proportion of the circulation, being only the amount consumed plus losses. If this relatively small flow can be met from a fresh inland source, we can have the arrangement as in Figure 6b.

A double circuit is a further possibility, as in Figure 6c. A fresh inland source goes (after treatment) into a high quality pipe network, for drinking, cooking, etc. The bulk supply for industrial processing, etc. is recirculated, and the waste water from the high quality circuit is added to it.

Finally, we come to the alternative illustrated in Figure 6d, where the comparatively small flow to meet actual consumption and losses is found by collecting the rainfall which falls on and around the area concerned, be it a city or an industrial plant.

All these sketches represent technical possibilities and possible considerations for the future. They can all be done. The extent to which they will actually be done depends on a range of other factors, especially the economic and the social factors.

Complementary, Competitive, or Both?

The two sets of schematic sketches illustrate the fact that the 'dilution' method, so far as concerns disposal of waste waters, is an obvious and natural phase in the evolution of man's settlements. It is in fact the 'open' or 'hatural' circuit of the sketch in Figure 5a. But when expansion of settlements and of their waste water discharge go too far, the natural process does not suffice. Specific re-use or re-circulation then becomes necessary, in some form or other.

Conservation takes over when dilution has been carried as far as it can go. But conservation does not necessarily replace dilution. So long as there are bodies of water, in rivers or lakes, where nature can contribute to the processes of purification, it is sound practice to carry the artificial treatment of waste waters no further than is needed to ensure that the natural processes of dilution can cope, without pollution. In this sense, conservation and dilution are complementary, not competitive.

In another sense, however, there may be (and almost certainly will be) competitive situations. One reason is that the dilution of waste waters is only one of the purposes of constructing reservoirs and other works for regulating rivers. Indeed, in any given situation, where there is still the technical possibility of improving pollution control by investing in more regulation which will bring other benefits besides more dilution, there will be a need for cross-comparison of costs and benefits.

As in so many sectors of human affairs, dilution and conservation are complementary as a whole, but often competitive across dividing lines where the balance of factors is debatable.

Ultimate Extremes

It is illuminating to see where one would get to (firstly) if we relied exclusively on dilution, with no treatment of waste waters and (secondly) if we relied exclusively on treatment, so that nothing but pure water is put back into the rivers and lakes, all the polluting elements having been removed.

With the first, more and more water is required for dilution and when the river systems have been regulated right up to the practical limit, more and more water has to be imported from somewhere else. When all the waters of the United States have been harnessed into the system, the water-hunters have to look outside the U.S. frontiers to other parts of the continent. When the resources of the American continent have been exhausted, an intercontinental hunt has to be started. The last, ultimate limit might be to go to the polar cap, melt the ice and pipe it down into the United States.

The other extreme is illustrated by a completely closed system, as in Figure 6d. In this extreme case, each unit, whether a city or an industrial plant, is self-supplied with its domestic and processing water through a closed circuit, topped up from the rainfall which drops within its own boundaries. Wastes in the discharge leg of the circuit are in solid form (because the water is vaporized) and are ultimately disposed of by transportation. Density of usage (population per acre, production per acre) is ultimately limited, so far as water is concerned, by the fact that consumption plus losses cannot be bigger than total rainfall over the controlled area.

Some Comparative Features of the Two Extremes

When we compare the two extremes, a very significant thing emerges. The dilution and regulation extreme ends up in a vast continental (or intercontinental) system of reservoirs, rivers, canals, and pipes, and the further we go towards the extreme, the more necessary it becomes to

interconnect the entire network inside itself, so that the natural variations of supply in various parts can be averaged out.

When we push conservation towards its ultimate limit, we tend
towards the exact opposite, i.e. towards smaller units, more and more
self-contained individually, each comprising its own capacity for
averaging out the natural variations of supply from the rain.

Again, in seeking the ultimate limit by regulation and dilution, we
are obliged to pin our explorations to the natural topography and
hydrology of the earth's surface. We have to search for and survey
the rivers and lakes as they are, the sites for reservoirs, canals, and
pipelines as they might be. The final pattern is dominated by nature's
actual disposition of lands and waters.

By this method, we follow faithfully in the footsteps of the early
settlers, who planted their first trading-posts at the nodal points where
nature had provided water, in rivers and lakes, in best relation to the
farmlands. We are still in the 'hunting and mining' phase of man's
hydronomic history.

When we seek solution by conservation, we are exploring new
technologies, and in the ultimate limit, any geographical locality will
serve as well as any other provided there is enough rainfall to charge
up the closed system and keep it topped up.

7. Waste Management

B. T. BOWER, G. P. LARSON, A. MICHAELS,
AND W. M. PHILLIPS

Basic changes in American life have combined to accentuate the problem of waste generation and disposal and to make it one of the most intricate and technically difficult problems. New factors have profoundly affected the problem in recent decades. Among them are population movement from farm to city, extensive spreading out of urban areas, a shift from rail transportation to motor vehicles driven by internal combustion engines, steadily increasing demand for electric power, expanding use of easily disposable but non-degradable materials, and greatly increased industrial production. These changes have combined to increase vastly the volume of wastes generated and discarded, and tended to concentrate them within the relatively small areas of urban cores. This has strained the assimilative capacity of the environment and accented the significance of waste accumulation.

The Problem: Some Examples

A dome of haze hovers over built-up parts of the New York region – especially on a calm sunny day. For the most part, this consists of automobile fumes. In 1965, some 6·5 million motor vehicles spewed 1·2 million tons of hydrocarbons into the air over the second regional plan study area.

In and around New York city, there is no escape from the patina of dust and soot. Nearly 300,000 tons of particulate matter are discharged annually to the region's atmosphere. Two thirds of this comes from the burning of refuse, either in apartment house and municipal incinerators or open dumps. The burning of fuels for heat and power generation produces particulates and sulphur dioxide gas. About

2 million tons of SO_2 are discharged each year, which, when combined with air moisture to produce sulphuric acid, lead to deterioration of masonry, paint, and clothing.

The potential damages of liquid wastes are measured by the amount of oxygen needed to oxidize them. About 700,000 tons of this biochemical oxygen demand (B.O.D.) are generated each year, and less than 40 per cent of it is removed by various waste reduction facilities.

Solid wastes, of which about half are paper and paper products, amounted to 17 million tons in the study area in 1965. About 30 per cent is incinerated; most of the remainder is disposed of in sanitary landfills and open dumps. Only some 4 per cent is salvaged. Generation of solid wastes, particularly disposable consumer products, has increased rapidly.

By the end of the century the region's population will have increased by about 60 per cent, from 19 to 30 million. Per capita income is expected to double. Both trends imply substantial increases in waste generation. If present trends and policies continue, vehicle-miles travelled will more than double and electric power demand will increase at least five-fold.

Solid wastes requiring disposal could more than triple by the year 2000. As urbanization engulfs greater segments of the region's vacant land, disposal space has become increasingly rare, especially in the developed core where most wastes are produced.

The Public Health Service sees municipal sewerage systems doubling their effluents before 1990, and the complex chemical composition of new industrial wastes may result in some difficult treatment problems.

Findings

1. Even without added population, upward trends in per capita waste generation and increasing public demands for improved environmental quality – particularly the cutting down of air and water pollution – will require much greater attention to waste management.

2. Efficient management of wastes requires analysis of the entire

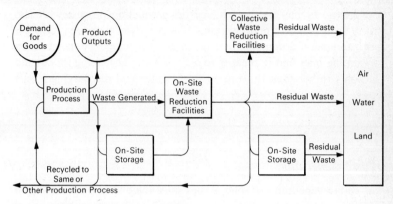

Figure 1. Waste management system.

waste management system, beginning with waste generation (Figure 1). Limiting waste generation offers a great opportunity for improved waste management. The usual approach to waste control – limiting waste discharges – may be less effective than controlling the generation of wastes. For example, limiting the sulphur content of fuel oil may be a better waste management technique than limiting SO_2 discharges.

3. One form of waste can be transformed to another during handling and disposal. Solid wastes, for example, may result in gaseous wastes when incinerated, liquid wastes when ground in garbage grinders, or remain as solid material disposed of in landfills. This suggests that integrated policies should be formulated for all forms of wastes at all stages in the waste management system, rather than separate policies for solid waste disposal, air pollution control, and sewage disposal – although administration of these programs might well remain separate.

4. Waste management policies should apply to the entire metropolitan area, even though elements of an efficient waste management system, such as refuse collection, can be carried out on a less than regional basis.

5. One way to achieve more economical waste management is to place the costs of waste handling and disposal on those who produce

the wastes. It may be that changes in production processes are less costly than handling and disposing of wastes after they are produced. For example, if a manufacturer is charged for dumping effluent into a stream, he may find it cheaper to recycle water he is using for cooling purposes rather than drawing in fresh water and discharging it as a waste.

Waste Generation

Per capita generation of solid wastes since the end of the First World War has increased by about 60 per cent. Contributors to this increase have been greater per capita consumption of paper products, the 'packaging revolution' which has virtually eliminated the purchase of goods in bulk, the decreased durability of many consumer goods, and the general proliferation of consumer goods. These are clear reflections of the spreading affluence of society.

An important factor in waste generation is that many decisions concerning the production of goods for consumer use are made without consideration of the impacts on waste generation or waste disposal costs. An obvious example is the decision to use non-returnable bottles rather than returnable bottles. Instead of a container which is recycled into the production–consumption process, the bottle becomes a waste which must be handled and disposed of after its contents are used.

The recycling of wastes, as illustrated by the environment of a space capsule, can have important effects on waste management costs. Although this will be evident from subsequent analyses, it is of sufficient importance to merit illustration here. In the United States, paper currently accounts for about 50 per cent, by weight, of the collected solid wastes generated per capita. Between 10 per cent and 20 per cent of this paper is salvaged and re-used. If we assume there is a market for recycled paper, waste management costs can be estimated for each level of recycling. Assuming that the paper which is not recycled is disposed of with the rest of the solid wastes by incineration, with subsequent disposal of the incinerator residue to sanitary landfill, the annual cost of solid waste disposal, with only 20 per cent of the paper recycled, is about 1·5 times the annual cost if 80 per cent of the paper were recycled, a difference of almost 100 million dollars for the New York region.

A waste management system consists of: (1) facilities for handling, treating, and disposing of wastes; (2) facilities for modifying the assimilative capacity of the environment; (3) regulations for modifying the generation and discharge of wastes (such as standards, charges, and controls on location of waste generating activities, and treatment facilities); and (4) facilities and procedures for collection and analysis of data necessary in monitoring environmental quality and performance of individual waste generators and waste reduction facilities. A simplified waste management system and its relation to waste generating units and to the environment is illustrated in Figure 1.

Measures which modify the assimilative capacity of the environment or allow better use of the existing assimilative capacity are important possible components of waste management systems. Examples of such measures are: releases of stored water to increase a stream's capacity to assimilate organic materials and to dilute non-degradable wastes; aeration devices which add oxygen directly to water courses, such as rivers, estuaries, and lakes; and the use of high stacks to allow the discharge of gaseous wastes at atmospheric levels where the assimilative capacity is greater.

After wastes are generated by a production unit, various types of on-site waste reduction facilities are available for use, to reduce the quantity of wastes prior to discharge to the environment or into collective waste handling facilities.

On-site waste reduction facilities include liquid waste treatment plants of various types and facilities for incinerating or compacting solid wastes.

Collective waste reduction may be used after on-site generation of wastes and their reduction at on-site facilities, if any. The wastes discharged from individual generators may be collected and conveyed to central facilities in which wastes from a number of units are handled. For example, liquid wastes from residences, offices, and industries are typically conveyed to municipal sewage treatment plants.

Solid wastes from homes and offices are collected and incinerated in municipal plants or disposed of in landfills. There are economies of scale (lower cost per unit of capacity as the size of the facility increases – up to some capacity) for some types of waste handling and reduction facilities. Use of collective facilities, in contrast to facilities at individual sites, therefore, is an important consideration in regional waste management. Economies of scale also exist with respect to some measures for modifying assimilative capacity of the environment.

There are many possible ways of managing the three forms of wastes. In addition to measures for influencing waste generation, various combinations of on-site and collective waste reduction measures are possible. Some of the existing and potential combinations of methods for handling and disposing of solid wastes are shown in Figure 2.

The Effects of Wastes Discharged to the Environment

The heart of the waste management problem involves: (1) determining the impact of waste discharges on quality of the environment, with impact measured by the time pattern of concentrations of wastes; and (2) determining the effects of time patterns of waste concentrations on users of water, air, and land.

Human beings and their activities may be affected, along with plant and animal life. Determining the impact on environmental quality and determining the effect of quality on users are complicated by interaction among wastes, which affects the resulting time pattern of concentration. That is, the degradation of one type of waste after discharge into the environment may be inhibited or increased by the presence of other wastes. The response of humans or animals to a particular waste may be attenuated or markedly increased by the presence of other wastes as, for example, the response of fish to low levels of dissolved oxygen in the presence of toxic materials.

Waste management involves the regulation of discharges from points of waste generation and from collective waste handling facilities. Various forms of regulations are possible – standards, fees on the

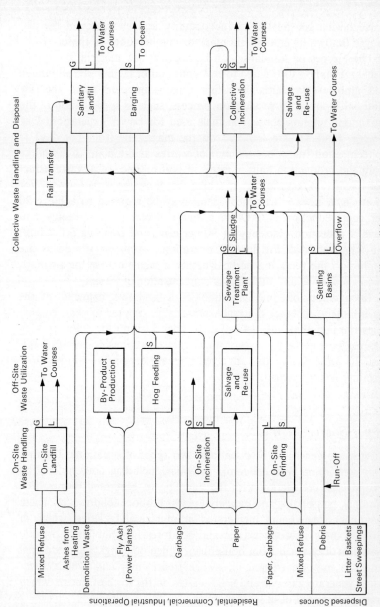

Figure 2. Combination of present and potential methods of handling solid wastes.

waste discharger related to the quantity and character of the discharge (known as effluent charges), or combinations of these.

Three types of standards can be applied: raw material standards, discharge standards (related to emissions and/or facility performance), and ambient standards. The first type is imposed upon the raw material inputs to a production process, such as specification of the maximum sulphur content in fuels used for power generation. Discharge standards are imposed on the magnitude (tons per day) or concentration (parts per million) of wastes at the point of discharge from the production unit, in terms of performance of a waste reduction facility, or on the way in which the discharge is performed. For example, a sewage treatment plant may be required to achieve 80 per cent reduction in B.O.D., a dust collector may be required to have a collection efficiency of 90 per cent, and covering procedures may be specified for landfill operations. Ambient standards are applied to the receiving body, whether a water course, or air mass, in terms of level and duration of concentration of wastes.

Recognition of time variation in assimilative capacity of the environment, whether diurnally, seasonally, or year to year, emphasizes the fact that any desired quality level cannot be achieved with 100 per cent certainty, except under rare conditions or at very large cost. In general, the costs involved increase rapidly as 100 per cent certainty is approached.

Major Sources of Wastes

Wastes are generated in essentially two types of situations. The first is in connection with economic activities, including households. The second is in connection with the handling of generated wastes. For example, households and industrial plants produce solid wastes. These may be collected and incinerated in municipal facilities, which in turn produce gaseous wastes and solid residue. Similarly, organic materials discharged from households, office buildings, and industrial activities may be treated in sewage treatment plants which themselves generate gaseous and solid wastes, in the form of sludge, which must be disposed of in some manner.

Some waste handling facilities, such as incinerators, yield a net reduction of wastes. That is, the total quantity of solid material discharged from an incinerator is less than the total input. The function of a waste handling facility is to transform one type of waste into other types, or into a modified form and/or quantity of the same type of waste, in order to achieve a material which can be disposed of more readily. Since these facilities end their process with wastes, they must be considered waste generators, though not in the same sense as a paper mill, power plant, or office building.

Table 1 shows the major waste generators in the New York region. These do not necessarily represent the major causes of air, land, and water quality deterioration in the region. In terms of proportion of total residual wastes discharge into the environment, some of these generators are relatively insignificant, in that their wastes cannot be 'found' in the environment in relation to all other wastes discharged.

TABLE ONE

Major Waste Generators in the New York Region

Waste Generator	Form of Waste		
	Gaseous (a)	Liquid (b)	Solid (c)
Individual			
Power plants, fossil fuel	X		X
Space heating: residential, commercial, industrial	X		X
Residential (other than heating)		X	X
Commercial (other than heating)		X	X
Industrial processes	X	X	X
Transportation, internal combustion	X		
On-site incineration	X		X
Collective			
Incineration	X	X	X
Liquid waste treatment plants	X	X	X
(a) SO_2, dust, and/or hydrocarbons			
(b) B.O.D. biochemical oxygen demand			
(c) Mixed solid wastes			

Policy Problems

What levels of air and water quality are 'desirable' in a region? If all the consequences (damages) of different levels of air, water, and land quality, in the form of relationships between themselves and the relationships between costs and modification of quality by various methods, were known, then the optimal level of quality could be determined by comparing costs and benefits (benefits measured in terms of damages reduced).

At the present time we do not know all the physical relationships between air and water quality and the responses of human, animal, and plant life, nor has the difficulty of relating physical responses to dollar damages been resolved. As a result, policy decisions must be based on economics and known physical effects. The known effects, which can be described in qualitative, physical terms, are such things as degree of eye irritation from smog, number of fish, such as shad, surviving upstream migration, and appearance of landfill areas. The economic criterion is based on costs defined in terms of the resources necessary to achieve different levels of quality. Thus, what can be established is the magnitude of additional resources necessary to achieve a higher degree of certainty of any specified level of quality. Whether the additional increment of quality and/or certainty is worth the additional increment in cost is a political decision.

The effluent control policies adopted by the relevant governmental agencies are part of the waste management system and hence influence waste management costs.

Policies which stimulate consideration of such modifications are essential components of an efficient waste management system. Just as the concern with the impact of detergents on water quality stimulated research and product development which eventually resulted in a change in the product, so consideration of the external costs imposed on society by the use of non-returnable bottles and non-degradable containers could lead to a change in product and process which would decrease overall costs.

Future Waste Generation

Estimating future waste generation coefficients is difficult because of the many variables which influence the coefficients. There is a large range of uncertainty attached to any coefficient estimated for a time almost thirty-five years in the future.

The most significant factors affecting the magnitude and characteristics of generated solid wastes probably have been changes in packaging practices and in household heating fuels. Packaging changes have increased significantly the amount of paper and paper products, have decreased food wastes, and have introduced plastic as a small but potentially important component. Non-combustible solid wastes have increased significantly as a proportion of the total, as a result of the popularity of non-returnable bottles and cans. On the other hand, the amount of household ashes has diminished and will probably continue to diminish to a point of virtual disappearance as a result of the increasing use of gas, oil, and, to a lesser extent, electric power for home heating.

Disposable containers for liquids and foods have virtually eliminated the returnable, re-usable bottle. Perhaps the first major shift was from milk bottles to coated paper cartons. The steel, aluminium, glass, paper, and plastics industries are all currently competing for the disposable container market. The 'mix' of container types which develops will affect the quantity and characteristics of solid wastes and the problems of their disposal. For example, aluminium and plastics are lighter in weight than the other materials and are virtually non-degradable. Aluminium may be incinerated at high temperatures, but this results in gaseous wastes which could lower air quality. Plastics generally have very high heat values and may cause gaseous waste problems if they are incinerated. Glass is heavy, will melt but seldom burn at normal incineration temperatures, and is non-degradable in landfills. A paper container may be plastic-lined and/or have various kinds of coatings and sizings; these affect its bio-degradability and increase its heat value if incinerated.

These are examples of potential changes in solid waste quantities and characteristics which may result from developments that can be foreseen or that are currently known and under way. But new developments are likely to take place by the year 2000. These may profoundly affect solid waste generation coefficients. The development of containers which can be used by the consumer would have such an effect. The classic example of this is the ice-cream cone. Physical changes in the structure of urban communities could result in purchasing and delivery systems which would reduce packaging needs.

8. Global Ecology: Towards the Planetary Society

JOHN McHALE

Within the closely knit interdependence of our now global community, the continued disparities between have and have-not nations may be viewed as a grave threat to the overall maintenance of the human community. The explosive rises in population, the pressures on food lands and other resources, the scale of wastage, disorganization, and pestilence now accompanying our 'local' wars, are also linked in due measure to the revolution in human expectations – a further, even if negative, aspect of the increase in awareness. As physical events, these press ever more critically upon the total resources and social energies of the developed regions. As world problems, they go increasingly beyond the capacity of any locally organized effort to mitigate or solve them, in anything but the shortest range.

In these terms, there are no 'local' problems any more – such as may be left to the exigencies and dangerous predilections of local economic or political 'convenience'. We have now reached the point in human affairs at which the ecological requirements for sustaining the world community take precedence over, and are supererogative to, the more transient value systems and vested interests of any local society.

The world, then, which the expanding network of electronic communication is fast reducing to a complex but single ecosystem, confronts the technological civilization with a profound and growing imbalance. The first step towards a human future is the acceptance of responsibility for meeting the emergency in our total environment by creating those generalized human conditions which will at least prevent the system from degenerating further. In the immediate term, the only way we know how to do this is by devoting the necessary physical resources to feeding the hungry; in the immediate term, we must do it by inventing the necessary means to graft our technological knowledge on all branches of the human trees.[1]

As we examine not only the local aspects of such problems within the less developed areas, but also their global effects on the more fortunate, it is clear that they form part of a larger context of eco-

Figure 1. The global ecosystem.

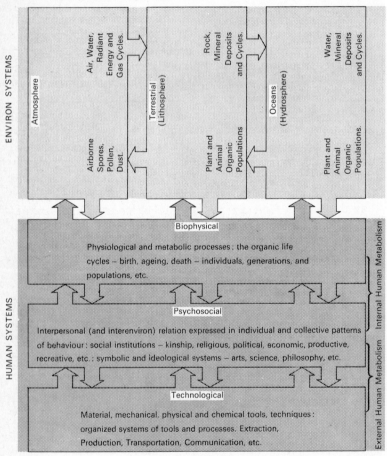

logical mismanagement. Wasteful resource-usage, soil exhaustion and spoliation, air, water, and earth pollution, etc., are world phenomena. They have all been contingent factors on human occupancy of the earth during historical time. Until recently, however, their effects were more localized and their scale relatively small. Now they may affect a whole region or continent in a few years – or in a few days, in the case of radioactive fall-out. Most of the problems of the less developed regions are all present in greater or lesser degree in the so-called developed regions. All are, in varying measure, contingent upon the 'piecemeal' nature of our present modes of knowledge integration, the gaps between such knowledge, its diffusion and effective application, and the lack of a consistent body of agreement on the physical 'stewardship' of the planet.

An Overview

Life on earth has been possible during the past billions of years only through the relatively stable interrelationships of the variables of climate, the composition of the atmosphere, the oceans, and the life-sustaining qualities of the land surface, the natural reservoirs and cycles.

Within the thinly spread biofilm of air, earth, and water space around the planet, all living organisms exist in various systems of delicately balanced symbiotic relations. The close tolerances of many of these relationships have only become known to us, generally through their disruption, in recent times.

Apart from the comparatively local disturbances of natural cycles brought about through hunting, herding, and primitive agricultural practices, man, until quite recently, did not have the developed capacities to interfere seriously with the major life-sustaining processes of the planet. He could live and find food only under conditions restricted by his technological development. The earth surface available to him, with breathable air, water, and arable land, was less than one eighth of the earth's area; the remainder – of the seas, mountain peaks, glacial, and desert areas – was mainly inaccessible to human

habitation or large-scale use. Though the evidence of ancient disruption of natural balance is still with us in the form of man-made
deserts – for example, deforested lands, etc. – these were essentially
local in their scope and consequences. It is only in the most recent
and brief historical period that man has developed sufficient power to
be actually, and even more potentially, dangerous to the overall
ecosystem – hence, to the maintenance of the human community
within that system.

As earlier inventions increased the amount of energy and survival
advantage available to man, so they had adjusted the ecological
balance to favour his increase, with corresponding adjustments in all
other living populations within the system. The last growth change in
human population since the onset of the industrial revolutions is,
within all previous contexts, an extremely 'abnormal' one: 'It represents, in fact, one of the greatest biological upheavals known in geo-
logical, as well as in human, history.'[2] In the longer range, of course,
this expansion may be viewed as the 'natural' evolutionary development of a unique species.

The first century of this new phase, of adaptation and 'species
extension' through intensive industrialization, seemed to confirm the
notion that man could indeed conquer nature – could free himself
from the biological laws governing other species' development. As the
series of such technological revolutions has multiplied in frequency
and power amplification, this has been somewhat tempered by the
equivalent increase of knowledge about the overall effects on the
planetary habitat. Both the extended possibilities of human control
of the environment and its present and potential limitations have
become the focal point of our mid twentieth-century dialogues.

Though it has been obvious, for some time, that we cannot simply
extrapolate human development in terms of 'natural laws', and that
Malthusian and other limits may not strictly apply, there are still more
central questions remaining. Since man, as a species, sidestepped the
normal biological sequence of evolutionary adaptation through his
capacity to externalize his intellectual and physical means, in symbolic and technological systems, he is, in this sense, more directly in
control of his own future evolvement. The extent of that control,
over the environment and over his 'uncontrolled' activities within it,

rests on his capacity to apply himself consciously to an adaptive process which has been largely unconscious.

Through his intelligence, man has enlarged his 'ecological niche' to include the whole planet. His activities are no longer constrained to horizontal deployments around its surface, but go increasingly into and beyond the atmosphere and beneath the oceans and include the transformation of vast amounts of the material resources of the planet to his purposes.

The scale of these activities and the expansion, and proliferation, of man-made systems now approach magnitudes in which they directly affect larger and larger areas, sectors, and relationships of the overall ecosystem.

Negative and Positive Aspects

Where such extended controls of man have increased survival advantage for greater numbers of men, and thus forwarded the human enterprise, we may count the overall balance till now as favourable. Our next priority – towards enormously extending such survival advantage to the greatest number of men – requires an even more rapid and extensive growth in scientific and technological undertaking on a world scale. This will require not only taking cognizance of the great positives of our recent acquisition of sufficient material power to carry out such a task, but also an immense stocktaking of the negatives which are inherent in the present lack of conscious integration and planning of our major technological systems.

Such systems now comprise not only local industrialization, in the sense of mass-production factory facilities, but all the globally interrelated systems complexes of transportation, communication, production, and distribution facilities. There is no longer a division possible between factory and farm or, in this sense, town and country; all are closely interlocked in a close symbiotic relation – a man-made ecology which we now see, almost for the first time, as an integrally functioning 'organic' sector within the overall ecosystem.

Though the growth of population has been accompanied by more intensive cultivation and higher food yields per acre, the amount of presently usable soil per capita is declining, and, in many areas, becomes impoverished through ill use. As the historical pattern of deforestation, which produced many of the great desert areas, continues, there is added to this the increasing amount of arable land claimed for building dams, roads, industrial installations, mining, etc. – all the necessary uses of an increasing technological system. In the United States alone, urbanization and transportation have been calculated to draw more than a million acres of soil, each year, from cultivation.

Other uses of the earth, incident on our developed technological capacities, have also increased enormously in the past hundred years. As against approximately 50 tons of raw materials per person consumed in 1880, we now use over 300 tons per person annually. When this is translated into amounts of iron, coal, oil, wood, and other products 'harvested' from the earth, processed and redistributed elsewhere, the operation becomes of considerable ecological magnitude. For example, of all the coal mined by 1960, only 20 per cent was mined before 1900, and the remaining 80 per cent since that time. The energies used in the extraction, processing, transportation, and use cycles of all the industrial materials are obtained mainly from burning the fossil fuels – each ton of which used releases large amounts of carbon dioxide and other gases into the atmosphere. From 1860 to 1960, this has been calculated to have increased the atmosphere's carbon dioxide concentration by 14 per cent; during the eight years from 1954 to 1962, the average rate of increase was 5 per cent. Sulphur oxides, a more immediately harmful aerial pollutant in highly industrialized countries, are expected to show a 75 per cent increase over present critical levels by 1980. A single fossil-fuel, power-generating plant may emit several hundred tons of sulphur dioxide per day and, under certain weather conditions, locally overburden the air of a whole city. When this effect is increased by larger multiple fuel uses in dense urban concentrations, the results may be lethally apparent – 4,000 persons died, directly or indirectly, from one week of such intense pollution in London in 1952, and 1,000 in 1956. The annual emission into the atmosphere of such pollutants, other than carbon dioxide, is estimated at 125 million tons for the United States alone. Even if present generating and production power technologies were converted 50 per cent to non-fossil fuels, it has been estimated that pollutant by-products from the remainder would still double 1970 levels every twenty years.

The dependence of one sixth of the world's food supply on 'artificial' nitrogen from the chemical industry is another factor in the overall ecosystem function. There is a tendency to separate agriculture from industry in everyday thinking, but the image of the farmer as conserver, and industry as the spoiler, of nature is no longer true — if it ever was. To make each million tons of such nitrogenous fertilizer annually, we use, in direct and related industries, a million tons of steel and five million tons of coal. Some fifty million tons of such support nitrogen are estimated to be required annually by A.D. 2000. The amounts of other agricultural chemicals which will require equally massive support technologies, to further maintain and increase crop yields, is only now becoming apparent.

When air, water, and earth uses are compounded with mounting waste and sewage disposal, the emphasis on the required redesign of all such human systems, becomes acute. The natural systems of air/ water/soil purification are now so overburdened, through increase and misuse in many areas of the world, that concern is now expressed about their overall malfunction in greater areas. These are no longer 'local' problems, as each subsector of the overall ecosystem eventually affects other sectors, if misuse occurs on a large enough scale.

Waste disposal, even in the most advanced countries, is still archaic. Those methods used in our larger urban concentrations are little improved from the traditional systems evolved for much smaller and less waste-productive communities of the pre-industrial period. The average city of a half million people now disposes of fifty million gallons of sewage daily and produces solid waste of about eight pounds per person each day.

The use of watercourses, or rivers, streams, and lakes has also been grossly affected, not only in the 'discard/residue' process of sewage disposal from cities and the increasing discharges of industrial wastes, but from intensified agricultural practices. Large amounts of soil additives in the form of fertilizers and chemical nutrients are washed off the lands through rainfall, irrigation, and drainage into the natural watercourses, where they disturb the aquatic life balances. The undue growth of algae and plant growths decreases the oxygen supply for fish and other organisms, thus attenuating the self-renewal of the water system. Again, such problems are not localized. In the case of the pesticide 'spin-offs' and other toxic agents, introduced into upper river reaches, their concentrated effects may only be felt thousands of miles away, for example, the massive fish kills, of around twelve million, in the Mississippi River and Gulf of Mexico in recent years.

Inadvertent poisoning of organic life through the unplanned and uncoordinated introduction of various toxins into the environment is not restricted to plants and animals. The effects on man are, in many cases, greater – but receive less direct attention. Some 500 new chemical compounds each year go into widespread usage in highly industrialized countries with little attention to their long-term dele- terious effects. Without going into the more publicized aspects of radioactive fall-out, a simpler case may be adduced of 'lead fall-out' – from tetra-ethyl lead in auto fuel additives. After almost fifty years of rapidly increasing use, such lead contamination is being monitored at levels approaching toxicity in waters, crops, and the human system.

Returning to the more positive aspects of man's ecological acti- vities, it is necessary to redress, in part, the semantic bias on 'pollu- tants, garbage, and poisons'. This usually tends to suggest vast quantities of alien substances being injected into an otherwise per- fectly functioning system. Rather – pollutants are, as we perceive and designate them: poisons and natural substances 'out of place', or in excess of tolerable levels. The gases and dust of forest fires, volcanic ashes, pollens, marsh effluents, etc., are all 'natural' pollutants of natural environments. Our concern here is to more fully appraise the role of man-made systems which are also *natural systems* in the overall integral functioning of the ecosystem.

The problem aspects which we have stressed are only problems through lack of 'design' and more thorough anticipatory planning. The naturally occurring forces operative in the environment can be more selectively and systematically used to absorb pollutants, reduce sewage/garbage, and reprocess discards and residue on a much vaster scale.

Our lack of adequate knowledge and equal lack of foresight and control are the main factors which overburden the natural regulatory systems and lead to their malfunction and breakdown. Some large-scale sectors, such as the global atmosphere, have enormous absorptive and regenerative capacities – others, such as a local soil area, forest, lake, or watershed, are more precariously balanced and may *not* be renewable or recoverable in anything but very long-range terms.

Some of the mandatory requirements for the merely adequate maintenance of the ecosystem are already clear.

We need to redesign our major social, industrial, and agricultural undertakings towards their more efficient and systematic functioning – as ecologically operating systems, rather than 'piecemeal' aggregates of unrelated processes. This would apply not only to environmental controls – such as houses, cities, and other facilities – but to all of our environmental control facilities which now comprise within themselves a vast 'socio-agri-industrial ecology'.

We need to refashion this system so that it can serve many more people at better standards and at higher performance levels than ever before:

1. *To 'recycle' the metals and materials in the system* – so that there is a swifter turnover with the least lag in scrapping and processing cycles. In high-grade technological process, each use cycle tends, through overall development, to achieve more, not less, performance per invested unit of materials.

2. *To employ increasingly our 'income' energies* of solar, water, wind, tidal, and nuclear power, rather than the hazardous and depletive fossil fuels. The latter represent major 'capital' investments, which once used are not replaceable. They are too precious to 'burn up' in our currently prodigal fashion, but they may be more efficiently – and more fractionally – employed in indirect conversion to plastics, foodstuffs, etc.

3. *To refashion our food cycle* that we may more swiftly augment the present starvation diets of more than half the developing world. We need, however, to go also beyond emergency satisfaction of immediate needs towards the more extensive ecological redesign of our whole agri-industrial system; employing the most efficient 'natural' means of food conversion through the plant/animal chains *and* the possibilities inherent in microbiological, biosynthetic, and other processes.

4. *To set up eco-monitoring and control centres* which will act as 'early warning' systems in relation to our large-scale scientific and technological undertakings – analysing and evaluating their immediate and long-range effects on the overall ecological matrix and their positive and negative implications on the quality of the human environment.

In essence, we have to redesign the presently chaotic elements of our developed and 'externalized' human metabolic system into a series of 'closed' ecological loops phased in with, and taking gainful symbiotic advantage of, the overall ecosystem. The wastes of one type of production cycle become the raw materials of another; thus energy converted and dissipated for one purpose may serve many more. The noxious 'garbage' of several processes may be valuable 'nutrients' materials in another sector. Each component subsystem now requires critical evaluation and redesign in terms of such higher performance and more economical function. The directly quantitative gains implied in this redesign are also qualitative in terms of more 'useful' function, in the reduction of pollution hazards, in less 'destruction' of the natural environment – and in the increased social and physical advantages available to all men.

Our thinking must obviously go beyond immediate preoccupation with locally vested interest in the prior solution of this or that isolated problem! The only context for all of our major problems is the global context. The range of our thinking is that which may extrapolate human ecological requirements, beyond subsistence survival, to the maximal advantage of all. It must also accept the challenge of designing not only for 'tomorrow' but for a century of tomorrows.

This may often entail 'non-use' as well as re-use. The scale of our present technological capacities is such that we cannot act without more accurate gauges of their immediate and long-range effects. Where it may be pleaded, for example, by special interest groups, that we have enough coal, oil, and gas reserves for 500 years, any *expanded* use at the present rate and level of technology is obviously precluded by their adverse side-effects on the ecosystem. In such cases, a resource, an invention or process which is evaluated as dangerous to the maintenance of the life systems should be left in 'storage' – until a more evolved society may use it less prodigally and less dangerously!

Need for Global Thinking

Such an orientation leads to further considerations involving our global, rather than local, commitments. As stated, there is no large-scale human problem which may not be solved outside of this context. Air, water, and soil pollution are not local – the air is not restrained within municipal or national boundaries, nor are the waters.

Where massive imbalances occur – whether biophysical in terms of earthquakes and other natural catastrophes or socio-physical in terms of hunger, disease, and the catastrophe of war – we need to recall that the resources of the planet can no more belong, by geographical chance, to any individual, corporation, country, or national group than can the air we breathe. National ownership of a key watershed, mineral deposit, or scientific discovery is as farcical, and dangerous, a proposition as our supposedly national sovereignty of an 'air space'.

The evolutionary transition towards 'world man' now faces a situation analogous to that of emerging national or empire man in the preceding two centuries. Then, the local ideological issues revolved around national control of public health, or child welfare, education, pure food and water legislation, etc. The same arguments now prevail at the world level, regarding the rights and privileges of individual nations – as if they were isolated, self-contained, and wholly autonomous physical and social entities. Though such a fiction may be a comforting 'prop' for local individual and social identity in a rapidly changing world, it is dangerously removed from reality.

The scale of our global systems of production/distribution, communication/transportation, etc., has now gone beyond the capacities of any single national or even regional group to wholly sustain and operate. They require, and are dependent upon, the resource range of the entire planet for the metals and materials of which they are built – and in which no nation is now self-sufficient. Each system is intricately and complexly interlocked with all others − production with transport, transport with communications, etc.

Ours is possibly one of the most critical periods in human experience up till this time. Poised in the transition from one kind of world to another, we are on the edge of a great transformation in the whole human condition. The next fifty years may be the most crucial in all of man's history. We have few guides to follow and almost no historical precedents. 'Many of the old moralities have suddenly become immoralities of the most devastating character.'[3] All of our previously local actions are now writ large on a planetary scale. The knowledge with which we might make the correct decisions is barely adequate − yet our gross ecological errors may reverberate for many generations.

NOTES

1. Hasan Ozbekhan, *Technology and Man's Future*, Systems Development Corp., Sp. 2494, May 1966.

2. National Academy of Sciences, *Energy Resources*, N.R.C. Pub. No. 1000-D, 1962.

3. R. C. Cook, 'Truth and Consequences in a New Era', *Population Bulletin*, Vol. XXII, No. 4, November 1966.

Part Two. Man: Balancing Inner and Outer Realities

Introduction

Man in equipoise with his environment is, says Giedion, one of the characteristics of periods of high civilization. His four groupings show where this balance is in grave danger today and provide a helpful framework for a discussion of human identity in megalopolis: (1) the balance between the human body and natural forces; (2) the balance between reason and emotion; (3) the balance between specialization and a comprehensive approach; (4) the balance between man's private life and the welfare of the community.

1. Balance Between the Human Body and Natural Forces

In ekistic terms, this means maintaining an equilibrium between man and nature. In Part One, evidence was put forward that showed how it is essential for man's survival that he designs his world in harmony with natural processes. In Part Two, both C. A. Doxiadis and Bertrand de Jouvenel lay stress on this same issue, noting how man's personal security is dependent upon his conscientious stewardship of the natural environment. Such an approach became necessary as soon as man started to dominate nature when determining the form of his physical environment.

Dr René Dubos reminds us that man is constantly transformed by the environment in which he lives. The health hazards of the recent past were mainly infectious and nutritional diseases, generated by the environmental conditions of overcrowding and poverty. Today's health hazards are no less environmental in origin, though their determinants are chemical pollutants and the stresses of life in noise-ridden and chaotic cities. Dr Dubos considers that the 'alarming increases in various types of chronic and degenerative disorders' may represent a delayed reaction to toxic conditions, and he paints a frightening picture of the long-term effects of developing apparent tolerances to a bad environment. Indeed, with considerable authority, he suggests that new and possibly very dangerous health problems are likely to arise, as we will not know the effect of some of our environmental pollutants for several generations. In other words, the growth of megalopolis will be accompanied by a race to detect, diagnose, and cure new diseases arising from the unforeseen effects of its transformation and pollution of the natural environment.

2. Balance Between Reason and Emotion

C. A. Doxiadis takes us swiftly through an analysis of the interrelation of man's body, senses, mind, and soul and – like Giedion – he concludes that only when these are all in equilibrium can man feel and perform at his best. This is happiness. De Jouvenel suggests that this equilibrium should be sought for in our daily round of urban life: 'the extraordinarily high value which people set on their vacation periods gives the measure of their discontent with their daily lives. . . . It is to the workaday world itself that pleasantness must be imparted.' De Jouvenel points out that man needs to determine what it is that he really wants: 'there is a vast difference between letting changes occur under the impact of technological advances and choosing the changes we want to bring about by our technological means'. He instances the misuse of economic cost-benefit analyses in which, for instance, a plentiful supply of bottled mineral water would automatically be considered an 'advance', whereas the causes of its demand – a polluted (therefore chlorinated) natural water supply – would go unrecorded. Giedion makes much the same point, insisting that all mechanization must be subordinate to the real needs of man. We need to resist the tendency to develop everything that technology makes possible.

To W. H. Auden, happiness consists not in leisure, but in work in which one is enchanted, which is at the extreme end of the scale from degrading, repetitive toil. Such 'work' – such happiness – requires concentration and one of the greatest needs of the present day, as he sees it, is to teach young people how to concentrate themselves upon something they consider worth while: 'The first prerequisite for leading any satisfactory kind of personal life in a technological society is the ability to resist distraction.'

However, it is fairly clear that many people find it very difficult to determine what it is they want or to find employment in something that seems of real value both to themselves and others. Such people have to find their satisfaction in their leisure time, and the use of growing leisure time is one of the preoccupations of our period. The man who rejoices in his work has few leisure problems. He tends to ration leisure so that it does not interrupt his productive work more than possible. But for the rest, leisure time represents the antithesis of the daily round of toil – of the rule of reason. It can be said that the essence of leisure-time activity is its spontaneity – its response to the free emotional choice of the individual. Such uses of leisure time have in the past been the prerogative of the rich, and, as Auden points out, their amusements have seldom benefited society or the environment. He then quotes Logan Pearsall Smith: 'To suppose, and we all suppose, that we could be rich and not behave as the rich behave, is like supposing that we could drink all day and stay sober.' In other words spontaneity becomes not only more difficult but also more dangerous as more and more people come to live in less and less space. We are therefore forced to accept de Jouvenel's dictum. The only way to plan for human happiness – for the balance of reason and emotion – is to aim at 'the ordinary man's good day'; which means enabling each man to find work in which he can take both joy and pride.

3. Balance Between Specialization and a Comprehensive Approach

Giedion's dictum that specialization has now to become integrated into 'a universal outlook' has long been a favourite theme of Buckminster Fuller, and we include a long quote from a paper he prepared in 1964.

The university student, having attained his first freedom of initiative, his optimum level of metabolic efficiency, bodily coordination and general-outlook idealism, is concurrently exposed to an awareness of powerful intellectual and technical disciplines of the university resources know-how. At the same time he is the recipient of frequent science-technology break-through news such as under-the-polar-ice-passages-of-atomic-submarines, new orbital achievements in rocketry and electronics. The student also receives an overabundance of news concerning *world want* and political stresses which break into open guerrilla warfaring and ever more frequent world crises.

Logically the students become exasperated and say 'why can't we make the world work? All the negative nonsense is the consequence of outworn, ignorant biases of the old-timers . . .'

There are now in the world several thousand powerful, high capacity, information storage, electronic computers. The number of them approximately doubles yearly. The computers both large and small are mathematical pattern cognition and recognition storage, retrieval and coordination machines of which the human brain is the prototype. As with the human brain all pattern processing consists of two main classes: *differentiation* and *integration*, i.e., *specialization* vs. *generalization*. Differentiation identifies, evaluates, selects, and separates out the uniquely developing patterns. Integration ratiocinates comprehensively the coordination rates and magnitudes of complex interactions, developments, or transformations . . .

In relation to the computer and the present significance of its development, as judged by experts, as far as the machine's differentiating function is concerned it can be said that the *computer is about to make man obsolete as a specialist*, due to the fact that the machine can differentiate and seek out much more accurately, swiftly, and persistently than can man. The computer can stay 'up' all night, night after night, selecting the blacks from the whites at incredible speeds and under humanly intolerable conditions of heat, cold, smells, etc., yet never tire. That the machine is to replace man as a specialist either in craft, muscle, or brain work, is an epochal event.

The computer as super-specialist produces, multiplies, and administers 'automation'. Because man's intellect had inevitably to invent the computer and because the computer is superior to man as a specialist – comprehensive, world automation has always been developing inexorably and is now inexorably imminent . . .

Displaced as specialist or differentiator, man is now being forced to become preoccupied exclusively with integrative patterning considerations. This means an epochal reorientation. All the universities, all the educational systems from now on must forsake specialization and cultivate powerful generalization. Everybody will be taught to be comprehensivists. Fortunately that will come naturally because man is born to be comprehensive. It is his most unique biological characteristic.[1]

In the world of today, the adult generations are finding themselves increasingly 'out-of-date'. With very few exceptions, they still belong to the era of specialization, and have problems in adjusting themselves to the universal approach of the new world. The mass media – in particular television and the international telephone service – are assisting this re-orientation by enabling them to take part, almost at first hand, in large and small events occurring simultaneously in different parts of the globe. But, in the main, the adult generations are becoming increasingly dependent upon learning from the young: professors from their junior faculty, and the junior faculty from their graduate students.

Problems also arise as to how the young child is to be brought up in our exceedingly complex and rapidly changing world, so as to preserve his birthright of a comprehensive approach. Delos Six was concerned with this, noting that natural abilities can become 'closed off' both by 'standard' educational systems and by an over-complex environment. It concluded that the child 'needs an environment which protects him from over-stimulus while allowing him to develop flexibility in facing simultaneously the small neighbourhood and the megalopolitan complexity'.

4. Balance Between Man's Private Life and the Welfare of the Community

Both Delos Three and Delos Six were very much occupied with the relation between the privacy of man's home life and growing population densities. Edward T. Hall noted at Delos Three that attitudes towards the size and character of a desirable living space vary greatly between different cultures, and several examples were then given of different approaches to the notion of density – or crowding in space. Very high density apartments may be tolerated if one is not confined to them for too long stretches of time: if open country and wide views are immediately at hand, or if they alternate with a week-end country cottage, or if, as in the case of college dormitories, they alternate with a more spacious family home.

It was pointed out that: 'people live at different tempos and different densities every day, week, and year. The changes can be stressful or wholesome'. Indeed the 'problem' of density is basically related to the conditions of life in a particular area. An instance is cited in Part Three of this book (Society) of a district in Boston that was torn down because, statistically speaking, its housing density was considered too high. But Chester Hartman describes how the people there lived a very full and satisfactory social life outside the confines of their somewhat cramped, but greatly loved, apartments. The area was also noted for its low level of social pathology – a fact that should have given the city authorities pause before ordering its demolition. As was stated at Delos Three: 'Density is only one, limited and mechanistic, measure of community life which does not mean much on its own.'

Delos Six hinted that studies of animal and plant societies might enable us to derive 'significant analogies to man's societal relations', and Professor Waddington gives a succinct account of how several kinds of animals keep their numbers below the level of stressful overcrowding. He summarizes the forms of control as: 'competition for conventionally determined status symbols which give the right to reproduce'. These controls are set up well before problems of shortage of food supply or excessive overcrowding become critical, and there are distinct indications that animal populations are interested in achieving a quality control of their offspring.

Giedion states that man 'must discriminate between the domain reserved for private life and the areas of collective life', and one of the most crucial of these areas in our period is the whole issue of population control. Unless restraint is practised, the burgeoning population of the world will inevitably outstrip not just its food supply, but the possibilities of living with personal dignity. Family planning is not a new idea. Both Plato and Aristotle advocated methods of birth control, not because they had a Malthusian fear of food shortages, but because they believed in striving for excellence.

The problem of changing value systems regarding family size is used by Dr Berelson as a measure of testing a number of different control devices on the basis of six criteria: the scientific readiness of the method, its political viability, its administrative feasibility, its economic availability, its ethical capability, and its practical effectiveness.

However, one of the major problems of population control is that, while it is discussed and advocated in public, it can only be practised in intimate privacy. This is a dilemma that is recognized by Dr Berelson, who points out that society has now developed the technical means to regulate population growth, but the individual human being has not become convinced that this applies directly to him. In other words, individual measures of birth control are only likely to become widespread (and ultimately universal) when the large family is widely accepted as a form of social disgrace.

In this, as in so much else concerning man, the influence of the social environment is crucial. Part Three specifically discusses the role of the small community in megalopolis for, as Dr René Dubos states: 'environmental planning plays a key role in enabling human beings to actualize their potentialities'. Part Four (Shell) follows, spelling out the more detailed environmental specifications, to provide, in Doxiadis's words, 'a place which satisfies the dreamer and is acceptable to the scientist, a place where the projections of the artist and the builder merge'.

NOTES

1. R. Buckminster Fuller, 'The Prospects of Humanity', *Ekistics* 107, October 1964, pp. 232–42.

9. Anthropocosmos: The World of Man

C. A. DOXIADIS

Man and the space surrounding him are connected in many ways within a very complex system. Man's space is just a thin layer on the crust of the earth, consisting of the five elements which shape man and are shaped by him: nature, in which he lives; man himself; society which he has formed; the shells (or structures) which he builds; and the networks he constructs.

This is the real world of man, the anthropocosmos, half-way between the electron and the universe. It is with this world, and with its relationship to man, that I will deal.

The human society does not operate as it did in the past, since, with increasingly lower densities, natural human contacts are fewer in our cities. Of course, we have cars – but not all of us do; certainly not the children (who miss their grandparents) and certainly not the underprivileged citizens. Of course we have telecommunications – but how can a telephone replace a father at bedtime, and how can television replace the contact of the two sexes? More and more people pour into the cities and often social or racial elements come into conflict which we are not prepared to face.

We have built larger and taller buildings, but at the same time we have isolated man inside them. We have limited our life within their sterilized atmosphere, and we have eliminated such natural expressions of it as works of art in the open. The age-old love affair between man and buildings is being destroyed in our cities.

It is in this environment that civilized man has to live – safe from infections but threatened by degenerative diseases; safe inside his home but not in the streets, isolated in the crowd, exposed to neuroses and psychoses. How many of these conditions are caused by the fact that our children must be caught by the hand in the streets and taught that they live in hostile surroundings?

We must face the fact that modern man has failed to build adequate cities. In the past his problems were smaller, and he solved them by trial and error. Now human forces and mechanical ones are mixed and man is confused: he tries and fails. We say he will become adapted. Yes, he is running the danger of becoming adapted. Prisoners, too, become adapted to conditions! For man to adapt to our present cities would be a mistake since he is their prisoner.

Setting Goals

What man needs is a place which satisfies the dreamer and is acceptable to the scientist, a place where the projections of the artist and the builder merge.

What is our goal? At this point we have a technology that is changing our life, yet we have set no goal for it. No businessman would buy machinery at random when building a factory, no housewife would collect furniture at random for her home. And yet this is exactly what we are doing in the case of our cities, the physical expressions of our life. For them we are producing and collecting at random.

What will our goal be? From the present I turn to the past and remember what Aristotle said: that the aim of the city is to make man happy and safe. I can find no better definition.

So if, in the chaos of our present situation, we can accept this, then we have something firm to stand on, provided we can define what we mean by *man*, *happiness*, *safety*, and *city*.

Man

I begin with man, so close to us and still 'man the unknown'. But he is also man the unique and complex organism, the ascending arrow of evolution according to science.

But which man are we talking about? Which best represents the nature of man? Is it primitive man (to whom some romantics want us to return) or the ancient Greek? The medieval or renaissance man, or the modern technocrat? The only possible answer is: the contemporary man as a human being in general abstract considerations, and as an individual, since in life we deal only with individuals.

Which man, then, is our ideal? To answer we have to look at man from every possible angle (Figure 1). We have to look at the body, and when we see people stretching, or youngsters dancing, we must realize that their bodies are revolting against the inactivity we have

Figure 1. Total man.

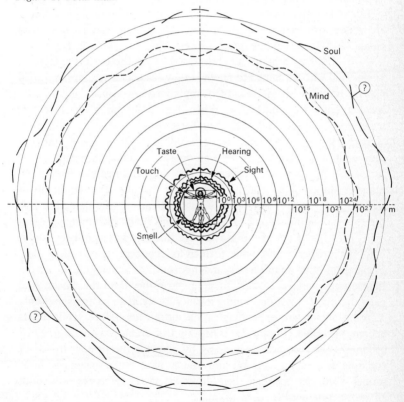

condemned them to. We have to realize how ignorant we are as to whether the taller, larger people that our children are becoming are more or less resistant to the hardships of life.

And we must look beyond the body. Beyond the sphere of his body are several concentric spheres defined by man's senses. No sensation can be overlooked: a sweet or bitter taste; caressing a marble carving, or a loved one; walking on sand with bare feet; the smells, the sounds, the sights; all physical sensation; and then all metaphysical sensations, like faith and religion.

The mind of man carries him into areas beyond those that can be reached through the senses. So does his soul by way of sentiment, for sentiments, too, are shaping factors.

I cannot forget the peasant on the mountains of Kabylia in Algeria. He was aware that it was in his interests to abandon his destroyed village and move to the plain. 'Then why do you still live here?' I asked. 'C'est un amour,' was his answer. Then there was the Cypriot intellectual who explained to me the many reasons why Cyprus should not be united with Greece, then applauded enthusiastically when a speaker defended unification. When I asked about it he placed his hand over his heart and said, 'You forget this.'

Body, senses, mind, and soul are only partial aspects of man, but they cannot be separated; they all operate together in health and in sickness. The real link between music and architecture lies within man. A dancer may find his motivation through stimulation of his senses, or mind, or sentiments. The mind can be stimulated through the rhythmical movement of the body walking or swimming.

At present we are at a disadvantage since we have not been studying man properly and have formed no concept of our ideal man. Because of this, man's body and his soul are developing in a nonharmonious way, according to the mind rather than the senses. And even the mind is not developing harmoniously in all its areas, but only in some, which are expanding much more than before, while others become atrophic (Figure 2). What kind of creature is man going to become? The risks we are running by allowing the present trends to continue are very great. We may be turning out monsters without proper balances between their different parts, monsters who may annihilate one another or mankind.

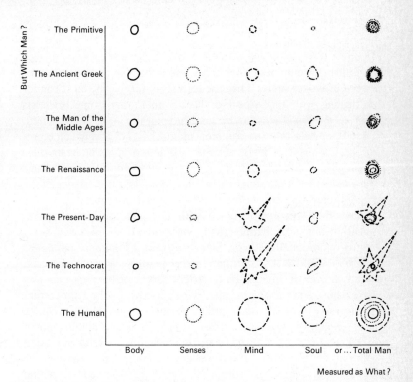

Figure 2. Man is the measure.

Confronted with such a threat I think we have an obligation: to study man as a whole, without rejecting anything that he has learned throughout his history unless we can prove scientifically that it is harmful. This we can achieve not by coordinating existing sciences — man does not consist of externally coordinated parts since he forms a whole — but by anthropics, the science of man. There is no proof that we can produce a better man by changing the relationship between the body, the senses, the mind, and the soul. Thus, our goal should be to work towards a harmonious development of all his elements: total man.

Happiness

Now I turn to happiness, although I know that the mere mention of the word provokes smiles. I beg the sceptics to forgive me but I cannot omit dealing with this aspect of life. Even though some scientists cannot accept this discussion because happiness cannot be measured, it is still happiness that the common man dreams of and which represents the fulfilment of his goals, the satisfaction of his interests. This is admittedly a difficult subject but we cannot work towards man's welfare unless we understand it. We should not let the existence of the immeasurable stop us from measuring what is measurable.

Rather than become involved with the philosophical or metaphysical meaning of happiness, I will proceed to measure it by standard operational methods. Since we speak of 'human' happiness we should measure it according to the quantity of satisfaction felt by man as seen in his different aspects. One can be very unhappy if one's trousers are too tight, the ceiling too low, or the temperature uncomfortable – or for other physiological reasons. But one can be equally unhappy if the senses suffer – through violent colours, noise, smell, coarse clothes, or bad food, or through stresses exercised on one's mind or soul. Man's happiness depends on the alleviation of the stresses he is subject to within his social environment or within himself.

These stresses can be relieved. There is, for example, the story about the man who always wore tight shoes so that when he took them off at home the physical relief would help him put up with an unhappy home life. Man can also learn to enjoy these stresses. As the balance between man and his environment changes continuously his chances for happiness change too.

A scientific 'happiness quotient' would be of the greatest importance to man. Such an approach would enable man not only to alleviate or to enjoy stresses, as the case might be, but also to work towards his further betterment, drawing from within himself something better than himself. This will be gradually achieved as he begins to understand how to coordinate his internal rhythm with that of his environment, changing the one or the other. He will have a variety of choices, ranging from harmony with the physical world (matching his footsteps to the pavement slabs), to harmony with nature (swimming along with the waves), to harmony with others (in the rhythmical marching of parades or in work for the amelioration of his society), to harmony with external influences (dancing to a certain tune), to complete freedom (climbing a mountain or lying on its slopes), as it pleases his internal personal rhythm.

When we come to understand all these, we can develop a formula for the lasting happiness of the total man, based on the interplay of man and environment which is a dynamic balance; a happiness which he can reach without endangering the happiness of others.

Safety

Safety is a concept just as difficult as happiness and just as indispensable. Civilization started when man first felt safe within his city. Today – for the first time in history since then – man is no longer safe, and this constitutes the greatest problem to be faced by him and his civilization. How can the city be made safe once more?

This question has to be answered through an analysis of all five elements of the anthropocosmos since the neglect of any one would upset the whole system. Nature has to be preserved, since without the proper development of all its resources there can be no hope for man's safety. The survival of man depends on his evolutionary resources and on his inborn diversity; consequently, he needs a free democratic society which will allow for the survival of the greatest variety of individuals, since we do not yet know which type is going to lead to a better total man.

Every single individual must feel and be safe, which means that safety within a safe society can regulate personal and group conflicts. The question is, at what cost can this be achieved? A man would be much safer if he never left his home, but he wouldn't be happy and he wouldn't develop further. We cannot sacrifice happiness and evolution in the cause of safety, nor safety in the cause of happiness.

So we come to the conclusion that what we need is a safety which can guarantee a basis from which to begin our endeavours towards happiness and the fulfilment of our duties to society. This leads to the concept of a system which will allow for different environments offering all degrees of safety, ranging from an absolutely safe environment, if this is possible, for new-born babies and invalids, to a completely natural environment which young people will have to conquer: thus ranging from sterilized rooms to jungles.

In such a habitat we can hope for the best balance between a controlled and an uncontrolled environment; an environment that can offer maximum safety, and yet allow for a dynamic balance of man and environment which is indispensable for lasting happiness – the only goal.

The New Frame

We can now turn our attention to the city of man, but without those preconceived notions about limiting the operation of forces which are independent of man that people often have. It is these forces which create a new frame for the city to come.

The dynamic forces of developing humanity show that we must be prepared for a continuing increase of population which may well reach 20 to 30 thousand million people by the end of the next century, at which time it may level off. This will mean a universal city, ecumenopolis, which will cover the earth with a continuous network of minor and major urban concentrations of different forms. This means that urbanization will continue, and that eventually farming may be carried out from urban settlements. This also means that the pressure of population on resources will be such that measures will have to be taken so that a balance can be retained between the five elements of the anthropocosmos in a universal scale.

But, more than all, we should be concerned with the survival of man, who, long before the earth has exhausted its capacity for production, will be subjected to forces pressing him to the point of extinction, forces caused by the elimination of human values in his settlements. When we realize that the average urban area is going to have twenty to thirty times more people and a hundred times more machines, and that difficulties grow much faster than the forces causing them, we must understand that this new frame is going to be *inhuman in dimensions.*

On the Measure of Man

Once we recognize the scale of these dynamic forces, we see that our real challenge lies not in changing these historical trends – something we cannot do anyway – but in using them for the benefit of man: shaping this universal city not only so that it will not crush man, but so that it will provide him with human settlements much better than those of today. To do this we have to build a city of human dimensions *on the measure of man.* We have repeated for centuries that man is the measure of all things – the time has come to put that principle to use again.

We cannot just talk about human scale and human happiness, we have to identify them and attempt to measure them. This can be done, since man has, for ten thousand years, been building a great laboratory in which he is both the guinea pig and the research director. This laboratory we have before us and we have to make use of it. We don't have to invent the 'human' solutions since they already exist – we have to understand them and use them within the new frame.

As an example I will mention that studies of the cities of the past show that the maximum distance from their centres was ten minutes, and the average was six minutes, meaning that people walking for a total of thirty minutes a day could visit the centre or other places two or three times. This shows that there was a human dimension influencing social and other contacts. It also shows the value of measuring such aspects of the city on the basis of time dimension and not on physical distance.

The need for such measurements arises from the consideration that in order to build a shell for a snail we must first know how the snail moves. Building the city of man requires an understanding of the laws governing his movements, not as it is manifested in his present prison, but as it would be ideally.

Up to now, measurements in cities have been based on economic criteria, but these define feasibility more than goals. We must introduce abstractions that combine goals and feasibilities. Man's most precious commodity – the one which cannot be replaced and which we don't yet know how to expand – is his own life, which is expressed by its length, or lifetime. This is the basic commodity (qualified by man's satisfaction and safety and limited by economic considerations) upon which our formula for the city will have to be based.

The average American citizen spends 76 per cent of his lifetime at home (males 69 per cent and females 83 per cent), and 24 per cent away from it. He spends 36 per cent sleeping, 20 per cent working, and 10 per cent eating, dressing, and bathing. He is left with 34 per cent, or one third of his life, for leisure, pleasure, thought, etc. It is this one third which constitutes the basic difference between man and animal. But males aged between 20 and 59 have only 20 per cent free time, of which one third is spent in commuting. On the basis of such calculations we can develop a time budget, which is more important than any other budget for man, and we can estimate how much time each man can afford to spend on each of his activities.

We can then quantify the satisfaction that man gets at every time period. Is it better for him, for example, to walk for twenty minutes, to drive in a Volkswagen for ten minutes, or in a Cadillac for two hours? We can also try to measure the degree of safety at every time length. In principle, total satisfaction would be the product of time multiplied by satisfaction. A happy life would be the product of time multiplied by satisfaction multiplied by safety. In this way we could arrive at a formula of happiness. This does not mean at all that such a formula would be a compulsory one, just as no economic formula can be imposed on anyone, nor does it mean that we should confuse the average or normal with any particular individual case.

If we now insert into the picture the factor of economic feasibility for satisfaction, we have the formula of feasible happiness, leading to the human city that we can build.

The goal set by Aristotle, which at that time did not need scientific interpretation, since all units of space were small and all dimensions at the human scale, has now to be achieved by new methods for the co-ordination of the many superimposed natural and artificial dimensions into one system.

The Human City

If we have managed to define total man, natural happiness, and reasonable safety, and then to measure them, we can define the human city. It will be very big, but it will consist of two categories of parts, the cells and the networks. The cells are going to be the size of the cities of the past – no larger than 50,000 inhabitants, no larger than 2,000 by 2,000 yards, no larger than a ten-minute average walk. They will be built on a human scale on the basis of human experience.

The networks are going to be absolutely mechanical and automatic, interconnecting the cells by transportation and communications, forming enormous organisms, with the cells as their basic units. Their vehicles will reach speeds of many hundreds of miles per hour, but their arteries will be underground; not highways but deepways – as they are in the bodies of all mammals. The higher the speed the deeper they will go.

In the cells, man will be offered all choices, from isolation and soli-tude to very intense participation in social and political life. The fact that we need TV should not lead us to eliminate the market-place. We don't need only one-way communications, we need a natural human dialogue as well.

The surface of the city will allow the flora to spread again, begin-ning with small gardens within the cells, and moving to major zones of forests above the tunnels of the networks, and big farming areas and natural reserves where man will find the tough conditions which he also needs for his health and happiness.

Society will operate much more efficiently, and people will come together in a multitude of ways, both natural and artificial.

Houses will not be formally specified, since the individual will want to express himself. Multi-storey buildings will need much greater areas per floor, so that a whole community with its shopping centre, playgrounds, and public squares, will be able to operate at each level. Automated factories will be placed within the earth, especially in hills and mountains.

Man will be free to move over the surface of the whole city, and even though the buildings will be as pleasant as possible, he will have many chances of staying out in the open without shelter or protection, since his whole organism must be kept fit for all sorts of adjustments that the future may necessitate.

In such a city we can hope that man, relieved of the stresses that arise from his conflict with the machine, will allow his body to dance, his senses to express themselves through the arts, his mind to dedicate itself to philosophy or mathematics, and his soul to love and to dream.

Epilogue

It has often been said that man may exterminate himself through science. What we must add is that man's hopes for a much better evolution also lie in science which, after all, is the acquisition of proven universal values that man can transmit from generation to generation. The whole difference between extermination and evolution lies in the goals that are set.

Our habitat is the world of man, our goal can only be human happiness and safety, leading to the human city. To achieve it we need *anthropics*, the new science based on the wholeness of man, to help us study and develop him, since we cannot achieve this by simple coordination of his separate aspects. We also need *ekistics* to help us study and develop the world of man, the *anthropocosmos*. To develop these sciences we have to break the barriers between disciplines. The task is hard but it can be accomplished through proper research and careful training. Very few minds today can work so synthetically that at every moment they can rise above the uni-directional evolution of ideas of specialists to a multi-dimensional one.

The task is hard. People have to learn how to be very conservative when dealing with man, and very revolutionary when dealing with new systems and networks.

The task is hard since man does not yet have a system of values with which to define what a good life it is.

Personally, I am convinced that the root of all problems in our cities lies in our minds, in our loss of belief in man and in his ability to set goals and to implement them. We can never solve problems and tackle diseases unless we conceive the whole. We cannot build a cathedral by carving stones but only by dreaming of it, conceiving it as a whole, developing a systematic approach, and only then working out the details.

But dreaming and conceiving are not enough. We have also to carve the stones and to lift them into place. Thus, I turn to myself and ask whether we can build the human city. My body is beginning to get weaker, my senses, especially my eyesight, do not help me as in the past, but my mind advances in knowledge and sees the confirmation of this possibility, and my soul mobilizes my whole self into a very positive affirmation: yes, mankind can build the human city.

10. Utopia for Practical Purposes

BERTRAND DE JOUVENEL

The obtaining of so-called 'mechanical energy' from inanimate sources has utterly changed the means available to human societies. I have seen an estimate by World Resources Inventory (the Buckminster Fuller group) according to which the North American population enjoys the services of 185 'energy slaves' per inhabitant, or 460 energy slaves per family. An arresting figure!

But also a misleading statement. What it calls to my mind is that each family severally is served by 460 slaves, thus enjoying the same autonomous power as the wealthy Roman of the late Empire, lording it in his villa over his own food providers and his own artisans, with many personal servants responsive to his beck and call. With such forces at its service, each family could set its own style of life after its own taste, and this without any scruples or compassion, since its pseudo-slaves would be insentient, incapable of feeling or suffering. The vivid picture thus aroused in my mind bears, as we well know, not the slightest relation to reality.

Firstly, these pseudo-slaves are not distributed among families: I do not mean that they are not distributed evenly or fairly, but that they are not distributed at all, save with some exceptions, mainly those used for individual transport. Chiefly, they are involved in a collective process of production, and it is the fruits of their energy which are made available to us. This brings us to the second point. Take as a basis of reference the pleasant setting and the unhurried pace of a mere bourgeois' life in the eighteenth century. One might think that the great increase in our powers has brought the life of even the most modest worker of our day beyond this line of reference. But it is not so. A problem arises, therefore, of how all this slave-power is being spent. What does it go into? This question involves us in complications: the use of the term 'slave-power' implies a versatility in mechanical energy which it has not up to now displayed; at its best in procuring speed, it is not much use in procuring gardens. We tend to get what it can best give us rather than what is most desirable.

But my third objection to the 'energy slave' formulation goes even deeper. Our mastery has many traits of a symbiosis: the machines do not serve us unless we service them, and we have to adjust our human organization to our equipment.

Finding out what we want should become a major object of our attention. It is a trite saying that we live in an age of very swift change. But there is a vast difference between letting changes occur under the impact of technological advances and choosing the changes we want to bring about by our technological means. I see with some alarm that we feel bound to carry out whatever technology happens to make possible. It is not clear to me that because we can now build super-sonic transport planes we should, therefore, hasten to build them – many other things are more pressing for human convenience. While it was a senile attitude towards technological change to fear and oppose it in every form, we have gone over to a childish attitude: whatever can possibly be done, let's do it! But the very abundance of the opportunities accorded by technological progress bids us to choose, brings us to an adult, responsible attitude of drawing upon the potentialities of technological progress as possibilities to be wisely exploited for the promotion of a sane and happy way of life.

The lack of any clear images of the style of life we are building is a cause of anxiety. This anxiety is revealed in the most characteristic literature of our time – science fiction. This displays what might be called a new fatalism, a feeling that our ways of life are being deter-mined entirely by technological advances through no choice of ours. Such a belief is widespread, and fed by many incautious expressions.

Why worry about the future way of life if increasing wealth increas-ingly enables each member of the wealthy society to elaborate his own specific and distinctive manner of life? If that assumption is justified, it is not only useless, it is even dangerous to picture a way of life in advance, since this is apt to steer towards convergence upon a single model an evolution which, left to itself, would lead to a far greater variety of styles, corresponding to a diversity of tastes. This is an objection to which I am highly sensitive, as I regard with horror any arrangements apt to herd individuals into a pattern of conformity: such enforced conformity is an odious trait of all but a very few utopias. I would not like to incite the designing of utopias if this were to work towards the narrowing down of individual choices.

We are increasingly integrated both as producers and consumers in a vast organization which need not be collectivist to be empirically collective. We are not forced to fit in, but the inducements to do so are very great indeed. If I choose to travel on horseback rather than by car not only do I forgo the advantages of the car, but, moreover, I shall endure many inconveniences which did not attend horseback travel in the past. The horseman caught in a rush of cars can serve to symbolize the discomforts of 'bucking the trend'. It is hardly reasonable to refuse the advantageous bargain offered to us by modern civilization. Realizing that the very process which makes it possible for us to get successively more for less toil clearly commits us to the typical way of life of our fellows, we must make every effort to improve this way of life as best we know.

Our age of agglutination has many unpleasant aspects: our environment is ugly and noisy, we are hurried and worried, people speak eagerly of 'getting away from it all' – pathetic attempts to do so crowd the roads on weekends and crowd the beaches in vacation periods. It will be found that there is no escape – quite soon Greece will resemble Coney Island – then it will be realized that what needs to be done is to improve Coney Island. The extraordinarily high value which people set upon the vacation periods gives the measure of their discontent with their daily lives. But surely it is a crying absurdity that the emphasis should be on that small fraction of the year. It is to the workaday world itself that pleasantness must be imparted, failing which, the palliative of escape will in time make the resorts as unpleasant as the residences.

What we need is to address ourselves to the ordinary day of the ordinary man. Instead of starting with some *a priori* doctrine concerning the causes of human happiness or unhappiness, we should pay the closest attention to whatever we find is apt to cloud or light up man's day.

We must beware of taking one part of the picture for the whole. In the course of the day, our man reaches several times in his pocket to pay either directly or through his wife and dependants for the acquisition of goods and services. We may regard the collection of such acquisitions as 'the family shopping list'. Our man's ability to lengthen the shopping list of the family is surely a very good thing – I have no patience with the austere moralists who belittle this aspect of welfare. On the other hand, it is not serious to take the length of this list as the exclusive measure of welfare. This unfortunately is the present propensity.

From the far-off days of Wilford King and Josiah Stamp through the works of Colin Clark and Simon Kuznets, I have been an enthusiastic supporter of National Accounting. This is a quite admirable tool in the hands of those who understand it – I am sorry that even some economists have to be included among those who do not understand it. In order to wield it effectively, one must never lose sight of the conventions on which it is based. It is a pleasure of the same nature to attend a baseball game or to follow the Olympic Games from one's home, and while the first ·was possible to the past generation, the second has only been made possible in our day. Yet the first figures in the statistical measure of the standard of life (private consumption) and not the second, because the costs thereof are counted as 'costs of productions' of the firms which provide this entertainment as a part of their advertising. But even if the costs figured, would they be a true measure of the benefit? Conversely, transport expenses of going to work are not distinguished from transport expenses incurred for pleasure. If you buy perfume, that figures, but the stink you may have to endure from the environment does not figure. If ordinary water becomes so polluted that you have to use mineral water, the mineral water figures as an improvement.

These are but anecdotal inconsistencies. Far more serious is the fact that the journey to work may become longer and more tiring, the environment may become murkier, uglier, and more noisy, without any trace of these phenomena being noted as negative components of material welfare. One must conclude that measurement of consumption (in itself extremely useful) should not be mistaken for a measure of material welfare. This is well understood by specialists of National Accounting, but too often forgotten by others.

Human felicity depends, of course, on many other than material conditions. That some of these conditions are moving unfavourably may be surmised from the rapid increase in the consumption of tranquillizers. Indeed, just as we can point to a successive improvement of the shopping list but some deterioration of the environment, so we can, in the realm of health, point to considerable improvements regarding organic health but notable deterioration in the nervous balance.

It is hardly necessary to press home points which have been made, often with exaggeration, by denouncers of our industrial civilization. Such is by no means my own mood. The negative features I do not regard as inherent traits of our progress. If I deemed them such, I would regard them as an acceptable price to be paid for unquestionable gains. But my point of view is very different; they are not a necessary price. I feel convinced that if we put our mind to it, we can quite transform the daily existence of man. Putting our mind to it means that we must begin to consider our man's day in all its aspects, instead of proceeding analytically as we tend to do.

By proceeding analytically, I mean, for instance, thinking in terms of the reduction of hours on the job without attention to those wasted in transport; thinking in terms of housing without regard for the environment; in general, cutting up the problem of man's existence into discrete problems.

It is a natural outcome of this procedure that each problem is treated in such a way as to give rise to unpleasant by-products, known to economists as 'external costs'. For instance, you provide a remarkably efficient solution of the problem of cleaning – the detergents; but this solution has the worst conceivable effect upon the water which is spoiled beyond the possibility of recycling by any simple method. The lesson of water is indeed important: because it was given, it has been treated without respect; because of such treatment, water has now become a problem; because it has become a problem we now set a value on it.

We are enthusiastic about rational calculation but we do not practise it reasonably. It is striking that economists start out by speaking of land, labour, and capital, and then immediately drop out land as of no account. While any industrialist knows that he must provide for the upkeep of his plant, the basic 'plant' we have received – the earth – seems to us to call for no stewardship.

In fact, the spirit of our industrial civilization represents a set-back relative to the spirit of agricultural societies. What I mean is this: societies of hunters took no care of preserving their stock of game. They were predators and depredators. When men settled down to agriculture it became important to provide for the maintenance of fertility. It was only very gradually that the agriculturists mastered that problem. We have not reached that stage in our industrial civilization, which is again a system of depredation of natural resources. At a more advanced stage of our skills, we have returned to a less advanced stage of foresight.

When a man awakes, he recovers awareness of his surroundings. If he thinks gladly of his family and looks forward to the day's work, he can be called happy, though I would like to add to these criteria a less essential but important component, the pleasantness of his surroundings. There is not much we know how to do, towards causing this major blessing of life, a united family. It is quite easy on the other hand to make the physical setting of life one which is delightful. Yet how can we pride ourselves on our wealth, as long as we do not make our towns as beautiful as the renaissance cities of Italy? Most people prefer to open their eyes upon trees, and I would like our man to walk to his work amidst pleasant scenery.

From the journey to work, I naturally pass on to the work itself. We have been engaged in making work more efficient: is it not important to make it more attractive? This great theme, broached by Charles Fourier, has practically not been followed up at all. Work is currently regarded as the cost of getting what we want, a negative value, the less of it the better. But is this the view which we intellectuals take of our work? Do we anxiously watch the clock to see whether we are allowed to knock off? Do we not feel that it is our work which imparts meaning to our life? Do we work to earn our leisure or do we regard our rest as enabling us to do better work? What we most want is to do 'good work' and such also is the wish we form for our best friends. Why then should our interest in the many take the quite different form of wishing them only to do 'less work'? There is reason for that contrast in that we recognize the unpalatable character of many labours. But should we not regard it as our problem to recast our organization of labour so that each man can rejoice in his work as we do? We should not accept it as a datum that the enjoyment of work is a privilege of some few: this is an immoral doctrine, and our concern should be to put our fellow men in that same position which is presently, but not by necessity, a privilege.

I recognize that the interest taken in 'the problem of leisure' is well meant, but I think this is a false track. It is treating men as children to seek means of entertaining them harmlessly. Indeed, children themselves sense it as a promotion when they are invited to do something apparently significant. You cannot make men contented through entertainments but only through achievements. It is therefore 'the problem of work' which is essential. You cannot have a good society if you do not offer to each man a man-sized job, which he can take joy and pride in. This is an immensely difficult problem but quite an essential matter.

If we aim at 'the ordinary man's good days' we may find a great change in our priorities, quite possibly that our efforts are misallocated, and that some things which are being done are not worth doing. This would be of great importance for the 'developing countries'. While we offer them valuable 'know-how', the value of our psychological impact is questionable. As a machinery for the production of happiness our arrangements have a low yield. Are there not simpler social machineries with a higher yield in happiness?

With the best intentions in the world, quite a disparaging view has been foisted upon the non-westerners: it has been pointed out to them how far they trail behind the Joneses. Is there no smoother path to a good life? Can we confidently assert that our way to a good life is necessary, when it has apparently not proved sufficient?

11. Culture and Leisure

W. H. AUDEN

For most of us, I imagine, the essential prerequisites for happiness appear to be two.

1. Freedom. That I shall not be prevented by others or by fate from doing what I enjoy doing or believe I ought to do.

2. Importance. What I do shall seem of value both to myself and to others.

Human activities can only be understood in their context of human relations. I can distinguish three kinds of relation I have to other human beings.

1. The involuntary, impersonal he-to-him relation I have to hundreds of individuals, farmers, mailmen, bus-drivers, garbage collectors, etc., whom I do not know personally and most of whom I shall never see, although my life depends upon them. Since there is no contact, we cannot like, dislike, or judge each other.

2. A professional, asymmetric, I-to-him relation I have to doctors, lawyers, teachers, priests, etc., which I voluntarily enter into at certain times for specific reasons. It is a personal relation to a degree that it involves personal confrontation and, on my side, a trust in their skill and wisdom, but impersonal to the degree that it is their skill and wisdom, not themselves as persons, which cause me to enter into the relation. Once I have got the prescription or the legal or spiritual advice I require, the relation is broken off. It is possible, of course, that we shall become friends, but we don't have to.

3. The personal I-thou relation between friends, husbands and wives, parents and children. This is voluntary, symmetric, involving mutual responsibility and, in intention at least, permanent. In addition there is a special kind of personal relation one can have to a work of art. Here the relation is not between me and the artist – the chances are he is already dead – but between me and a personal object.

In the following classification of human activities, I shall take my terms from Hannah Arendt's remarkable book, *The Human Condition*. I can distinguish three kinds: labour, work (and under the head of work I include, as Miss Arendt does not, deeds as well as fabrication), and play.

Labour is an activity imposed by necessity and lacking any element of free choice. While I am labouring, I have no sovereignty whatever over my time. In our society, I am a labourer if what I do to support myself and my family has no personal significance or interest to me, and, which, therefore, if I did not have to earn my living, I would not do. As a labourer I am a slave of society; I am aware, however, that my labour is important to others because, if it were not, I should not get paid for it.

At the opposite extreme is play. Play is a completely gratuitous activity in which I enjoy absolute sovereignty over time. I am free to play or not as I choose, and my only reason for playing is that I enjoy it for its own sake. But this absolute sovereignty necessarily implies that my play is of no concern to others and has no consequences beyond itself. Professional sportsmen who earn their living by playing a game, and compulsive gamblers who play for stakes which may ruin them or make their fortune, are not playing. Time spent in play is, as we say, *time out*, without relation to past or future. Among our games must be counted the 'play' of thought. As Rosenstock-Huessy has written: 'We play gladly and think gladly because in these activities we feel ourselves masters of the situation; the space of play and the space of thought are the two theatres of freedom.' However, 'Games give pleasure but bear no fruit, and only that which bears fruit is real. All games and all thoughts seek to exclude the necessity of death, suffering, injustice, downfall. The thinker turns the pangs of birth into causes, death into evolution.'

Between these two extremes comes the activity of work. I have the extraordinary good fortune, granted to – what shall I say? – not more than 16 per cent of the population, to be a worker. I am a worker if what I do is, like play, something I enjoy doing for its own sake because it is in accord with my interests and talents, but, like labour, is of importance to others, so that I can earn my living by doing what I enjoy doing.

In the special case of the artist (Cézanne, for example) who is not recognized during his lifetime, what makes him a worker and not, like a Sunday painter, a player, is his conviction that sooner or later his art will be recognized for what it is, work of public importance.

Among the many blessings enjoyed by a worker, not the least is the knowledge that for him leisure can never become a problem. He does not want and does not allow himself more leisure than he can cope with. Indeed the danger for a worker is that he will not allow himself sufficient leisure to rest his mind and body and to cultivate satisfactory personal relations. Workers are apt to die of coronaries and to forget their wives' birthdays.

Up till now, the machine, by reducing the need for manual skill and by rationalizing the process of fabrication, breaking it down into a series of sub-operations which have no meaning in themselves, has had the effect of degrading many who formerly were workers into labourers. It is possible, I dare say, that further technological developments will make such forms of senseless labour as an assembly-belt unnecessary; it is certain, however, that technological progress must continue to render our bodies more and more irrelevant to social needs. For those of us who derive our greatest satisfaction from using our minds, a technological society offers few obstacles and may even increase our opportunities, but the outlook is gloomy for those, and they are many, whose satisfaction requires the exercise of their muscles.

From my own observation, I would say that the majority of juvenile delinquents are second-class mesomorphs, that is to say, their strength and muscular coordination is not of the exceptional quality which enables a man to become a professional athlete, or an aeroplane pilot, or a ballet-dancer, which today are the only occupations left in which the human body has an economic value. It is all very fine for well-meaning social workers and clergymen to provide the young with gymnasia and playing fields, but the young are not deceived. They know that their athletic activities are on a par with being a Sunday painter, a hobby of no concern to anyone but themselves, and this is not enough. What they need is a job which calls for the use of their muscles, and all society has to offer them are white-collar jobs. The Biblical curse on labour – 'In the sweat of thy brow thou shalt eat thy bread' – is not removed by substituting – 'In boredom of spirit thou shalt eat thy bread'.

A labourer must find his happiness outside the activity by which he earns his living, and the most obvious place to look for it is in the field of personal relationships, particularly sexual relationships.

In the past the personal lives of the poor have been made difficult and often brutalized by exhausting toil, physical want, squalor, and overcrowding. These evils are still with us, but in an affluent society it is possible that we shall be able to eradicate them. Mere eradication, however, will merely substitute one difficulty for another. We seem to be so made that our personal relations work out most satisfactorily when both parties have impersonal interests of their own, in addition to their mutual interest in each other. When such interests are absent, so that men and women are wholly dependent upon personal relations for a meaningful life, there is apt to be trouble, and their relations tend to become either hysterically intense or promiscuous and trivial.

If the future confronting us is what the technicians prophesy, then the majority of the population are going to have to cope with the problem which has hitherto been confined to aristocracies, namely, excess of free time; time in which no demands are made upon them and they are free to do exactly as they please and, when one considers the behaviour of aristocracies throughout history, such a future gives cause for disquiet.

All aristocracies have attempted, and with some degree of success, to deal with the problem of excessive freedom by ritualizing their behaviour and their time; by submitting themselves, as in playing a game, to arbitrary rules about dress, forms of speech and the right season at which to do things – when to be in town, when in the country, when to shoot grouse, etc. I very much doubt if such ritualization is possible except in a small non-industrialized society. In a mass, democratic, commercially minded society, I suspect that the substitute for a conventional, unchanging ritual will be blind obedience to the latest fashion, which it will be to the profit of certain powerful sectors of the economy to change as often as possible. Once he had been taught the ritual, the aristocrat enjoyed the security for the rest of his life of knowing exactly what is and what is not done.

The rituals of the aristocracy were the most satisfactory and charming side of their behaviour. There were others which were not so pleasant. To escape boredom – to have 'kicks' – they made war, they slaughtered animals for fun, they risked their fortunes at the gaming table and their lives in duels. Why should we expect a mass society with the same excess of leisure to behave any better? As Logan Pearsall-Smith said: 'To suppose, and we all suppose, that we could be rich and not behave as the rich behave, is like supposing that we could drink all day and stay sober.'

Of course, some of the amusements of an aristocracy are denied us. We cannot go in for private wars, like feudal knights; we cannot hunt, like the landowners of the eighteenth and nineteenth centuries, because there are so many of us that, in a very short time, there would be no animal alive to hunt. But who can doubt that we shall find substitutes? Who does not expect the increase, already marked, in acts of criminal and gratuitous violence, slaughter by automobile, drug-addiction, sado-masochistic pornography, etc., to get worse?

One of the most obvious results of technological advance is its multiplication of choice both in material and spiritual goods. This means that the importance of choosing rightly (rightly, that is, for the person who makes the choice) is greater than it has ever been. Choice necessarily implies rejection of what is not chosen, so that the importance of being able to say 'No' is greater than it has ever been. 'To be cultured', said Hoffmansthal, 'is to know what concerns one and to know what it concerns one to know,' and in a society of multiple choices, this knowledge is much more difficult to acquire than when choices were more restricted. If, in order to hear a piece of music, a man has to wait six months and then walk twenty miles, he knows that his desire to hear the music is real. If all he has to do is put a record on his phonograph, then it is much harder for him to know whether he really wants to hear the music or merely wishes to forget himself for a short while.

Where gratuitous or spiritual goods are concerned, I must know not only my personal taste, but also the limits of my mental capacity for full response. Technology, by creating the paperback, the colour reproduction, the stereo phonograph record, has made the enjoyment of works of art, hitherto confined to the rich, possible for all but the very poor. This case of access is in itself a blessing, but its misuse can make it a curse. We are all of us tempted to read more poetry and fiction, look at more pictures, listen to more music than we can possibly respond to properly, and the consequence of such over-indulgence is not a cultured mind but a consuming one; what it reads, looks at, listens to, is immediately forgotten, leaving no more traces behind than yesterday's newspaper.

The first prerequisite for leading any satisfactory kind of personal life in a technological society is the ability to resist distraction. Human beings are not born with this ability but, from about the age of seven onwards, we are all capable of learning to direct our attention on this rather than that, down this path not down that. This concentration of attention is to the inner life what deliberate action is to the outer. A man is as responsible for what he attends to as for what he does, and, as in the case of his actions, the consequences of attending are never foreseeable. The proper name for such direction of attention is, I believe, prayer. Whenever a person so concentrates his attention on a subject – be it a landscape, a poem, a geometrical problem, an idol, or the Living God – that he completely forgets himself and every-thing else, he is praying. The primary task of the schoolteacher – more difficult and more important than ever before – is to teach the young, in a secular context, the techniques of prayer.

In giving our complete attention to anything, the greatest aid – only the most highly trained and practised minds can do without it – is enchantment. To quote Hoffmansthal again: 'Where is yourself to be found? Always in the deepest enchantment you have experienced.' To that which enchants us, whether truly or falsely, we find it easy to attend. Indeed, in the case of an enchantment which we know to be false, we can only stop attending by taking immediate flight before the spell has taken full hold. Enchantment cannot be taught because it works at a subconscious level, but it can be aroused by social contagion. The primary requirement in a teacher (an interest in his pupils and a knowledge of educational techniques are secondary) is that he should be enchanted by the subject he teaches. He may not succeed directly in infecting his pupils with the same enchantment, but as an example of what it means to be enchanted, he may help them to discover their own. An enthusiastic Latin teacher may be the means by which one of his pupils becomes enchanted with physics. For learning a foreign language, a teaching machine may possibly be a more efficient instructor than the average human teacher, but only on condition that the pupil is already eager to learn. No machine can impart eagerness.

12. The Crisis of Man in His Environment

RENÉ DUBOS

The general worry about the environment has resulted in a distortion of the meaning conveyed by the phrase 'human ecology'. At present, this phrase is exclusively identified with the social and biological dangers that man faces in the modern world. But there is more to human ecology than this one-sided view of man's relation to his environment. In the long run, the most important aspect of human ecology is that all environmental factors exert a direct effect on the development of human characteristics, in health as well as in disease. In fact, it can be said that the body and the mind are *shaped* by the adaptive responses that man makes to the physico-chemical, social, behavioural, and even historical stimuli that impinge on him from the time of conception to the time of death. Genetically and phenotypically, man is being constantly transformed by the environment in which he lives.

Human ecology therefore involves both the pathological and the formative effects of the total environment. I shall first illustrate by a few examples these two aspects of the problem, then attempt to formulate a general approach to the study of the interplay between man and environmental forces.

The general state of public health has greatly improved during the past century, but therapeutic procedures have played a relatively small role in this achievement. Advances in health and in the expectancy of life have come chiefly from higher standards of living, and from the application of natural sciences to the *prevention* of infectious and nutritional diseases.

Although the early sanitarians did not use the phrase 'human ecology', their slogan 'pure air, pure water, pure food' implied sound ecological concepts. Their awareness of the effects that environmental factors exert on biological health was furthermore supplemented by a shrewd understanding of man's emotional needs. For example, they advocated that urban areas be ornamented with trees and flowers and that city dwellers be given ready access to country lanes.

Thanks to their efforts, we have gone far towards solving the problems of infectious and nutritional disease generated by the first Industrial Revolution. Unfortunately, the new revolution in the ways of life and in the environment that is now occurring in technological societies is bringing about profound changes in the pattern of diseases, causing in particular alarming increases in various types of chronic and degenerative disorders.

Whereas the nineteenth century was concerned with malnutrition, overwork, filth, and microbial contamination, the diseases most characteristic of our times result in large part from economic affluence, chemical pollution, and high population densities. The medical problems are still largely environmental in origin, but they have different ecologic determinants.

The average expectancy of life has increased all over the world and especially in prosperous countries as a result of the prevention of early deaths that used to be caused by acute infections and malnutrition. But, contrary to general belief, life expectancy past the age of forty-five has not increased significantly anywhere in the world, not even in the social groups that can afford the most elaborate medical care. It is no longer permissible to take comfort in the belief that various types of vascular diseases, of cancers, of chronic ailments of the respiratory tract, have become more prevalent simply because people live longer in affluent societies. The increase in chronic and degenerative diseases is due in part at least, and probably in a very large part, to the environmental and behavioural changes that have resulted from industrialization and urbanization.

The so-called diseases of civilization are certainly the results of man's failure to respond successfully to the stresses of the modern environment. But there is as yet no convincing knowledge of the mechanisms relating the environment and the ways of life to the increased incidence of chronic and degenerative diseases among adults. Granted the deficiencies in etiological understanding, it is obvious nevertheless that man feels threatened and is threatened by the constant and unavoidable exposure to the stimuli of urban and industrial civilization; by the varied aspects of environmental pollution; by the physiological disturbances associated with sudden changes in the ways of life; by his estrangement from the conditions and natural cycles under which human evolution took place; by the emotional trauma and the paradoxical solitude in congested cities; by the monotony, the boredom, indeed the compulsory leisure ensuing from automated work. These are the very influences which are now at the origin of most medical problems in affluent societies. They affect all human beings, irrespective of genetic constitution. They are not inherent in man's nature but the products of the interplay between his genetic environment and the new world created by social and technological innovations. To a very large extent the disorders of the body and mind are but the expression of inadequate adaptive responses to environmental influences which differ drastically from the conditions under which man evolved.

As already mentioned, hardly anything is known concerning the natural history of the diseases characteristic of modern civilization — let alone concerning methods for their treatment. It is urgent, therefore, to develop a new science of human ecology focused on the conditions prevailing in the technological environment.

One can take it for granted that medical science will continue to develop useful techniques for treating cancers, vascular diseases, and other degenerative disorders; methods for organ transplants and for the use of artificial prostheses will certainly be improved during the forthcoming decades. But most of the conditions that will thus be treated need not have occurred in the first place. Greater knowledge of the environmental determinants of disease would certainly constitute the most important factor in helping biomedical sciences to improve human health. Prevention is always better than cure, and also much less expensive.

As presently managed, the technological urban civilization subjects all human beings to endless and dangerous stresses. Yet men of all ethnic groups elect to live in huge megalopolises, and indeed manage to function effectively in this traumatic environment. Most of them seem to develop tolerance to environmental pollutants, intense stimuli, and high population density, just as they develop herd immunity to microbial pathogens that are ubiquitous.

The acquisition of tolerance, however, is not an unmixed blessing. Air pollution provides tragic evidence of the fact that many of the physiological, mental, and social processes which make it possible to live in a hostile environment commonly express themselves at a later date in overt disease and in economic loss. During the past two centuries, for instance, the inhabitants of the industrial areas of Northern Europe have been exposed to large concentrations of many types of air pollutants produced by incomplete combustion of coal, and released in the fumes from chemical plants. Such exposure is rendered even more objectionable by the inclemency of the Atlantic climate. However, long experience with pollution and with bad weather results in the development of physiological reactions and living habits that obviously have adaptive value, since Northern Europeans seem to accept almost cheerfully conditions which appear unbearable to a non-experienced person.

Unfortunately, adaptation to the stresses of the present often has to be paid in the form of physiological misery at some future date. Even among persons who seem to be unaware of the smogs surrounding them, the respiratory tract registers the insult of the various air pollutants. Eventually, the cumulative effects of irritation result in chronic bronchitis and other forms of irreversible pulmonary disease. Generally, however, this does not happen until several years later.

Chronic pulmonary disease now constitutes the greatest single medical problem in Northern Europe, as well as the most costly. It is increasing in prevalence at an alarming rate also in North America and it will undoubtedly spread to all areas undergoing industrialization. There is good evidence, furthermore, that air pollution contributes to the incidence of various cancers – not only pulmonary carcinoma. It also increases the number of fatalities among persons suffering from vascular disorders. The delayed effects of air pollutants thus constitute a model for the kind of medical problems likely to arise in the future from the various forms of environmental pollution.

Noise levels that are accepted almost as a matter of course bring about a progressive impairment of hearing; pathogens that do not cause destructive epidemics because they are ubiquitous and have therefore elicited herd immunity can generate endogenous infections when resistance to them is decreased by physiological or mental stress; crowding, regimentation, or intense stimuli that become acceptable through habituation indirectly elicit physiological or behavioural disorders. In brief, most adaptive adjustments to deleterious influences are achieved at the price of bodily or mental disturbances later in life. Some at least of these disturbances contribute to the diseases of civilization.

From the point of view of the general biologist, an environment is suitable if it enables the species to reproduce itself and increase its population; but this concept is not applicable to man. An environment allowing man to produce a family and to be economically effective during his adult years should be regarded an unacceptable one if it generates disease later in life. This, of course, is the case for many modern technological and urban environments, which rarely destroy human life but frequently spoil its later years.

Human ecology thus differs from orthodox biomedical sciences in the much greater emphasis that it should put on the indirect and delayed effects of environmental forces, even when these do not appear to cause significant damage at the time of exposure.

Man's responses to the environmental forces that impinge on him determine to a very large extent how his genetic potentialities are converted into existential, phenotypic reality.

Contrary to what is commonly assumed, genes do not determine the traits by which we know a person; they only govern the responses he makes to environmental stimuli. Such responses become incorporated, usually in an irreversible manner, in the person's whole being and thus mould his individuality. This is true not only for emotional characteristics, but also for most other physical, physiological, and mental characteristics. Man makes himself in the very act of responding to his environment through an uninterrupted series of feedback processes. Since each person continues to respond to environmental stimuli throughout his life and to be lastingly modified by such responses, individuality can be defined as the continuously evolving phenotype.

Many of the most striking differences in size, shape, attitudes, and mental abilities between ethnic groups are not innate; they are expressions of environmental influences. In other words, men are as much the products of their environment as of their genetic endowment. This is what Winston Churchill had in mind when he asserted: 'We shape our buildings, and afterwards our buildings shape us.'

The influences experienced very early in life during the formative phases of development deserve emphasis, because they exert profound and lasting effects on the anatomical, physiological, and behavioural characteristics of the adult. Experimentation in animals and observations in man have revealed that the foetus and the newborn can be so profoundly affected by environmental conditions acting indirectly through the mother, or directly after birth, that the adult reflects throughout his life the consequences of this early experience. Early influences are of particular importance because man's body and brain are incompletely developed at the time of birth. Hence, the need for precise observations and searching experimental studies concerning the conditions of prenatal and early postnatal life.

Biological and social deprivation are well known to have deleterious effects on development. For example, there is now overwhelming evidence that various types of deprivation early in life exert irreversible damage on learning ability – a fact of obvious importance in all underprivileged populations. On the other hand, it is also possible that some of the conditions prevailing in affluent societies have undesirable consequences.

It is known that injection into newborn mice of particulate materials separated from urban air greatly increases the frequency of various types of tumours during the adult life of these animals. If this observation can be extrapolated to human beings, the worst effects of environmental pollution are yet to come, since it is only during the past decade that large numbers of babies have been exposed to high levels of pollutants in urban areas.

It is known also that animals offered a rich and abundant regimen early in life thereby become conditioned to large nutritional demands as adults and tend to become obese. This may explain why the bigger baby does not necessarily become a healthy adult.

By acting on the child during his formative stages, the environment thus shapes him physically and mentally, thereby influencing what he will become and how he will function as an adult. For this reason, environmental planning plays a key role in enabling human beings to actualize their potentialities.

Children who are denied the opportunity to experience early in life the kind of stimuli required for mental development do not acquire the mental resources that would be necessary for the full utilization of their free will. It is not right to say that lack of culture is responsible for the behaviour of slum children or for their failure to be successful in our society. The more painful truth is that these children acquire early in life a slum culture from which escape is almost impossible. Their early surroundings and ways of life at a critical period of their development limit the range of manifestations of their innate endowment and thus destroy much of their potential freedom.

It would be unethical and in any case futile to try creating one particular type of environment optimum for all of mankind. Such a course would impose a common pattern of development on all human beings and thus would be tantamount to suppressing their freedom. Society should instead provide as wide a range of environmental conditions as practically and safely possible so that each human being can select the experiences most suitable to the development of his attributes and to the prosecution of his goals.

Human potentialities, whether physical or mental, can be realized only to the extent that circumstances are favourable to their existential manifestation. For this reason, diversity within a given society is an essential component of true functionalism; the latent potentialities of human beings have a better chance to emerge when the social environment is sufficiently diversified to provide a variety of stimulating experiences, especially for the young. As more and more persons find it possible to express their biologic endowments under a variety of conditions, society becomes richer and civilizations continue to unfold. In contrast, if the surroundings and ways of life are highly stereotyped, the only components of man's nature that flourish are those adapted to the narrow range of prevailing conditions.

Thus, one of the most important problems of human ecology is to study the effects of environmental forces not only in the here and now, but also with regard to their future consequences.

13. The Regulation of Population Density by Animals

C. H. WADDINGTON

The phrase 'population density' refers to two related but somewhat different ideas: firstly, the total number of the animals in a given locality; and secondly, the pattern in which they are dispersed, for instance, evenly spaced throughout the whole area, or concentrated in a few places, such as rookeries, rabbit warrens, and the like. The study of animal numbers and dispersion is a large and elaborate section of biology. It will only be possible here to give a few notes of the general outline of the subject. A good recent, fairly short book, which concentrates rather on the mathematical theory of the subject, is *Growth and Regulation of Animal Populations* by Lawrence B. Slobotkin. An important discussion of the whole field, paying particular attention to the social factors involved, is *Animal Dispersion in Relation to Social Behaviour* by V. C. Wynne-Edwards. This is a long book of over 600 pages. Most of the ideas and the notes that follow come from it or are fully discussed in it.

All animals can reproduce at rates which are more than sufficient to make good the inevitable losses due to death and old age. If, in an experiment, a small number of animals are introduced into a space containing the necessary food, and free of predators, pests, etc., the number of the population will start increasing. The rate of increase is, at first, dependent on the number of animals present. Thereafter, as the number of the population increases, the speed at which the population is expanding gets faster and faster. The population grows 'exponentially'. Clearly this cannot go on indefinitely. Eventually we find in such experiments that the rate of increase of the population slows down, and finally ceases altogether, when the population attains a steady size which it can usually maintain indefinitely thereafter. If we plot the numbers in the population against time we can usually distinguish three different phases (Figure 1):

1. An initial 'lag' phase during which the growth of the population is slow (this does not always occur, but often does so, for instance, for such reasons as the difficulty of finding a mate when there are only a small number of animals in a large space).

2. An 'exponential' phase of rapidly increasing numbers.

3. A phase when population growth slows down. This slowing down must be due to the operation of factors tending to limit population growth and these factors must be 'density-dependent', i.e. they must get more powerful as the density of animals in the space increases.

The ultimate density-dependent, growth-limiting factor is, of course, the availability of food. Theoretically it would seem possible for an animal population to increase in numbers to the point at which

Figure 1. Typical growth curve.

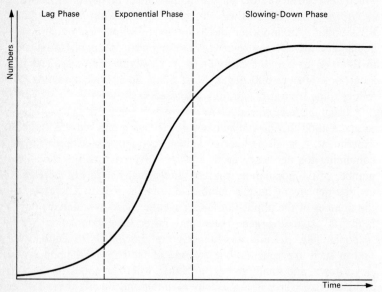

the available food could not feed all of them, and some would actually die of starvation. In practice, however, it is found that this scarcely ever occurs. Animals are found to regulate their numbers by some other means which do not involve direct competition of individuals for food in which the loser starves to death. There are many reasons why competition in which the losers starve would be an unsatisfactory way of regulating population density. For one thing, at a level of nutrition at which some individuals are going to starve, even the more successful animals are likely to be undernourished and weak. Again, many animals are dependent on some sort of crop which is only produced from time to time. Consider, for instance, birds which live on plant seeds which are produced during the summer and ripen in autumn. If by the autumn the bird population had reached the number which could be fed during the next two or three weeks, they would eat out the whole supply and all starve to death during the winter, before the next crop of seeds came along. There must be some way in which the number of birds in autumn are kept to a level which the plant seed crop can sustain throughout the whole winter. This is a very simple example of an extremely basic principle. All animals ultimately depend for their food either on other animals or on plants. All animal populations are, therefore, faced with the problem of leaving enough of their food crop alive and uneaten so that it can reproduce and grow again in later years.

This problem has been most fully studied in a quantitative manner in connection with man's exploitation of fish in the sea. It has been clearly shown, both in theory and in practice, that, if an area of sea (e.g., the North Sea) is fished too heavily, not enough adults are left to replenish the population and the total crop that can be harvested goes down. Some species, for instance some of the whales, have been almost totally eliminated by over-exploitation. Man has had to adopt the policy 'to fish less and catch more'.

The vast majority of animals have evolved devices by which they can escape the danger of eating their offspring out of a living. These devices have presumably been brought about by the operation of natural selection. Populations which fail to produce effective devices of this kind would eliminate themselves from the scene, so that only those populations which evolve successful control devices can persist.

The control devices depend essentially on some method by which the effective population density (i.e. number of animals in relation to the available food supplies) can be assessed, and the animals' reproductive behaviour modified accordingly. The devices employed are found nearly always to involve many elements which are basically conventional, in the sense that their importance is not intrinsic (as it is with actual food), but depends on the social organization of the population. For instance, the amount of space available to a population is usually determined as being some rather arbitrary 'territory', which the population 'owns'. Within this space individuals compete, not so much for actual food, but for some conventionally accepted status symbol. The competition for these status symbols is usually not so much by actual fighting but rather by some form of display or conventional competition. Such displays are technically known as 'epideictic' displays, in contrast to 'epigamic' displays, which are concerned solely with winning mates.

Epideictic behaviour, i.e. behaviour which exhibits in some way the total number of animals in the population, may take very many forms. Any of the sensory modes – sight, hearing, smell, touch – may be used. For instance, some of the beetles which inhabit flour stored in warehouses give off a smelling gas as they burrow through the mass of flour. As the concentration of this rises with increased numbers of beetles, the behaviour of the beetles changes. The females start laying fewer eggs, the adults start going in for cannibalism, and various other changes occur, all of which result in slowing the rate in population increase. Again the well-known dawn and dusk choruses of birds, frogs, cicadas, and other vociferous animals are cases in which the whole population makes itself felt simultaneously, at the easily recognizable times when light intensity is changing, so that the total number present is registered.

It is more interesting to consider the various types of epideictic display, and the kinds of status symbol competed for, in connection with the geographical dispersion of the population over its territory. The types of dispersion can be classified according to two criteria. A. Whether the individuals (or family parties) are either scattered more or less evenly over the whole area, or live in clusters concentrated at one or two places. B. Whether or not there is overlapping of the feeding territories associated with the separate living quarters. We thus have a four-fold classification:

1. Separate family parties with non-overlapping feeding territory.
2. Separate family parties with overlapping feeding territories.
3. Separate clusters with non-overlapping feeding territories.
4. Separate clusters whose feeding territories overlap.

We will consider each of these in turn.

1. *Separate living quarters and separate feeding territories.* Most song birds are typical examples of this type of population organization. At the beginning of the breeding season each male takes possession of a certain territory, from the produce of which he proposes to feed himself and his family (Figure 2a). The size of the territory depends on the available food supply. The male in possession defends his boundaries primarily by display, only very occasionally by actual fighting. His song, and often his bright plumage, are essentially used to give notice that there is a male in possession. This is a much more important part of their function than anything to do with courtship or the attraction of a mate. Any males which fail to secure a territory are thereby debarred from breeding. There are always a number of bachelors and spinsters around in an area occupied by such territorial birds. They keep themselves alive until next year by scrounging surreptitiously over the territory of a number of different breeding cocks. Many of them are young birds capable of breeding, but not able to do so because of the social organization.

2. *Separate living quarters but overlapping feeding territory.* This sort of organization is found in many carnivorous animals, such as lions, badgers, foxes, etc. In such cases the symbol which confers on its owner the status of a breeder is not the actual territory over which he will crop his food, but conventionally recognized living quarters; for instance, a badger's earth or fox's den (Figure 2b). These living quarters are occupied by a succession of tenants for periods of many years. Within the whole area covered by the population there are probably many other places which could make suitable foxes' dens, but what is found is that there are certain conventionally recognized foxes' dens whose owners are accepted members of the population

and can breed, but that through some social pressure, not very fully understood, the surplus bachelors are not allowed to set up house for themselves in new places.

3 and 4. *Clustered dwelling, non-overlapping or overlapping feeding territories.* These two categories may be treated together, since the most interesting point is how the animals regulate the numbers accommodated within the dwelling clusters, and the way they disperse themselves for feeding is of rather minor interest.

Figure 2. Four-fold classification of living quarters.

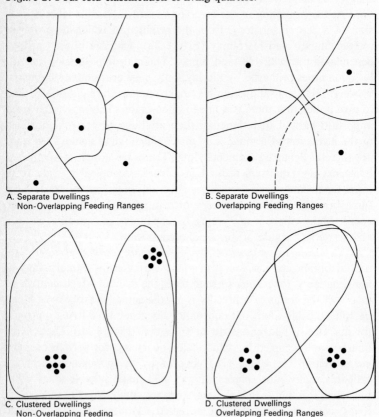

A. Separate Dwellings
   Non-Overlapping Feeding Ranges

B. Separate Dwellings
   Overlapping Feeding Ranges

C. Clustered Dwellings
   Non-Overlapping Feeding

D. Clustered Dwellings
   Overlapping Feeding Ranges

The organization within a clustered dwelling place may be carried out in terms of (a) individual families; (b) neighbourhoods containing several families; (c) the cluster as a whole.

When the organization is in terms of individual families this may take two forms, comparable to those under sections (1) and (2) above. For instance, many sea birds nest in enormous flocks on certain particular rocks or small islands. Each family there owns as its own property a small nesting site, which is far too small to provide food but is adequate for the laying of eggs and the rearing of chicks. These nesting sites are competed for, owned and defended, by epideictic display behaviour very comparable to that by which song birds own the much larger feeding territories. Since the limit of the whole clustered dwelling places is fixed (often as much by convention as by geographical factors) the total number of the breeding population is also fixed. In other clustered dwelling species, competition is not for a minimum sized nesting area but is for one of a number of conventionally recognized nesting places. For instance, in rookeries there are a certain number of nests, which persist from year to year. The owners of these nests are permitted to breed in them, but if an enterprising young rook tries to build himself a new nest elsewhere it will usually be destroyed by the rest of the community. There are, of course, many intermediates between these two extremes. For instance, in flocks of starlings there are certain commonly recognized breeding areas, and within these the nesting sites are moderately well recognized, and each tends to belong to one pair, but there is a good deal of jostling about and the situation seems to be half-way between that in the rookery, in which nesting sites are firmly sanctioned by tradition, and in a colony of gulls where there are no specific sites and anyone can nest if he can find room to do so.

Organization in terms of neighbourhoods has been most fully studied in the case of the prairie dog in America. These animals live in large townships, which contain the burrows of a large number of animals which go out to feed over a much wider area than the one they actually live in. Within the townships, groups, which seem to be considerably larger than single families, live and spend most of their leisure time within particular neighbourhood areas. An animal runs quite freely about within its own neighbourhood, and when it meets one of the other members of the neighbourhood community, acts in a friendly way towards it, often indulging in mutual grooming, or exchanging amicable grunts, etc. When in other parts of the town, out of its own neighbourhood, the animal tends to look scared, to run rather fast, to avoid encounters with other animals, and in general behaves like a rather apprehensive foreigner.

Organization in terms of the whole community is usually done by some mechanism which involves a complete separation of the life of the sexes, so that no biparental families are set up. It nearly always depends on all the males coming together in one place and competing in epideictic displays for social status. The dominant males are then available to fertilize as many of the females who turn up as they think fit. The classic example of this behaviour is in the bird known as the ruff. The males from a large area assemble in one locality, known as a lek. They then engage in elaborate displays, holding themselves in tense artificial positions, ruffling out feathers and exhibiting their plumage and aggressive potential to each other. By this behaviour, in which practically no actual fighting ever occurs, they sort themselves out into some sort of status order. From time to time the modestly plumaged females show up in ones and twos, and some male high enough up in the social order (depending on the rate of flow of customers) will serve them, after which they retreat, lay their eggs and rear their families with no further dealings with the male at all.

In these communities with clustered dwellings, the brake on population increase may be competition for a status symbol, such as a recognized nesting site, those individuals who fail to attain such a symbol being excluded from breeding altogether. However, in such communities there are certainly ways of reducing the rate of reproduction other than total exclusion from breeding. It has been found by experiment that excessive crowding produces a number of effects on animal behaviour and physiology which tend to reduce the overall fertility. For instance, the growth rate may be slowed down, and the age of entry into the breeding period be delayed. Again the number of eggs produced by a female may be reduced; for instance, crowded rats tend to have smaller litters. Again the prenatal mortality (abortions and resorption of foetuses) may be increased. Excessive crowding may lead to unhealthy nervousness and aggressiveness. There may be a great deal of fighting between animals, so that most individuals spend half their time nursing their wounds. Frequency of copulation is probably reduced. The females fail to build proper nests or abandon the nest early. There is often a good deal of cannibalism of the young. It has been shown that the balance of the pituitary and adrenal hormones may be quite upset. All these physiological and behavioural abnormalities tend to occur long before the onset of actual starvation. However, they are manifestations of rather extreme conditions of overcrowding, such as are achieved in experimental situations. It is rather doubtful whether they often occur in animals living in a state of nature. (There are some animals, such as lemmings, which have not evolved an efficient method of keeping their population level constant, but which fluctuate in numbers rather violently over periods of a few years, and in them this 'stress syndrome' seems to be one of the important ways of reducing their numbers from the exaggerated peaks which they gain at the high point in the population cycle.) In most well regulated, clustered-dwelling animal populations, such as the neighbourhoods of the prairie dog towns, excessive reproduction seems to be restrained by social factors long before the population has got to such a density as to reduce its individual members to neurotic wrecks. Basically, as we have seen, these social factors can be reduced to competition for conventionally determined status symbols, which confer the right to reproduce.

Addendum

In a species which has no effective methods of contraception the right to reproduce is effectively the same thing as the right to copulate. In relatively primitive human communities the forces of social convention, in the form of organized priesthoods, have based their power on control of reproduction through control of copulation. Nearly all the Churches in the world – Christian, Mohammedan, Hindu, etc. – have acquired the enormous power which they possess because they have persuaded society that the sexual instincts must not be fulfilled until the Church has given its licence. With the development of effective contraception the social power to control copulation loses its raison d'être, and is in fact very widely disregarded. Most Churches are at present fighting a rearguard action to preserve their social power by controlling a causal sequence which is no longer operative (namely that copulation leads to reproduction) which is something with which society must now concern itself. The solution, both of the position of the Churches in society, and of the population explosion, would seem to lie in transferring the attention of the Church from the trivial matter of immediate sexual satisfaction to the undoubtedly important matter of reproduction. The Church's control of marriage will undoubtedly disappear if 'marriage' is interpreted as licence to copulate. This control could be preserved – and it might be useful to preserve it – if 'marriage' was interpreted as licence to reproduce.

14. Beyond Family Planning

BERNARD BERELSON

This article rests on four propositions: (1) among the great problems on the world agenda is the population problem; (2) that problem is most urgent in the developing countries, where rapid population growth retards social and economic development; (3) there is a time penalty on the problem in the sense that, other things being equal, anything not done sooner may be harder to do later, due to increased numbers; and accordingly (4) everything that can properly be done to lower population growth rates should be done, now. The question is, what is to be done? There is a certain agreement on the general objective (that is, on the desirability of lowering birth rates, though not on how far and how fast), but there is disagreement as to means.

The first response to too high growth rates deriving from too high birth rates is to introduce voluntary contraception on a mass basis, or try to. Why is family planning the first step taken on the road to population control? Probably because, from a broad political standpoint, it is the most acceptable one; since it is closely tied to maternal and child care it can be perceived as a health measure beyond dispute, and since it is voluntary it can be justified as a contribution to the effective personal freedom of individual couples. On both scores, it ties into accepted values and thus achieves political viability. Moreover, it is a gradual effort and an inexpensive one, both of which features contribute to its political acceptability.

How effective have family planning programs been as a means towards population control? There is currently some controversy among qualified observers as to its efficacy, and this is not the place to review that issue. There is agreement, however, that the problem is of such magnitude and consequence that additional efforts are needed to reach a 'solution', however that is responsibly defined.

For the purpose of this article, then, let us assume that today's national family planning programs, mainly based on voluntary contraception, are not 'enough' — where 'enough' is defined not necessarily as achieving zero growth in some extended present, but simply as lowering birth rates quickly and substantially. 'Enough' begs the question of the ultimate goal and only asks that a faster decline in population growth rates be brought about than is presently being achieved or in prospect — and, within the range of the possible, the faster the better. Just to indicate roughly the order of magnitude, let us say that the proximate goal is the halving of the birth rate in the developing countries in the next decade or two — from, say, over forty births per thousand per year to twenty to twenty-five. For obvious reasons, both emigration and increased death rates are ruled out of consideration.

What is to be done to bring that reduction about, beyond present programs of voluntary family planning? I address that question in two ways: first, by listing the programs or policies more or less responsibly suggested in recent years for achieving this end; second, by reviewing the issues raised by the suggested approaches.

Proposals beyond Family Planning

Here is a listing of the several proposals, arranged in descriptive categories. The list includes both proposals for consideration and proposals for action.

(a) Extensions of Voluntary Fertility Control

1. Institutionalization of maternal care in rural areas of developing countries: a feasibility study of what would be required in order to bring some degree of modern medical or paramedical attention to every pregnant woman in the rural areas of five developing countries, with professional back-up for difficult cases and with family planning education and services a central component of the program, aimed particularly at women of low parity.[1]
2. Liberalization of induced abortion.[2]

(b) Establishment of Involuntary Fertility Control

1. Mass use of a 'fertility control agent' by the government to regulate births at an acceptable level. The 'fertility control agent', designed to lower fertility in the society to a level 5 to 75 per cent below the present birth rate, as needed, would be a substance now unknown but believed to be available for field testing after five to fifteen years of research work. It would be included in the water supply in urban areas and administered by 'other methods' elsewhere.[3] A related suggestion is the 'addition of temporary sterilants to water supplies or staple food'.

2. 'Marketable licences to have children', given to women and perhaps men in 'whatever number would ensure a reproduction rate of one' (say, 2·2 children per couple). For example, 'the unit certificate might be the "deci-child", and accumulation of ten of these units, by purchase, inheritance, or gift, would permit a woman in maturity to have one legal child'.[4]

3. Temporary sterilization of all girls by means of time-capsule contraceptives and of girls and women after each delivery, with reversibility allowed only upon governmental approval. Certificates of approval would be distributed according to national popular vote on desired population growth, and saleable on the open market.[5]

4. Compulsory sterilization of men with three or more living children;[6] a requirement of induced abortion for all illegitimate pregnancies.[7]

(c) Intensified Educational Campaigns

1. Inclusion of educational materials on population in primary and secondary school systems.[8]

2. Promotion of national satellite television systems for directly disseminating information on population and family planning and for indirectly promoting acceptance of modern attitudes and practices in general.[9]

198 Man: Balancing Inner and Outer Realities

(d) Incentive Programs

As used here, the term *incentive programs* refers to payments, or their equivalent, made directly to couples who use contraceptives or to couples who do not have children for specified periods. It does *not* refer to payments to field workers, medical personnel, volunteers, and others, for securing acceptance of contraceptive practice.

1. Payment, or the equivalent (for example, the gift of a transistor radio), for accepting sterilization[10] or for the effective practice of contraception.[11]

2. A bonus for child spacing or non-pregnancy;[12] a savings certificate to couples for each twelve-month period in which no child is born;[13] a lottery scheme for preventing illegitimate births among teenagers in a small country;[14] 'responsibility prizes' for each five years of childless marriage or for vasectomy before the birth of a third child, and special lotteries, with tickets available to the childless.[15]

(e) Tax and Welfare Benefits and Penalties

That is, a system of social services that would discourage childbearing rather than encourage it, as present systems tend to do.

1. Withdrawal of maternity benefits perhaps after the birth of n (three?) children[16] or in cases where certain limiting conditions, such as adequate child spacing, knowledge of family planning, or attainment of a given level of income, have not been met.[17]

2. Withdrawal of child or family allowances, perhaps after the birth of n children.[18]

3. Levy of tax on births after the nth child.[19]

4. Limitation of governmentally provided medical treatment, housing, scholarships, loans, subsidies, and so on, to families with fewer than n children.[20]

5. Reversal of tax benefits, to favour the unmarried and the parents of fewer rather than more children.[21]

6. Provision by the state of n years of free schooling, at all levels, to each family, to be allocated among the children as desired.[22]

7. Pensions for poor parents with fewer than *n* children, as social security for their old age.[23]

(f) Shifts in Social and Economic Institutions

That is, broad changes in fundamental institutional arrangements that could have the effect of lowering fertility.

1. Raising the minimum age at marriage, through legislation or through imposition of a substantial fee for marriage licences;[24] through direct payment of bonuses for delayed marriage;[25] through payment of marriage benefits only to parents of brides over twenty-one years old;[26] through government loans for wedding ceremonies when the bride is over a given age, or with the interest rate inversely related to the bride's age;[27] through a 'governmental "first marriage grant"... awarded each couple in which the age of both [sic] partners was twenty-five or more';[28] or through establishment of a domestic 'national service' program for all men for the appropriate two-year period in order to develop social services, inculcate modern attitudes towards (among other matters) family planning and population control, and delay marriage.

2. Measures to promote or require the participation of women in the labour force (outside the home), in order to provide roles and interests for women that are alternative or supplementary to marriage.[29]

3. 'Direct manipulation of family structure itself – planned efforts at deflecting the family's socializing function ... or introducing non-familial distractions ... into people's lives', specifically through employment of women outside the house;[30] 'selective restructuring of the family in relation to the rest of society'.[31]

4. Promotion of 'two types of marriage, one of them childless and readily dissolved, and the other licensed for children and designed to be stable'; marriages of the first type would have to constitute 20 to 40 per cent of the total in order to allow free choice of family size for marriages of the second type.[32]

5. Encouragement of long-range social trends leading towards lower fertility – for example, 'improved and universal general education, or new roads facilitating communication, or improved agricultural methods, or a new industry that would increase productivity,

or other types of innovation that may break the "cake of custom" and produce social foment';[33] improvement in the status of women.[34]

6. Efforts to lower death rates even further, particularly infant and child death rates, in the belief that lower birth rates will follow.[35]

(g) Political Channels and Organizations

1. U.S. insistence on 'population control as the price of food aid', with highly selective assistance based thereon, and exertion of political pressures on governments or religious groups that impede 'solution' of the population problem.[36]

2. Reorganization of national and international agencies to deal with the population problem: within the United States, 'coordination by a powerful governmental agency, a Federal Department of Population and Environment ... with the power to take whatever steps are necessary to establish a reasonable population size';[37] within India, creation of 'a separate Ministry of Population Control';[38] development of an 'international specialized agency larger than W.H.O. to operate programs for extending family limitation techniques to the world ... charged with the responsibility of effecting the transfer to population equilibrium'.[39]

3. Promotion of zero growth in population as the ultimate goal, and acceptance of this goal now in order to place intermediate goals of lowered fertility in proper context.[40]

(h) Augmented Research Efforts

1. More research on social means for achieving necessary fertility goals.[41]

2. Focused research on practical methods of sex determination.[42]

3. Increased research directed towards improvement of the contraceptive technology.[43]

Proposals: Review of the Issues

Since several of the proposals tend in the same direction, it seems appropriate to review them against the criteria that any such proposals might be required to meet. What are such criteria? There are at least six: (1) scientific, medical, and technological readiness; (2) political viability; (3) administrative feasibility; (4) economic capability; (5) moral, ethical, and philosophical acceptability; and (6) presumed effectiveness. In other words, the key questions are: Is the scientific, medical, technological base available or likely? Will governments approve? Can the proposal be administered? Can the society afford the proposal? Is it morally acceptable? And, finally, will it work?

The table shows how the various proposals seem to fit the six criteria. This is only one observer's judgement of the present situation, but whatever appraisal is made of specific items, it would appear that the overall picture is mixed.

Conclusion

This review leaves us with some conclusions concerning proposals that go beyond family planning.

1. There is no easy way to achieve population control. If this review has indicated nothing else, it has shown how many obstacles stand in the way of a solution to the population problem.

2. Family planning programs do not compare unfavourably with other specific proposals, especially when one considers that any *actual* operating program is at a disadvantage when compared with any competitive *ideal* policy. Indeed, on this showing, if family planning programs did not exist, they would have to be invented; it appears that they would be among the first proposals to be made and the first programs to be tried, given their generally acceptable characteristics.

TABLE ONE
Illustrative Appraisal of Proposals, by Criteria

Proposal	Scientific Readiness	Political Viability	Administrative Feasibility	Economic Capability	Ethical Acceptability	Presumed Effectiveness
(a) Extension of voluntary fertility control	High	High on maternal care, moderate-to-low on abortion	Uncertain in near future	Maternal care too costly for local budget, abortion feasible	High for maternal care, low for abortion	Moderately high
(b) Establishment of involuntary fertility control	Low	Low	Low	High	Low	High
(c) Intensified educational campaigns	High	Moderate-to-high	High	Probably high	Generally high	Moderate
(d) Incentive programs	High	Moderately low	Low	Low-to-moderate	Low-to-high	Uncertain
(e) Tax and welfare benefits and penalties	High	Moderately low	Low	Low-to-moderate	Low-to-moderate	Uncertain

(f) Shifts in social and economic institutions	High	Generally high, but low on some specifics	Low	Generally low	Generally high, but uneven	High, over long run
(g) Political channels and organizations	High	Low	Low	Moderate	Moderately low	Uncertain
(h) Augmented research efforts	Moderate	High	Moderate-to-high	High	High	Uncertain
Family planning programs	Generally high, but could use improved technology	Moderate-to-high	Moderate-to-high	High	Generally high, but uneven, on religious grounds	Moderately high

204 Man: Balancing Inner and Outer Realities

In fact, when such proposals are made, it turns out that many of them call for *more* family planning, not less, but in a somewhat different form. In the present case, at least a third of the proposals listed above put forward, in effect, simply another approach to family planning, often accepting the existing motivation as to family size. In any case, family planning programs are established, have some momentum, and, importantly, can be useful as the direct instrument through which other proposals would take effect.

What is needed is the energetic and full implementation of present experience. Much more could be done on the informational side, on encouraging commercial distribution of contraceptives, on the use of paramedical personnel, on logistics and supply, on the training and supervision of field workers, on approaches to special groups of individuals, ranging from women after childbirth to young men drafted into the armed forces. If workers in this field did well what they know how to do, that in itself would in all likelihood make a measurable difference, competitive in magnitude with the probable effects of other specific proposals – not to mention the further impetus of an improved contraceptive technology.

3. Most of the proposed ideas are not new; they have been around for some time. So, if they are not being tried, it is not because they have not been known but because they have not been accepted.

4. All of the proposers are dissatisfied to some degree with present family planning efforts, but that does not mean that they agree with one another's schemes for doing better.

5. In a rough way, there appears to be a progression in national efforts to deal with the problem of population control. The first step is the theoretical recognition that population growth may have something to do with the prospects for economic development. Then, typically, comes an expert mission from abroad to make a survey and report to the government, as has occurred in India, Pakistan, South Korea, Turkey, Iran, Tunisia, Morocco, and Kenya, among others. The first action program is in family planning, and most of the efforts are still at that level. Beyond that, it apparently takes: (1) some degree of discouragement about progress, combined with (2) some heightened awareness of the seriousness of the problem to move the effort forward. To date, those conditions have been most prominently

present in India – and that is the country that has gone farthest in the use of incentives and in consideration of further steps along the lines mentioned above.

6. Proposals need to be specific – proposals both for action and for further research. It is perhaps too much to ask advocates to spell out all the administrative details of the way their plan is to operate in the face of obstacles and difficulties, or even to spell out how it is to get permission to operate; the situations, settings, opportunities, and personalities are too diverse for that. But it does seem proper to ask for the fullest possible specification of actual plans, under realistic conditions, in order to test out their feasibility and likely effectiveness. Similarly, advocates of further research ought to spell out not only what would be studied, and how, but also how the results might be applied in action programs to affect fertility. Social research is not always readily translated into action, especially into administrative action; and the thrust of research is towards refinement, subtlety, precision, and qualification, whereas the administrator must act in the large. Short of such specification, the field remains confronted with potentially good ideas, such as 'raise the age at marriage', or 'use incentives', or 'substitute pension systems for male children', without being able to move very far towards implementation.

7. Just as there is no easy way, there is no single way. Since population control will at best be difficult, it follows that every acceptable step that promises some measure of impact should be taken. The most likely prospect is that population control, to the degree it is realized, will be the result of a combination of efforts – economic, legal, social, medical – each of which has some effect but not an immediately overwhelming one. Accordingly, it is incumbent upon workers in the professional fields concerned to look hard at various approaches, including family planning itself, in order to screen out what is potentially useful for application. In doing so, it may be the path of wisdom to move with the 'natural' progression. Some important proposals seem reasonably likely of adoption – institutionalization of maternal care, population study in the schools, the TV satellite system for disseminating information, a better contraceptive technology, liberalization of abortion laws in some settings – and we need to know not only how effective such efforts will be but, beyond

them, how large a money incentive would have to be to effect a given amount of fertility control and how effective those indirect social measures are that are morally acceptable and capable of realization. It may be that some of these measures would be both feasible and effective – many observers fifteen years ago thought that family planning programs were neither – and a genuine effort needs to be made. The 'heavy' measures – involuntary measures and political pressures – may be put aside for the time being, if not for ever.

8. In the last analysis, what will be scientifically available, politically acceptable, administratively feasible, economically justifiable, and morally tolerated depends upon people's perceptions of consequences. If 'the population problem' is considered relatively unimportant or only moderately important, that judgement will not support much investment of effort. If it is considered urgent, much more can and will be done. The fact is that, despite the large forward strides taken in international recognition of the problem in the 1960s, there still does not exist an informed and firm conviction in high circles that this is a matter with truly great implications for human welfare. Such convictions must be based on sound knowledge. Here it would appear that the demographers and economists have not sufficiently made their case to the world elite – or that, if made, the case has not sufficiently commanded their attention and support. Population pressures are not sharply visible on a day-to-day or even year-to-year basis, nor, short of major famine, do they show themselves in dramatic events. Moreover, the warnings of demographers are often dismissed, albeit unfairly and wrongly, on the basis of past forecasts that were not borne out. After all, only a generation ago we were being warned about a decline in population in the West. Asking government leaders to take steps towards population control is asking them to take very substantial steps indeed – substantial for their people as well as for their own political careers – hence the case must be virtually incontrovertible. Accordingly, the scientific base must be carefully prepared (and perhaps with some sense of humility about the ease of predicting or urging great events, for the record is not without blemishes). Greater measures to meet the problem – measures which exclude social repression and needless limitation of human

freedom – must rely on heightened awareness of what is at stake, on the part of leaders and masses alike.

What is beyond family planning? Even if most of the specific plans are not particularly new, that in itself does not mean that they are to be disregarded. The questions are: Which plans can be effected, given such criteria? How can they be implemented? What will be the outcome?

NOTES

1. H. C. Taylor, Jr, and B. Berelson, *Amer. J. Obstet. Gynecol.*, 100, 885 (1968).

2. K. Davis, *Science*, 158, 730 (1967); P. R. Ehrlich, *The Population Bomb*, New York, Ballantine, 1968, p. 139; S. Chandrasekhar, *Population Rev.*, 10, 17 (1966).

3. M. M. Ketchel, *Perspect. Biol. Med.*, 11, 687 (1968); see also Ketchel's article in *Med. World News*, 18 October 1968, p. 66.

4. K. E. Boulding, *The Meaning of the Twentieth Century: The Great Transition*, New York, Harper & Row, 1964, pp. 135–6.

5. W. B. Shockley, in a lecture delivered at McMaster University, Hamilton, Ontario, December 1967.

6. Chandrasekhar, as reported in the New York *Times*, 24 July 1967.

7. K. Davis, op. cit.

8. K. Davis, op. cit.; S. Wayland, in *Family Planning and Population Programs*, ed. B. Berelson et al., University of Chicago Press, 1966, pp. 353–62; P. Visaria, *Economic Weekly*, 8 August 1964, p. 1343.

9. P. R. Ehrlich, op. cit., p. 162; R. L. Meier and G. Meier, 'New Directions: A Population Policy for the Future', unpublished manuscript; *Preparatory Study of a Pilot in the Use of Satellite Communication for National Development Purposes in India*, UNESCO Expert Mission, 1968, especially pp. 13–14; W. Schramm and L. Nelson, *Communication Satellite for Education and Development – The Case of India*, Stanford Research Institute, California, 1968, pp. 63–6.

10. K. Davis, op. cit.; T. J. Samuel, *Journal of Family Welfare*, 13, 11 (1966).

11. T. J. Samuel, op. cit.; S. Enke, *Population Rev.*, 4, 47 (1960).

12. M. Young, 'The Behavioral Sciences and Family Planning Programs: Report on a Conference', *Studies in Family Planning*, No. 23

(1967), p. 10; D. Bhatia, 'Government of India Small Family Norm Committee Questionnaire', *Indian J. Med. Educ.*, 6, 189 (1967); S. Enke, 'The Gains to India from Population Control', *Rev. Econ. Statist.*, 42, 179, 180 (1960); J. W. Leasure, *Milbank Mem. Fund Quart.*, 45, 417 (1967).

13. M. C. Balfour, 'A Scheme for Rewarding Successful Family Planners', *Population Council Mem.* (1962).

14. W. P. Mauldin, 'Prevention of Illegitimate Births: A Bonus Scheme', *Population Council Mem.* (1967).

15. P. R. Ehrlich, op. cit., p. 138.

16. K. Davis, op. cit.; T. J. Samuel, op. cit.; D. Bhatia, op. cit.

17. R. M. Titmuss and B. Abel-Smith, *Social Policies and Population Growth in Mauritius*, London, Methuen, 1960, pp. 130–31.

18. K. Davis, op. cit.; D. Bhatia, op. cit.; R. M. Titmuss and B. Abel-Smith, op. cit., pp. 131–6.

19. T. J. Samuel, op. cit.; D. Bhatia, op. cit.

20. K. Davis, op. cit.; D. Bhatia, op. cit.

21. K. Davis, op. cit.; P. R. Ehrlich, op. cit., pp. 136–7; T. J. Samuel, op. cit.; D. Bhatia, op. cit.; R. M. Titmuss and B. Abel-Smith, op. cit., p. 137; A. S. David, *National Development, Population and Family Planning in Nepal* (1968), pp. 53–4.

22. J. Fawcett, personal communication.

23. T. J. Samuel, op. cit.; G. Ohlin, *Population Control and Economic Development*, Development Center of the Organization for Economic Cooperation and Development, New York, 1967, p. 104.

24. K. Davis, op. cit.; A. S. David, op. cit., pp. 53–4.

25. D. Bhatia, op. cit.

26. R. M. Titmuss and B. Abel-Smith, op. cit., p. 130.

27. K. Davis, personal communication.

28. P. R. Ehrlich, op. cit., p. 138.

29. K. Davis, op. cit.; A. S. David, op. cit., pp. 53–4; P. M. Hauser, in 'The Behavioral Sciences and Family Planning Programs: Report on a Conference', *Studies in Family Planning*, No. 23 (1967), p. 9.

30. J. Blake, in *Public Health and Population Change: Current Research Issues*, ed. M. C. Sheps and J. C. Ridley, University of Pittsburgh Press, 1965, p. 62.

31. K. Davis, op. cit.

32. R. L. Meier, *Modern Science and the Human Fertility Problem*, New York, Wiley, 1959, Ch. 7.

33. P. M. Hauser, *Demography*, 4, 412 (1967).

34. 'Family Planning and the Status of Women: Interim Report of the Secretary-General', United Nations Economic and Social Council, Commission on the Status of Women, New York, 1968, especially pp. 17 ff.

35. R. Revelle, quoted by M. Viorst, *Horizon*, Summer 1968, p. 35; D. M. Heer and D. O. Smith, 'Mortality level and desired family size', paper presented before the Population Association of America, April 1967.

36. P. Ehrlich, op. cit., pp. 161–6.

37. P. Ehrlich, op. cit., p. 138.

38. S. Chandrasekhar, in *Asia's Population Problems*, ed. S. Chandrasekhar, New York, Allen & Unwin, 1967, p. 96; Chandrasekhar cites a suggestion made in 1961 by Julian Huxley.

39. R. L. Meier and G. Meier, 'New Directions: A Population Policy for the Future', unpublished manuscript.

40. K. Davis, op. çit.

41. ibid.

42. S. Polgar, in 'The Behavioral Sciences and Family Planning Programs: Report on a Conference', *Studies in Family Planning*, No. 23 (1967), p. 10.

43. *The Growth of World Population*, National Academy of Sciences, Committee on Science and Public Policy, Washington, D.C., 1963, pp. 5, 28–36.

15. Living at High Densities

Extract from the Report

Between 12 and 19 July 1965 the Third Delos Symposion brought together once again a group of men and women of different professional, cultural, and national backgrounds to consider the continuing and accelerating crisis of world urbanization.

The starting point of their discussions was the simple fact that the container available for human activities – the earth's surface – is strictly limited. Its population grows more explosively than ever. Since the beginning of the decade, more than a score of censuses conducted by the U.N. have shown, in every case, that human beings are multiplying even more rapidly than was supposed as recently as 1960. The density of population in the entire inhabited world is reaching the level at which, in the Greek city states, drastic changes in economic and civic institutions had to be made in order to cope with the pressure of rising population.

Density is not simply a question of more people. It is also determined by the vast technological changes which continuously transform man's ways of living. Modern transport has enabled men to spread their urban settlements over much wider areas than ever before. In many modern cities densities are far less than the 100–300 per hectare average of earlier centuries. In the city of New York the average is only forty to the hectare and in the city of Los Angeles only twelve. But this transport system, at certain hours and in certain areas, brings millions back to the centre, creating intolerable densities on the journey and at the destination. Similarly, it is world-wide networks –

---

* Participants in the Third Delos Symposion included: Thomas Dobzhansky, C. A. Doxiadis, J. M. Fraser, R. Buckminster Fuller, S. Giedion, L. B. Granger, E. T. Hall, R. Llewellyn-Davies, Margaret Mead, H. S. Perloff, J. M. Richards, Arnold Toynbee, C. H. Waddington, and Barbara Ward.

transportation, power, commerce, finance – that enable countries such as Belgium to maintain in reasonable comfort densities of population which are catastrophic in underdeveloped lands not yet fully geared into the world-wide economy.

These pressures of population, of technology, of economic transportation, are not self-correcting. Urban spread can threaten, as in South East England, to submerge the whole region. In many developed cities, visual monotony, lack of satisfying urban design, pollution of air and water are among the elements which reduce man's pleasure and pride in his urban setting. In most states in the developing world urban growth is intensified by a massive movement of migrants from the countryside before work in the cities can be provided for them. In short, danger signals are appearing all over the globe to warn the world community that it has come to just such a critical threshold as was reached in ancient Greece during the period of formation of the city states, when only the transformation of a rural, conservative, hierarchical society into a trading, colonizing, urban democracy enabled them to confront the crisis. Mankind as a whole has to think of changes on a comparable scale within the far wider framework of a world community.

There are daunting difficulties in such a transformation. The avalanche of technical change and population growth, the whole drive towards involvement in a world-wide society, have caught mankind largely unawares. We do not sufficiently know what is happening to us. We lack precise data on the nature of modern urbanization – its densities, its positive and negative pressures, its cultural determinants, its rates and lines of expansion. We have only the beginnings of an agreed methodology to permit fruitful comparative urban studies and of a scientific framework within which research can take place.

Points Made in Discussion

When the *Serrus nippon* deer on Chesapeake Bay multiplied to a density of more than one per acre they died off. There was ample food supply, but their adrenals were over twice normal size. They had died from stress.

Our problem is really tempo, not density. Up to recently the horse was the fastest thing there was and the whole tempo was much slower. The car goes too fast for ordinary things. Cities need places where the tempo is slower. Only in a few places like Greece can you sit in a taverna for two hours and not expect anything much to happen. We need places where the car is kept out and man uses his legs only: this is an inherent human tempo. Aeroplanes make many things possible, but they are also extremely taxing. Long plane journeys mean six hours added on to or subtracted from a day. It is difficult for people to make vital decisions at major conferences when under this kind of strain.

People live at different tempos and different densities every day, week, and year. The changes can be stressful or wholesome. Low income families tied to a high density area have a different living pattern from wealthier people. Density may be a helpful variable but intensity – rather than tempo – is the central problem. There is a whole sequence of levels, some related to time/tempo, others not: thresholds of noise levels, intrusion levels, etc.

Density cannot be discussed without taking the technological level of the society into account. We cannot directly compare the densities of today with those of the past, which had a different technological level. Density is only one, limited and mechanistic, measure of community life which does not mean much on its own.

Should we use density merely in a descriptive way or is it a valid normative/prescriptive tool? One middle-class American does not equal one Asian peasant in terms of density. In addition to his dwelling, the American's living space includes his impedimenta of car, boat, out-of-town house, and the web of communications. If varying 'atomic weights' were given to their degree of encumbrance of the land, the western city would have a much higher density than cities of the past.

People prefer to put up with considerable discomfort of congestion (density) in order to be in a place that has a magnetic attraction. The qualitative differences between densities are more important than the numerical ones.

Some like the excitement of life in big cities but ancient Athens had excitement with 30,000. We need not just passively allow a trend to grow endlessly. Can a size be considered apart from its density? No one has yet been able to limit urban size, but one could subdivide the total to give the impression of smaller units and increase local intensity.

If New York shows a gross density below that of Moscow this must mean that the use of overall density as a measure does not throw up what is wrong with New York, and thus it may be a deceptive tool by itself. When interpreted, it means that while Manhattan is over-crowded by any standards, the rest of New York City is not. The whole island of Hong Kong is twenty-six square miles with just over a million people. This is 60 people per acre, or 150 pph, though the city of Hong Kong itself has five times this density.

Density relates to interference. Many systems can coexist as long as they don't interfere with one another. We are considering a visible, tactile city but much that is going on is invisible. Thousands of waves are passing through this room. They could be tapped by a radio set but do not interfere with us as a solid building does. Downtown is a communication system, 99 per cent of which is off the visible spectrum. The new invisibilities will have a critical influence on urban form.

Densities can be negative and give rise to unpleasant interferences, but they can also be very positive and give rise to social cohesion, security, etc. Densities can define social contacts, and proper densities have contributed to the creation of civilization. Without sufficient density, people cannot come in contact with one another. It is only when it becomes too high that there is trouble. The same quantitative densities do not necessarily result in the same qualitative ones. However, certain quantitative densities make good frames within which to work, since they can easily satisfy needs for sunshine, traffic access, etc.

While the central conception of density is the relation of numbers of inhabitants to units of space, these figures can be misleading if used to calculate various considerations that the ekistician planner must take into account (for example, the transportation and communication facilities generated by densities of various sorts) in the absence of a commonly accepted set of ideas for their understanding and measurement. Such a set of criteria would relate various aspects of human activity to the different spaces in which they take place: work, residence, recreation, etc.; house plots, neighbourhoods, cities, etc.

Densities of various dimensions are important to life in human settlements as they may promote or interfere with the attainment of different sorts of human values: in some areas population may be too sparse to permit the attainment of satisfactory conditions of life; in others so dense as to interfere with the attainment of a good life. High densities are frequently related to culturally and technologically determined variables which greatly increase the tempo of life, stress, noise, and population. The effect of an increase in densities upon the attainment of human values in a given situation will vary with its culture, technology, and economic wealth.

Edward T. Hall

The first question to be considered is how does one go about measuring human density? The term *density* refers to the distribution of objects in space, but what kind of objects and what kind of space? Mathematical space? Physiological space? Cultural space?

In my own research on man's use of space I have found no universal standards which can be used in judging density. Not only do people move constantly in space, at different rates and in different ways, but each of us carries around with him a concentric series of bubbles which vary in size. For five years I have been studying six different sensory modalities used as measuring scales: visual, auditory, kinaesthetic, olfactory, thermal, tactile. It seems that different cultures have different mixes of these.

The determining factors are personality, relationship to others, what is happening, and how people feel about it; all of which are set in a culturally determined matrix. Culture is possibly the most significant single variable in determining what constitutes stressful density. Density which would distress a North European is not likely to bother a Japanese. While there are many reasons for this variety in response, the chief one is that peoples around the world perceive space quite differently. This is because no two peoples learn to use their receptor systems in the same way.

In a word, people brought up in different cultures live in different perceptual worlds. We see examples of this in the way people handle space in interpersonal encounters. Consider for a moment the difference between a Greek who garners information from the way people use their eyes and look at him, and the Navajo Indian whose eyes must never meet those of another person. Or consider the disparity between a German who must screen both sight and sound in order to have privacy, and the Italian who is involved with people visually or auditorially almost twenty-four hours a day. Compare the sensory world of the New England American, who must stay out of other people's olfactory range and who avoids breathing on anyone, and the Arab who has great difficulty interacting with others in any situation where he is not warmly wrapped in the olfactory cloud of his companion.

The visual emphasis of most architects derived from the system of perspective developed during the Renaissance. This concept is inconsistent with the way many people of the world perceive space. Not only is space perception not restricted to the visual mode, but it is seriously distorted in the absence of correcting data from the other senses. All the senses are involved in the perception of space; there is auditory, tactile, kinaesthetic, and even thermal space. It is possible to think of the cultures of the world as spread out along a continuum of sensory involvement. The position of a given culture on this scale depends on which of the senses (immediate or distant receptors) are used in interpersonal encounters. The kind of private and public spaces that should be created for people in towns and cities depends upon their position on the involvement scale.

This also suggests a relationship between public and private spaces that bears on density as it is perceived by man. As the English have discovered, urban man living in crowded conditions looks for respite in open spaces. In considering density and crowding, it is important to remember that there is a vital relationship between indoor and outdoor space. If there is high density (as defined by the culture) in public space, there must be relief in the space in the home, or else in the readily available space beyond the city. Therefore, we must think in terms of the spatial experiences during total periods: a twenty-four-hour day, a week, a year, and possibly a lifetime. The great danger is that economic considerations and special interests will destroy the necessary balance between public and private spaces – as they are now doing in the United States.

Time, too, and the way it is handled have a lot to do with the structuring of space. In *The Silent Language*, I described two contrasting ways of handling time. Monochronic, which is characteristic of low-involvement peoples, and polychronic, more common with peoples high on the involvement scale. Monochronic peoples compartmentalize time. They schedule one thing at a time and become disoriented if they have to deal with too many things at once. Polychronic peoples, possibly because they are so involved with each other, are like jugglers and they tend to keep several operations going at once. Therefore, the monochronic person often finds it easier to function if he can separate activities in space, whereas the polychronic person tends to collect activities. If, however, these two types are interacting with each other, much of the difficulty they experience can be overcome by the proper structuring of space. Monochronic North Europeans, for example, find the constant interruption of polychronic South Europeans almost unbearable because it seems that nothing ever gets done.

To reduce the polychronic effect, one must reduce involvement, which means separating activities with as much screening as is necessary. The other side of the coin is that monochronic people interacting with people must reduce or eliminate physical screening so that they can establish contact. This often means physical contact. The American businessman who deals with Latin Americans finds the settee a more successful office fixture than a desk. The highly involved polychronic Neapolitans designed and use the Galeria Umberto, where everyone can get together. The plaza of the Spanish and Spanish colonial town and the Italian piazza serve both involvement and polychronic functions, whereas the strung-out Main Street so characteristic of the United States reflects not only our structuring of time, but our lack of involvement in others.

Since large American cities now incorporate a significant number of both kinds of people, I would suggest that it might have a salutary effect on the relationships between the two groups if both types of spaces were provided there.

I believe that we should design our cities to go even further in providing congenial spaces that will encourage and strengthen the cultural enclave. This will serve two purposes: first, it will assist the city and the enclave in the transformation process that takes place generation by generation as country folk are converted to city dwellers; and, second, it will strengthen social controls that combat lawlessness. As it is, we have built lawlessness into our enclaves by letting them turn into what John Calhoun calls 'behavioural sinks'. In the words of Barbara Ward, we have to find some way of making the 'ghettos' respectable, which means not only that they be safe, but that people can move on when the enclave has performed its educational functions.

How man treats density and copes with the urban crisis is a function of the conceptual models he has of himself and of the city. I suggest that man is above all else a living, evolving organism and, like all organisms, lives in a dynamic interrelationship with his environment. His survival, therefore, is contingent upon learning to use the city creatively. To do so means learning more about its functions as an expression of culture. Therefore, to act intelligently, we must discover the maximum, minimum, and optimum density of the different cultural enclaves that make up the cities of the world. The maximum, minimum, and optimum size of the viable component units for these different populations must also be determined. Furthermore, these two measures are dependent on knowing the involvement ratio of the different cultures and sub-cultures that inhabit our cities. Puerto Ricans and Negroes have a much higher involvement ratio than New Englanders and Americans of German or Scandinavian stock. Highly involved people apparently require higher densities than less involved people, but they may also require more protection or screening from outsiders.

16. Human Development, Densities, and Scale

DELOS SIX*

Human Development

A consideration of man and his needs is the preface to a consideration of the types of spaces necessary for a human environment. Child growth and development is emphasized in this context not only as a factor crucial for urban planning, but as an index of the important role physical environment plays in behaviour manipulation.

The first eighteen months of life is the critical period in learning how to learn, not just in learning itself. It is known that very young infants exhibit extreme variability – even when only a few days or weeks old – but little has been studied of the direct effects upon them of different environments. Child development follows a fixed sequence of stages (Figure 1) although there is a great degree of variability at each stage, which environmental planning must take into account. The child develops with the advent of curiosity from a strict dependence on one person, his mother, and one room, to a state of increasing autonomy and mobility in a number of rooms and the neighbourhood (Figure 2). The necessity for planning starts, therefore, with the room; then communication between rooms and the neighbourhood.

We must consider four orders of perceptual development in infant growth: sensory, orientation, body self-perception, and psychic self-perception. The infant is not only the result of his genetic past; he is

* Participants in the Sixth Delos Symposion included: R. A. Aldrich, Daniel Cappon, C. A. Doxiadis, S. A. Doxiadis, T. M. Fraser, Suzanne Keller, Gyorgy Kepes, R. S. Lourie, R. L. Meier, J. E. Salk, and G. Vassiliou.

Figure 1. (top) Stages of child development.
Figure 2. (bottom) The child's development of independence.

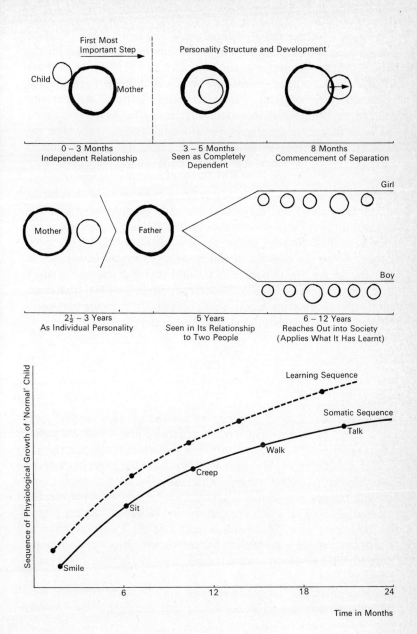

First Most
Important Step

Personality Structure and Development

Child

Mother

0 – 3 Months
Independent Relationship

3 – 5 Months
Seen as Completely
Dependent

8 Months
Commencement of Separation

Mother

Father

Girl

Boy

2½ – 3 Years
As Individual Personality

5 Years
Seen in Its Relationship
to Two People

6 – 12 Years
Reaches Out into Society
(Applies What It Has Learnt)

Sequence of Physiological Growth of 'Normal' Child

Learning Sequence

Somatic Sequence

Talk

Walk

Creep

Sit

Smile

6   12   18   24

Time in Months

a dynamic creature, and a potential adult. The impressions, the input and the decisions executed during the child's first three years predispose his perceptual and emotional attitudes as well as his use of space in later years. Although infants are born with different capacities for perception, psychological experiments reveal that small children with marked natural abilities in certain directions often have these closed off when they enter the standard educational system. At the other extreme, children from sensorily deprived homes find it impossible to recognize two-dimensional representations of common objects of daily use.

We face the problem of raising children to live in a highly complex world. Overstimulation may cause the child to close off, yet he has to learn to live in an environment in which TV and the aeroplane co-exist with the intimacies of the physical neighbourhood. We can no longer choose the moment at which the child should be exposed to certain factors. He is born into a world that is immediately larger than the room. He needs an environment that protects him from over-stimulus while allowing him to develop flexibility in facing simultaneously the small neighbourhood and the megalopolitan complexity.

The Human Scale

Considerations of space on a micro-scale, though easily agreed upon on a verbal basis, are highly controversial on a design basis. Also, it is often easier to agree on the statistics of the macro-scale than the size and shape of a room. We must also emphasize the importance of the intervention of cultural patterns in the use of space.

With respect to distances in space, it appears, for example, that the greatest distance at which one can see and recognize another person is 200 yards, and 2,000 yards seems to be the longest distance at which one can see a monument (indeed ancient cities – seldom larger than 50,000 population – were scarcely ever larger than 2,000 yards across).

Although traditional standards still work in some contexts, they do not invariably apply. By combining time and sight a visual experience is not confined to a distance of 2,000 yards. Distance depends on the interaction between man and the object sighted.

With respect to minimum acceptable space, there is evidence that the individual, properly motivated, can endure comfortably in a unit of only 600 cubic feet, given infinite resources and varying sensory stimuli. Varying psychological and physiological factors can, of course, change an individual's requirements. However, the difference must be noted between geometric space and pattern space: for example, an elephant's foot and a human head occupy the same geometric space, and the 600 cubic feet recorded as a minimum acceptable space may include a wide range of hidden variables.

There is a parallel between the dynamic ecological systems of human beings and that of plants and animals. There is also a sociology of things – of objects made to fulfil needs. From the ways in which they accumulate and group themselves we might derive significant analogies to man's societal relations.

Human Densities

Planning must take account of densities of people per volume of space, not merely densities of area (Figure 3). It is important to point out that densities vary from the horizontal to the vertical during the night and the day. In terms of relative space requirements, density is not a straight line function: it is dynamic, not static. Also density statistics can be misleading since they normally only include internal spaces, but many cultures use streets and other public areas as extensions of their internal living spaces.

We must recognize two types of densities – geometric density and sociometric density – which include a wide spectrum of interconnections. A low density on a macro-space may sometimes be a high density on a micro-scale, in terms of its social and communication contents.

In seeking for certainties we must not leave out the Sundays of our lives, the atypical densities which, as fleeting experiences, deepen our experience. People must be provided with greater choices from very

Man Seen as		Densities Related to															
		People				Type of Space			Use of Space				Time				
		Age	Sex	Personality	Culture	Size	Quality		Type ?	Order	Entropy						
	Body																
	Senses																
	Mind (memory)																
	Psyche																

Figure 3. Human densities in space.

high to very low densities, and many types of spaces in which to live and to move around.

McLuhan says that a kind of cultural law suggests that the greater the density, the greater the social distance. Another theorem of social life suggests that people accept society exactly to the extent that they can reject it. Planning must accommodate the possibility of peak points as well as isolation points.

In considering the transactions between sociometric units there are at least six errors to note: noise (except perhaps in Hong Kong where noise is utilized as a security device), accidents (in terms of human relationships as well as between humans and artefacts), illness, crime, social injustice, and faulty distribution of services. These categories indicate density degree, and are density related phenomena in all cultures.

Densities of functional groups reveal realistic aspects of communities: for instance, an assessment of family units per space in suburbs and working units per space downtown. These concepts move not from different levels, but from different foci. We are dealing with patterns. Patterns studied in space appear as structures, while patterns studied in time appear as functions.

We have to consider not uniform densities, but clumpings of people to be calculated statistically as they change in time under a wide variety of influences. Space must be so allocated as to avoid conflict between organizations and encroachments on life styles.

17. Man in Equipoise

S. GIEDION

Never has mankind possessed so many instruments for abolishing slave labour. But the promises of a better life have not been kept. All we have to show so far is a rather disquieting inability not only to organize the world, but even to organize ourselves.

Control over our increasingly mechanized environment demands that everything become subordinated to the needs of man – to human needs. Mechanization is an agent – like water, fire, or light. It is blind and without direction of itself. Like natural forces, the value of mechanization to man depends on his capacity to use it to the full, while simultaneously protecting himself against its inherent perils. But, because mechanization sprang entirely from the mind of man, it is more dangerous and less easily controlled than natural forces since it reacts on the senses and the mind of its creator.

From the very first, it was clear that mechanization involved a division of labour. This has proceeded until now it is increasingly difficult for man to be in control of any given situation. When his car goes wrong, the owner seldom knows what part is causing the trouble; an elevator strike can paralyse the whole life of New York. The individual has become increasingly dependent on large-scale production and the operation of society as a whole, and relationships are far more complex and interdependent than in any earlier period.

One of the reasons why contemporary man is overpowered by means is because his powers of integration gradually atrophied under the pressures of the fragmented and specialist approach of the nineteenth century. It is only recently that we have seen a gradual rebuilding of the use of universal concepts as the basis for scientific research.

In order to function, man's organism requires a specific temperature, a specific quality of climate, air, light, humidity, and food. To preserve his bodily equilibrium, man needs contact with the earth and with things that grow. To this extent man's body is subject to the laws of animal life.

The human organism can be regarded as a constant. On the other hand, the relations between man and environment are subject to constant change. From generation to generation, from year to year, from instant to instant, they are in continual danger of losing their equilibrium. There can be no static equilibrium between man and his environment, between his inner and his outer reality. We cannot lay hold in any tangible way of the processes of action and reaction. We can only experience the forms in which they crystallize. The very different creations of the Romans, of medieval man, and of the Baroque period demonstrate the perpetually changing relations between man's inner nature and his outer world.

No closed circles and no repetitive patterns exist to define the constantly adjusting relations of man and environment. They evolve in curves, never duplicating themselves.

Our period demands a type of man who can re-create an equilibrium between his inner and his outer reality, who can regain control over his own existence by balancing forces that are often regarded as irreconcilable. This equilibrium can never be static but must be involved in continuous change, proceeding – like a tight-rope dancer – by a series of small adjustments that maintain a balance between himself and empty space: man in equipoise.

To attain this equipoise, man must establish a balance in four main fields:

1. Between his private life and his community life. He must discriminate between the domain reserved for private life and the areas of collective life. As our civilization desires neither extreme individualism nor overpowering collectivism, man must establish a balance between the rights of the individual and the rights of the community. Today both lack form and content.

2. Between his methods of thinking and his methods of feeling. The nineteenth-century gulf between rational thinking and emotional expression resulted in the rise of a split personality. An equilibrium must be regained between reason and emotion, between tradition and the unknown, between repetition of the past and exploration of the future, between the temporal and the eternal.

3. Between the different fields of knowledge. The specialist approach has now to be integrated with a universal outlook. All new developments and discoveries must be related to their social implications.

4. Between the human body and natural forces. The human organism demands a balance between the organic environment and his man-made surroundings. Totally separated from the earth and the natural processes of growth, man can never attain the equilibrium needed for contemporary life.

It is time we became human again and let the human scale rule over all our ventures. The man in equipoise that must arise is new only in contrast to a distorted period. He expresses age-old demands that must be satisfied in terms of our own time if our civilization is not to collapse.

History does not produce repetitive patterns. The life of a culture is limited in time, just as is the life of an individual. Everything depends on what is accomplished within the allotted span.

*Part Three. Society: The Human
Community*

Introduction

The larger the urban concentration of people, the more intelligence is required for living together successfully.

Granted the truth of this definition, it follows that a minority of the people in metropolitan areas are fully civilized, and their proportion in metropolitan population becomes progressively smaller as the size and density of the total population increases.

From this point of view the community is composed of three different layers of population. At the top, a layer of the civilized – the well-trained, well-informed, socially responsible – who cooperate for their own benefit and for the good of their community. The middle layer is composed of those for whom the sole purpose of cooperation is profit and whose methods are predatory. These may cooperate with 'the system' by remaining within close touch of the law's limits, but only for the purpose of exploiting opportunities to be found in the system's weaknesses, or among the weakest, least experienced, and most credulous members of the community.

These latter form the bottom layer of metropolis – those from whom civilization's benefits are withheld by reason of their poor education and training, the handicaps they must suffer because of their social origin and general conditions of life. They can never attain, under such conditions, the benefits of civilization.[1]

Mr Granger speaks from a wide experience as a social worker in New York, but the huge lower layer 'from whom civilization's benefits are withheld' may be found around the world, in run-down middle-class housing, new public housing apartment blocks, and squatter settlements, etc. These people are unique to no culture but have become more numerous as urbanization has snowballed. The solution to the degenerative situation described by Lester Granger lies in involving this layer of society in the organization – and thus the amelioration – of their own environment. But how can the common man participate in megalopolis?

Directly he cannot. Megalopolis is a theoretical construct devised to describe and explain the increasingly complex interrelationships between tens of millions of people over long distances. Between this abstract megalopolis and the individual man in his dwelling, there is a whole range of other categories of settlement, some of them administrative units and some of them functional units. In our context, the urban neighbourhood is of particular importance: the place from which man relates himself socially and functionally with the complex whole.

Man's immediate urban environment acts as an interface between his personal interests and the large depersonalized urban structure. It provides the individual's window to the world. Although numerous institutional and administrative units are essential for the organization of urban life, it is the urban neighbourhoods that – in the words of Suzanne Keller – provide humanity with 'stepping stones in the pursuit of happiness'.

Yet the great majority of the inhabitants of megalopolis step from their front door straight into the impersonal, faceless city with no 'human scale' intermediary. The theory of ekistics holds that a hierarchy of spatial experiences is as necessary in human settlements as in biological and ecological phenomena. The way this operates as a freely interacting network of places within a total system, and not as a one-way hierarchical 'tree', is described by Christopher Alexander in Part Four, 'Shell'.

The abortive history of the too facile notion of building self-contained 'neighbourhood units' is described in this present section by Norman Pearson and Margaret Willis. How then is the bridge to be built between man and the larger anonymous world of urban affairs? Two main threads of discussion weave through this section. As so often, their bases are primarily economic and social: population size and population composition. In other words, how many and what sort of people can there be on this stepping stone? Immediately we are brought to realize that man has a number of different relationships on his way from the nuclear family to the impersonal city: the extended family, the next-door neighbours, 'neighbouring', and his relations with various focusing points of local community feeling: church, school, shops, clubs, etc.

Thus, it is helpful first to consider 'how many', which is an ekistic problem for administrators and technicians as well as economists.

Community Size

Administrators desire governable units, engineers want generally applicable utility standards, economists seek for commercially viable organizations. The evolution of contemporary concepts of appropriate neighbourhood size is traced by Norman Pearson and Margaret Willis. In Figure 1, nine of these sizes are compared with three theoretical scales: one devised by the German geographer Walter Christaller (1933),[2] one by the French sociologist Chombart de Lauwe (1953),[3] and the ekistic scale conceived by C. A. Doxiadis.[4] The resulting twelve examples show that small-scale communities can be divided into several different levels of size.

The smallest grouping is around fifty families. It is equivalent to the sociologist's face-to-face group, or the number of households with a common frontage upon a street, or sharing the common hallway of an apartment block. These fifty-odd families are the physical neighbours discussed in this section by Suzanne Keller and Dan Soen. They are not necessarily either friends or relations, though these are frequently included. They represent the typical urban grouping of people living in physical proximity who are, almost inevitably, on 'nodding acquaintance' terms.

The next grouping ranges from 150 to 450 households. This represents roughly 500 to 1,500 people, which has been the traditional size of villages and small towns throughout the world, based upon easy walking distances. The upper level probably marks the maximum size of an entirely pedestrian island: an area with no carrying distances longer than 200 metres. This scale of grouping also represents the smallest number of people who can support several social functions – from local food shops to nursery schools and community clubs. It is essentially the area of movement of the small child and the old person, and it is significant that this scale occurs in ten of the twelve examples. The only exceptions are Perry's theoretical study of 1929

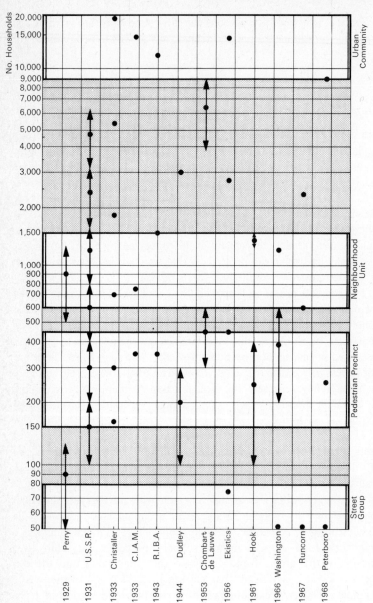

Figure 1. Numbers of households in small communities: twelve examples.

and the recent British New Town of Runcorn. But both Perry and the Runcorn plan lay special stress on the smaller unit.

It is when we come to the larger scale groupings that sharper differences occur. In the era before widespread car ownership, a figure of 600 to 1,500 families was widely accepted as the 'best' size for a self-contained urban neighbourhood. This was mainly based on the number of children needed to support a primary school, and the number of adults needed to support a local shopping centre. Differing systems of education and the advent of the family car have altered these estimates, and the figure for this unit has become raised to around 2,000 to 3,000 households. However, even this cannot provide the range of choices that the housewife and the schoolchild both rightly demand today. This is met by the next ekistic unit of around 40,000 population. It is this scale of community that is referred to in the opening article to this section: a discussion at Delos Seven between experts from many fields, who recognized that if the megalopolis is to serve man, it must be composed of a network of communities rather than a mere assembly of administrative units.

In the following paragraphs on population composition, the four levels we have identified are called, for the sake of brevity, the street group, the pedestrian precinct, the neighbourhood unit, and the urban community.

Community Composition

Margaret Mead makes a strong argument for population diversity but opens the question of how much diversity can be tolerated at the smallest scale:

. . . living in large cities is disastrous for those who have not learned to deal with a variety of people and who have not learned to expect that the strange will be interesting and rewarding or to recognize that it must be treated with a certain wariness. The inclusion of the strange has implications for the size of the basic neighbourhood.

Suzanne Keller draws careful distinctions between the neighbour 'as a special role and relationship', neighbouring 'as a set of socially defined activities', and the physical neighbourhood in which neighbouring may or may not occur. These three distinctions can be directly related to our series of community scales.

1. Diversity at the level of *the street group* should ideally at least include people of widely different ages, but there is a general tendency for this level of grouping to be culturally homogeneous.

In a study of U.S. suburbia, Herbert Gans pointed out that forced heterogeneity often arouses latent hostilities and little cultural adaptation results.[5] Margaret Willis reinforces this finding from English examples, noting that the housing group only becomes a socially important unit if there is a homogeneity of interests.

However, Dan Soen's study of racial tolerances in Israel showed that, while immigrants found that adaptations to local urban conditions were facilitated by the moral security of similar neighbours, there was a direct correlation between households with next-door neighbours of a different background and tolerant attitudes towards mixed cultural groups.

In Musil's case study of several urban areas in Czechoslovakia, it was noticeable that people especially desired to live in close proximity to their younger or older relatives during those periods of life when they needed more help than casual neighbours could be expected to give – when they were very old, or when they had very young children. At these times, the benefits of family help far outweighed the irritations of excessive interference.

Although it is clear that mixed age-groupings occur and are desired at the level of the street group, they are rarely planned for. Indeed the rapid growth of urban populations has brought with it the development of extensive housing estates which are often filled uniquely with young families. Similarly, segregated age-groupings occur in the retirement communities which are growing in number in the wealthier countries.

2. At the level of *the pedestrian precinct*, we ideally enter a realm of varied activities at the pedestrian scale: not a microcosm of the city as a whole, but an area within which the stay-at-homes – the old and the very young – can reach on their own feet the range of facilities they need, and can have some contact with the wider activities of the

outside world. The fact that they are not car drivers should not mean that they are disenfranchized from participation in urban life.

The kind of richness that an urban environment of this scale can provide in the eyes of its inhabitants is well illustrated in Chester Hartman's description of the attitudes of the inhabitants of the West End area of Boston. At Delos Seven, Margaret Mead made a statement that brings out very clearly the different functions of the two smallest community levels.

From the earliest years children should be exposed to the widest range of physical types that are available. In the U.S., children should experience both black and white children and adults. One of the dangers of the present black power movement is that we will have black children that will not have experienced a single act of kindness from a white person, just as we have in many parts of the U.S. white people who have never seen black people close up. This does not mean that we should mix the ethnic or race groups indiscriminately. In Israel the planners initially tried to put all the immigrants in mixed communities, but this did not work at all. Then clusters were built with five little villages, each for a different ethnic group, and a centre where children went to school, adults and children attended a clinic, etc. The five resident villages were a protective milieu; the centre was the place where the process of assimilation was begun. Ideally we want an environment where children, from birth on, experience care and affection from people of different physical types, so that they can learn to appreciate each type and still feel proud of the beauty of their own people.[6]

3. We now come to *the neighbourhood unit*, the third community grouping, and the one that has been the focus of most systems of neighbourhood planning. Up to recently, its size has usually been set at somewhere around 5,000 people. Yet, as Margaret Willis points out, high automobile ownership has made this scale of population quite insufficient as a basis for an economic 'service unit', and sociological studies have repeatedly shown that it is too large ever to function in terms of 'neighbouring'. Equally such units are too large to operate as true pedestrian precincts. The car has to enter, and the dead-end street is a makeshift solution that tends to backfire. Studies show that it is the car entrance that becomes the children's playground, increasing the danger of accidents. Children naturally gravitate to where the action is, as is shown in the study of a Tokyo neighbourhood included in Part Six, 'Synthesis'.

238 Society: The Human Community

Experience in many countries now indicates that the physical de-limitation and separation of 'neighbourhood units' tends to lead to isolation rather than integration. This unit is not large enough to support the variety of choices that the mobile town dweller demands, and it is too large for the purposes of the immobile old and young. They need the closer-in and more limited conveniences of the smaller-scale unit, that can easily be made entirely pedestrian, for, at this scale, car access can always be on the periphery – either above ground or underground according to the type of development. And the periphery marks that junction with the outer world that presents a challenge to the child when he is ready to tackle it: not a danger that penetrates into the intimate environment of his secure home base.

In other words, the small unit that is too large for its sociological purposes tends to become a trap, holding back the less advantaged people from a wider range of choices and opportunities. In certain conditions it can (and has) become a ghetto: a means of segregating different groups of the population under the specious cloak of com-munity planning.

4. *The urban community.* This is not to say that people do not need larger groupings than the small-scale unit that meets the daily needs of the stay-at-homes. But the groups that are voluntarily formed by the mobile members of the population tend not to be tied to a single limited locality. They may be cultural groupings, age-groupings, or interest groupings but their membership tends to be spread over the more accessible part of the urban area, the metro-polis, or even the megalopolis, depending upon the income and degree of mobility of the individual members of the group.

As will be seen in Part Four, all evidence goes to show that people will make every effort to organize themselves in small groups of a par-ticular flavour or content (Elizabeth Wood gives examples from Chicago and India, John Turner from Peru, and Chester Hartman from Boston). This is something that can and should be planned for, for while the simplistic notion that a city can be built up from a col-lection of identical neighbourhood units of 5,000 people, a primary school, and a few shops is patently ridiculous, a faceless metropolis with no identity of place is even more hurtful to the human spirit.

NOTES

1. Lester Granger, 'Community Organization and Tomorrow's Urbanism', *Ekistics* 123, 1966, p. 85.

2. Walter Christaller, *Die Zentralen Orte in Suddeutschland*, Jena, 1933, trans. Carlisle W. Baskin, *Central Places in Southern Germany*, New Jersey, Prentice Hall, 1966.

3. Paul Chombart de Lauwe, et al., *Paris et l'Agglomeration parisienne*, Paris, Presses Universitaires de France, 2 vols., 1953.

4. C. A. Doxiadis, *Ekistics*, Hutchinson, London, 1968.

5. Herbert Gans, 'The Balanced Community, Homogeneity or Heterogeneity in Residential Areas?', *Journal of the American Institute of Planners*, Vol. XXVII, No. 3, August 1961, pp. 176–84.

6. Margaret Mead, 'Preparedness for Participation in a Highly Differentiated Society', *Ekistics* 167, 1969, p. 243.

18. The Scale of Settlements and the Quality of Life

DELOS SEVEN*

Discussion

In between the mega-scale of the total environment and the micro-scale of man there are a number of other categories. In a way, the notion of the total environment is an attempt to view man together with all the different systems operating within and around society. The total environment, in fact, is the system of systems, the sum total of all the various relationships between factors in society, at present and in the future. When we move from man to society we move into an area where experimentation is of a quite different nature, and the projection of settlements into the future involves us in a study of the controls of society which becomes increasingly difficult as the scale of the social phenomenon increases.

Generalization in literature means covering too much territory to be persuasive; in science it means the discovery of a principle that holds true in every case — like the principle of leverage. We can make some generalizations about size. If you take a steel needle seven feet tall and put it into water it will sink to the bottom. If you shorten it to an inch long, with the same slenderness ratio, it is a sewing needle. If you put this in the water it will float. When we increase dimensions geometrically, from a dimension of one linear diameter to two, the surface increases at two to the second power and the volume at two to the third power. Changes in dimensions create changes in the properties of the object.

We can no longer use the word 'city' without thinking twice because we all have an image of the city as a built-up area, and we forget that the ordinary man and his family no longer live within a

* Participants in the Seventh Delos Symposion included: R. Buckminster Fuller, C. A. Doxiadis, Jean Gottmann, T. A. Lambo, Richard Llewellyn-Davies, C. Marston, Martin Meyerson, Jerome Monod, and V. Sarabai.

city but within a system of life processes which extends well beyond the city, which it only touches at certain points. This system is growing continuously in space. This is not the only thing. Man is developing other forces which grow faster than the population itself. The curve of area growth rises more steeply than population growth; the curve of growth of the economy – the G.N.P. – goes higher still; and the curve of energy growth very much higher than that. For example: in Detroit, population rose fifty-fold in a century; the area sixty times; the incomes 450 times; and the energy 550 times. This is the real potential inside the system that forces us to live at a completely different scale. For instance we can take two families with incomes of $5,000 and $20,000 and say that their incomes are in a ratio of 1:4. But their ability to participate in life is a factor of the energy at their disposal which is more like 20:600, expressed in terms of the number of places they can easily reach for different purposes, i.e. a ratio of 1:30. This explains why the greatest segregation today exists between the isolated peasant (who can only move in space in a very small area) and the average urban dweller. The isolated peasant has very few choices, because he cannot dispose of the energy that enables him to move around. In consequence we have to recognize that our notion of villages and cities belongs to the past: in a few generations there will be no isolated villages left on the earth. Instead we have to think of the systems that organize our life, primarily the daily urban systems that encompass our daily movement and which can extend from twenty to thirty miles (Europe) to eighty to ninety miles (U.S.A.). These daily urban systems have to be planned immediately, because the situation is rapidly becoming more and more confused. In addition we need to consider other systems, such as the weekly systems that deal with our weekend movements and which take a different rhythm. We have to try to rationalize man's conquest of space, and not try to keep him back.

Size is usually measured in terms of numbers of people, area, density, transport time, economic volumes, the variety of transactions, etc. Doxiadis has added the measurement of available energy, and the great bulk of energy is used for transport, especially in the U.S.A. But in our concern for quality and the consequences for human life of different patterns of settlement we must go beyond these crude measures. Certainly, there is a great deal of evidence that larger settlements attract more people than smaller ones. This world-wide phenomenon seems to be related to the symbolism of the large city in popular culture. The larger centres have provided certain external economies of scale that enable many kinds of enterprises to function that could not have functioned elsewhere. New small business flourishes best in a setting of related enterprises that can service it. Also the growing sophistication of the population of the world leads to a search for a greater and greater diversity which can only be satisfied in those very large human settlements which have close linkages with other such settlements. For instance, the Stuttgart Ballet could not function without the urban audiences of London, Tokyo, and New York. Another feature common to large settlements is the growing homogenization of land. Instead of the former peaking of activity in the town centre, we are finding a spread of activity extending over the whole settlement. Also when we talk of size we have to recognize the problem of social interaction within large settlements. We must in fact talk of size in terms not only of a macro-scale but also of a micro-scale (there is some evidence that human beings do not interact with more than a hundred others).

The microcosm of all human settlements is a group that gives people a sense of community. World-wide settlements must first be thought of in terms of the organization of small communities. We should then forget the term 'city' and think of a matrix that could cover the whole world or be subdivided into regions, but certainly not into areas that are as arbitrary and unreasonable as the present administrative boundaries of cities.

In France we are laying more emphasis on the functions of a town than its size and we are trying to maximize the network of cities rather than maximize them individually. This seems the only way to avoid the isolation of towns in rural areas and to give a new value to nature.

There is trade-off between the advantages of living in the centre of a great city with short distances to a maximum range of services and contacts, and the amenities of freedom from congestion, space, privacy, and access to the countryside. The majority may prefer the second alternative, but we need a variety of situations. Maybe you can have your cake and eat it if you live in a small, low-density community, well linked to a metropolitan system. But you neither have your cake nor eat it if you live in a high-density small town, remote from, or poorly linked to, a metropolitan centre.

There seems to be an assumption that we can safely ignore villages and that the trend is going to be inevitably towards big cities or larger urban systems. In Africa the so-called isolated villages had already grouped themselves into systems long before we started using this concept. A survey in 1963 showed that as much as 40 per cent of one village intermarried and interacted with another village, in spite of the distance between them. Thus, in some parts of the world there may be a period of restructuring of the functions of the institutions of these village communities before their metamorphosis into an urban people. Conversely, we may find that the cities in England today may later become collections of villages.

There are vast areas of the world where we have an existing lattice of old settlements. Perhaps half the world's population, in China, Pakistan, India, and Indonesia, live in this situation. They have low economic standards and the large majority are dependent upon agriculture. With a few key inputs, such as energy, fertilizers, new varieties of seeds, credit and marketing cooperatives, you can truly transform the economic condition of these areas, even where land holdings are as small as an acre or two. In addition to fighting off starvation and increasing the G.N.P., the new life inserted into this lattice of settlements can act as a counter-force to the pull of the great cities. The major emphasis of national policy must be to improve the quantitative aspects of the economy of this lattice of settlements, and the quality of the life lived there. It has now been shown that if one can insert all these improvements simultaneously the impact is highly dramatic: of the order of 100–150 per cent. The signal is then clearly received by the people and no difficulty at all is encountered in countering traditional conservatism or traditional methods. If the effect is only 10–20 per cent (as it is if everything is not done together) the improvements can easily be wiped out by a monsoon failure or other catastrophe. But a most important aspect of this bringing new energy and new life into the small centres of this lattice is that a new focus is created for small-scale industries, and it is the maximization of family income through utilizing otherwise idle labour that is becoming increasingly important. These industries include spare parts for machine tools, components for the automobile industry, and the assembly of transistor radios. One can already see a transformation occurring in these localities. But the next moves must be improved systems of transportation and telecommunication that can remove their isolation and bring in not only physical and financial inputs, but also the information inputs required for transforming society. In this context, the advent of satellite television and the possibility of inexpensive receivers have made it possible for the first time to bring individual farmers in contact with the whole world. This is an example of how the new, advanced technology is no longer confined to optimum utilization in large centres of population, but permits dispersal and a new freedom that was impossible earlier.

19. Neighbourhoods and Human Needs

MARGARET MEAD

Human beings must be brought up among human beings who have learned from other human beings how to live in a particular way. There are very few cultural differences when we discuss basic human needs; that is, the floor below which the human being must not be permitted to fall.

Primarily, the neighbourhood is the place where children are brought up to become members of their own society. Inevitably, within a neighbourhood, children encounter various older adults from whose experience they learn how to adapt themselves to the kind of society into which they are growing. In a static society, older experienced people who have learned nothing new in their lifetime are the greatest asset, for they transmit the entire heritage to the children. But in a society that is changing, grandparents who are continually learning and who have themselves participated in change have the highest potentiality for transmitting a sense of adaptation. The neighbourhood, where children learn to meet basic human needs and to move towards the use of higher human capacities, is where they first encounter adults – parents and grandparents and unrelated adults of these two generations. The older people may not include their own grandparents (for in some parts of the world there is an extraordinary lack of tolerance of one's own relatives), but there will be some members of the grandparental generation who are treated with consideration.

Of course, any neighbourhood that we design, or that we attempt to ameliorate, must meet the basic physiological needs for all human beings – the essential needs that human beings share with animals: the need for food, water, space, sleep, rest, and a minimum of privacy.

Of these, privacy is one of the most variable. There are societies that have no word for privacy, and when the idea is explained to them they think it is horrible. In one society in which I worked – Samoa – a curtain hung between me and other members of the household gave me a certain privacy from them. But, in a house without walls, nothing separated me from the rest of the village, from whose eyes, obviously, I did not need the protection of privacy. Nevertheless, some sort of privacy, some small, identifiable spatial territory of one's own – even if it is only a hook on which to hang one's own hat – seems to be a basic human need.

A second basic need is for some continuity in human relationships. It need not be affectionate or even kind. One society that I studied – the Mundugumor – reared their children to be effective and happy cannibals, but Mundugumor methods of child-rearing would seem very harsh to us. It never occurred to a mother to give her baby the breast when it cried; instead, she put it in a flat scratchy basket, which she hung up high so the baby could see what was going on. Then, when the baby became restless, she scratched the outside of the basket, making a sound like the squeak of chalk on a blackboard, and the baby stopped crying. It was not an affectionate sound, but it was a sound that assured the baby of continuity in its human environment.

The idea that a baby must be brought up by its biological mother and that it will be traumatized by the mother's absence for a week derives from a recognition of this need for continuity. But, in fact, the child who is reared from birth to be accustomed to eight different human beings, all of whom are close, can be given a sense of continuity by any one of them. And where the immediate environment – the shape of its bed and the smell of its room – is part of what is continuous, the child can stand a greater variety of persons close to it.

This means that in planning neighbourhoods for the future, various possibilities are open to us. We can turn the family car into a house, and when the child, together with the cat and the dog and familiar toys, is moved to a strange place the car will still be a familiar home. Or we can bring children up to live in the same place every summer but in a different place each winter. We can do a great many different things, providing we keep in mind the basic need for continuity and familiarity. There is considerable evidence that failure to take this need into account may lead to severe conflict in young children, and so we are faced with the problem of how to move children safely from highly familiar to entirely unfamiliar environments, with nothing to bridge the gap. A familiar and trustworthy environment is necessary for the child to learn that things will be here tomorrow that are here today and that its hand, reaching out, will find what it is seeking for. But we must also recognize that continuity can be provided for in many different ways.

If children are to be ready to live in a changing world, they must also be prepared to deal with strangeness almost from the day of their birth. For those who live in the modern world, it is a disabling experience to grow up knowing only their own relatives. The fewer the relatives, the more disabling an experience it is. And yet, all over the world, as older forms of the extended family are breaking down into small, isolated nuclear family groups, the child is becoming disastrously over-dependent on its two parents. Disastrous in the sense that living in large cities is disastrous for those who have not learned to deal with a variety of people and who have not learned to expect that the strange will be interesting and rewarding or to recognize that it must be treated with a certain wariness.

The inclusion of the strange has implications for the size of the basic neighbourhood. That is, the neighbourhood cannot be modelled on the primitive village where everyone knows everyone else and everything is familiar. There are, however, some people who would like to keep everything within a safe, closed environment – keep all the cars out, keep all the strangers out, and turn the neighbourhood into a grass plot where all the children can run. There is no doubt that a neighbourhood must have something that is child-scale, some place where children can walk about. I am inclined to think that if children can walk enough, the question of whether or not adults are walkers is less serious. Adults can tolerate enormous specialization – even many kinds of deprivation – if, as children, their senses have been stimulated. One striking example of this can be seen in the experience of people who have suffered deafness, blindness, or paralysis in later life, but who still can draw on earlier experience of hearing, vision, and movement. Helen Keller is probably the best example of such a person. She could hear and see up to the time she learned her first word, and this early experience preserved for her a sense of the world that carried her through her later incredible sensory isolation. All this suggests that the better we can build into neighbourhoods ways of humanizing the small child in the fullest sense of the word, the greater tolerance the adult will have for the strangeness and stresses of a world in which some people may be physically highly restricted for long periods as they move into outer space or deep in the sea – experiences for which human beings have had little evolutionary preparation. Certainly, we need areas where young children are safe and where they can move on their own legs (and this, of course, will affect the location of nursery schools and primary schools); but we also need to provide for their living dangerously part of the time, even while they are very young. Strangeness and danger are part of living in an urban environment.

The anonymity of the city is one of its strengths as well as – carried too far – one of its weaknesses. Even the young baby, growing up to live in a city, needs to have windows on the unknown world. The shopping centre, in which the child encounters strangers and sees its mother encountering strangers, is one such window. But at the same time, the child needs the grass plot, the protected walk, and the nursery school where everything is close and familiar. Only in this way can the small child achieve the autonomy that is necessary at every stage of development. There must be play places and front yards where children can walk safely without fear of traffic. When children move into a newly built housing estate that is inadequately protected from automobiles, parents may be so frightened that the children – who have no preparation for dealing with traffic – will run under the wheels of the cars, that they give the children no freedom of movement at all. In one tribe I know of, the village was located at some distance from a big river. Then, one year, the river changed its course and ran right through the village. The adults, who had no idea what to do, were terrified of the water and, of course, their children fell into the river. In contrast, the people of another village who had lived on the river for a long time knew how to teach their children – and their children were safe. Today, we have to teach our children not only about rivers, but also about traffic: to realize its dangers and be wary of them and also to know how to take chances safely. So, too, in every neighbourhood, there must be places where older children can move freely away from areas of familiarity with confidence, trust, and toleration of strangers and the strange.

Children also need multi-sensory stimulation. There are several reasons for this. Because of tremendous individual differences, we do not know whether a particular child will be most dependent on hearing, sight or touch. Moreover, in different contexts, there may be a greater emphasis on the use of the eyes or the use of the ears. The child who, as an infant, has lacked multi-sensory stimulation will be handicapped in making the necessary transition from one to the other. But, beyond these considerations, there is evidence that multi-sensory cross-referencing is a very creative source of innovation in thought, and we want to bring up children who have the capacity for innovation in a dynamic world.

Children need an environment in which they can learn fine discrimination – in which they can hear small sounds and learn to differentiate between footsteps, learn to hear slight differences in tones of voice, learn to wake and know what time it is. Some peoples have a greater sensitivity to noise and want to shut more of it out than other peoples do. This is something in which whole cultures can be differentiated one from another. But in all cultures, human beings – in order to be human – must understand the non-human. They must have some understanding of plants and animals, water and sunshine, earth, the stars, the moon, and the sun. People who have not appreciated the stars cannot really appreciate satellites; they are confused as to which is which. This need to know about the non-human also affects what is necessary for a good neighbourhood. There must be water, preferably water that moves, for moving water is one of the major experiences through which a child's senses are amplified. There must also be earth – not merely a sandbox. There must be animals, although not necessarily large animals. A child can learn about animals as well from fish in a pond as from buffalo on a prairie, and he can dig in a miniature garden as well as in a great field.

Providing the pattern is complete, the scale can be reduced and the details of the arrangement can be different in different neighbourhoods. The child needs to learn what lives in the water, what lives in the air, what lives on earth, and how human beings are related to these growing, living, singing, fighting, and playing creatures. Any environment is crippling if it cuts the child off from such experiences. The child who has grown up in peach country – who has learned to register, as he wakes up, a drop in temperature and knows how this will affect what people will do – has acquired a lifetime familiarity. He can live in a city for forty years, but when he goes back to the peach country and sees the peach blossoms, he can still wake up at two o'clock in the morning and say what the people are going to do. Experience of this kind is never lost.

A principal aim in building a neighbourhood must be to give the child trust, confidence, and the kind of autonomy that can be translated into a strength to bear the strange, the unknown, and the peculiar. So children need some experience of the range of humanity in its different versions. It is nonsense that children do not have racial prejudices. Of course, they do not know which race is 'superior', and this is the root of racial prejudice. However, children are sensitive to differences in physique, and a child to whom only dark-skinned people are familiar may get used to seeing white faces but shriek with terror at the sight of a white man in a bathing-suit. Equally well, a white child may get used to seeing dark faces but be terrified at the discovery that the middle of someone's back is dark. We need an environment in which the child experiences differences in colour, type, and physique, with sufficient range so that no one group is solely associated with unskilled labour or with the exercise of some highly skilled profession. Instead of being presented with stereotypes by age, sex, colour, class, or religion, children must have the opportunity to learn that within each range, some people are loathsome and some are delightful.

I think we must also consider how children can be presented with models of the kinds of thinking that will be required of most educated adults. Though not all children will learn in the same way, in general it is known, for example, that children who have grown up in rooms that conform to ordinary geometric forms later learn geometric thinking with relative ease. Similarly, children can learn about volumes and ratios from blocks long before they learn words to express the ideas they have grasped. And today they need somehow to learn that their own language is only one of many languages. They need to experience the fact that this object – this container for holding liquids – is called 'glass' *in English.* This is something that must be learned very early, but it is part of learning that one's own culture is one of many cultures. It is part of acquiring freedom of movement in the modern world.

In building a neighbourhood that meets human needs, we start with the needs of infants. These give us the groundwork on which we can build for contact with other human beings, with the physical environment, with the living world, and with the experiences through which the individual's full humanity can be realized. For every culture, the criteria must be modified. We cannot set our sights too low, but we can aim at any height, for we have as yet scarcely begun to explore human potentialities. How these are developed will depend on the learning experiences we can provide for children through the human habitat in which they live.

20. Planning a Social Unit

NORMAN PEARSON

Whether it be called 'neighbourhood unit', 'residential unit', 'social unit', or 'planning unit', the aim is to carry out large-scale housing in a coherent fashion, paying due attention to the neglected fundamentals: human needs both individual and collective. What is aimed at is a social unit of sufficient size to support (from the point of view of use and social cost, rather than mere profit and loss calculation) a varied range of communal facilities, and to provide for what is called 'a satisfactory balance of income groups among the residents'. The unit is to be small enough to bring the communal establishment within easy reach of the groups of houses, and to have its own character and 'a well-balanced community life'.[1] There is, however, a vague quality about most attempts to define 'the neighbourhood unit', since often the aims and intentions of the proposers are doubtful. Early statements of the idea seemed to include the conception of some standard unit which would provide a panacea for all problems of residential development and somehow fit all cases and needs.

Despite the lack of precise statements containing adequate reasons for the area and population considered suitable for such a planning unit, certain purposes are clear. The conception is of a social unit comprising a certain number of people from a variety of classes, occupying a definite area of land, served with the amenities and facilities necessary to a healthy social life, sited at convenient distances, with a service centre where the social institutions of day-to-day life are grouped. Thus, the main function of such a unit is to meet the immediate needs of its inhabitants by the convenient location of its components, both in relation to the areas of housing and to its surroundings. The idea is to organize the physical form of a town so as to encourage the full development of community life. This resembles the statements made about 'self-sufficiency' of neighbourhoods, the desire to make them, even in the great conurbations, 'self-contained', with their arbitrary thousands of inhabitants – who may or may not be a purposeful community, and whose interests and activities are all too likely to reduce arbitrary bounds to meaningless conventions. Exaggerated and over-enthusiastic claims have been made for the neighbourhood unit idea and for units of a similar nature. Many of the purposes of the proposers, in their fight against what Mumford has often called the 'devitalized mechanisms, desocialized organisms, and depersonalized societies', can only be achieved by a complete alteration of our national, and even international trends and policies.

Origins and History

The idea of some unit of urban expansion, some theory of the organized growth of settlements, is by no means new. In ancient Greece and in some medieval countries, expansion was often in a 'satellite' manner. Thus, some Greek cities expanded by units; and there are frequent cases of medieval 'mother' cities and urban offspring. More's communities in his *Utopia* had a common purpose, and their cities (like the Greek ones which were in some ways a model) were similar: 'He who knows one . . . will know all, so exactly alike are they, except where the nature of the ground prevents.'[2] His citizens were filled with civic pride, and keenly competitive in the preservation of amenities. Similarly, houses were 'by no means mean', and were regularly exchanged by lot. The population was to be 60,000 in each of twenty-four towns in Utopia, and the largest city, Amaurote, was two miles across. This makes an interesting comparison, when cultural backgrounds are considered, with Plato's city of 5,000 electors, which implies a population, including helots, women, and children, of anywhere from 40,000 to 60,000 people.[3] In both these cases political and social convenience are the guiding factors.

The political and social theorists who reacted, like certain artists, writers, and poets, to nineteenth-century industrialism, frequently sought to express and achieve their alternative forms of social and industrial organization in what we might call 'planning units'. The cooperative communities of Robert Owen[4] in 1813 were suggested to combat the evils of postwar unemployment by combining small-scale factories with agricultural pursuits. They were to contain 1,200 people, with a high standard of community provisions. Similarities may be seen in the ideas of Charles Fourier,[5] who in 1822 produced his idea of a complete and standard dwelling unit: the association of about 1,800 people in 'phalansteries', living a communal life in one settlement, owning about ten square miles, and being able to reduce costs of distribution to a minimum in their dealings with the rest of society, and with other similar communities. We may also refer to the suggested industrial–agricultural settlement of Kropotkin,[6] and the 'vills' of Fawcett[7] early in this century. With the possible exception of the last, these were small planning units, more self-supporting than normal settlements. This was also the case, though the author was less explicit in this instance, with the communities in William Morris's *News from Nowhere* (1891),[8] in which London was transformed into a romantic-pseudo-medieval association of settlements separated by a well-defined park system, thus anticipating the Patrick Abercrombie plans of the 1940s[9] which, as often as was convenient, accepted the old historical components as bases for 'neighbourhood units' and the 'community units'.

The tragic ugliness of human life 'barricaded evermore within the walls of cities', and the apparent inefficiency of towns resulted in many suggestions and experiments. Ebenezer Howard's *Tomorrow: A Peaceful Path to Real Reform* (1898)[10] pointed to the need for local facilities for community life which is one of the bases of the 'neighbourhood unit' theory.

With the advent of large-scale motor transport came the ideas of planning for a transport age. Sometimes this took the form of planning for more rapid transit, more dormant dormitories and a nation of commuters. Sometimes there was more thought for human needs. Thus, Henry Wright and C. Stein at Radburn[11] applied in 1929 what is now a principle of the layout of neighbourhood units: they installed a complete system of footpaths with underpasses and footbridges so as to allow pedestrians to walk from one end of the site to the other, completely unhampered by motor traffic. This enabled the achievement of a clear segregation of traffic according to speed.

Meanwhile, that aspect of the neighbourhood unit theory concerned with the provision of community buildings was developing. In the 1880s in England, the Settlement House movement began: John Ruskin aided the work of Octavia Hill[12] in the slums of London, where she began a 'community centre' in Southwark, and attempted to carry out ideas which resemble current theory on housing management. Similarly in 1907, Edward J. Ward[13] in Rochester, New York, attempted to establish a school as a neighbourhood centre. He believed that in this way a great community interest could be created and kept up.

Radburn was a beginning. But with it came the more dogmatic ideas of those who attempted to formulate theories of residential units as a cure to the chaotic disorder of the modern city, with an insufficient factual background.

Clarence A. Perry first suggested a hierarchy of units in 1929,[14] and later spelled them out as follows:

1. Patriarchal unit: 5–10 families.
2. District unit: 50–150 families.
3. Parish unit: 500–1,500 families.
4. Multiples of the parish unit giving the neighbourhood unit.[15]

The 'neighbourhood unit' was to be a self-contained residential unit bounded by main traffic roads, without any main traffic routes. This unit was to provide all the housing, schools, and shopping and recreational facilities for its population within these boundaries, with the school and the community buildings at its centre.

A similar dogmatism seems evident in the proposals for the pyramidal town structure put forward by one school of thought in the U.S.S.R. in the 1930s:

1. The group: 100–200 families with kindergartens, crèches, and restaurant.
2. Two groups: 200–400 families with medical station and shopping centre.
3. The block: 400–800 families composed of four groups with an elementary school.

4. The rayon: 800–1,600 families composed of two blocks with a community centre.

5. Two rayons: 1,600–3,200 families with ambulance, fire brigade, and recreation centre.

6. The city: 3,200–6,400 families composed of four rayons with civic, health, educational, and main commercial centres.[16]

While the Soviet Russian example just quoted was for the creation of new settlements, the Royal Institute of British Architects in 1943 suggested a 'hierarchy of social units' mainly intended for application in the reconstruction of existing urban areas and conurbations, as follows:

1. The residential unit: 1,000 persons with small café, public house, nursery school, crèche, and shops.

2. The neighbourhood unit: 5,000 persons with extra shops for weekly demands, restaurant, places of worship, library, community centre, medical centre, and schools (five residential units).

3. The borough unit: 40,000 persons with theatre, cinema, hospital, specialized shops, shopping centre, public hall, and railway terminus (eight neighbourhood units).

4. The district unit: 240,000 in one urban aggregate, about 64,000 families. In its centre, technical schools, exhibition halls, concert halls, specialized services, and large hospitals (six borough units).[17]

These ideas were evolved in answer to rebuilding needs, before the sociologists had turned their attention to planning. A quotation from Frank Pick serves to illustrate the approach to the problem of reconstruction at this time:

The integration of society demands a special study . . . a social unit must be devised – rather must come to birth – not too large to destroy personal contact and not too small to fail to afford variety and diversity. And the social unit must involve all classes and carry within it no class distinction. However, much preliminary thought is needed here, for if the unit is not rightly and naturally conceived, the social structure will never be securely built up. The town, the city, the metropolis itself, and finally the region, will be aggregates of social units, differentiated and combined to fulfil even higher and broader conceptions of the good life.[18]

This approach is interesting. Although Pick is not sure of the worth of preconceived hierarchies of social units there is the same desire for a stable and secure society as is found in Lewis Mumford's writings. Pick's democratic opinions and high ideals are obvious. The 'preliminary thought' he looked for – the survey work for the planning of the material environment of large numbers of urban dwellers – is increasingly recognized as absolutely essential. The desired social relationship cannot be set up at the desire and command of an enthusiastic authority, but must grow.

This was the attitude of Forshaw and Abercrombie in the *County of London Plan*:[19] their purpose was 'to emphasize the identity of existing communities' and to provide each with its own communal buildings, open space, shops, etc. In this plan, the 'neighbourhood unit' was defined as the largest social unit in which domestic interests predominated, i.e. homes, public services intimately related to home life, including small shops, gardens, clinics, day nurseries and, especially, the primary schools. These 'neighbourhoods', which contained physically distinct residential units, were based on the population required to maintain, under existing educational provisions, one elementary school. Above these were existing 'communities', social units for the most part with historical roots, local customs and loyalties and definite physical boundaries. The size of these was between 50,000 and 100,000. This 'community' has been described as 'the first social group with which the planner has to deal in which all elements of home, work, and play receive clear expression'.

In this plan an attempt was made to analyse the conditions existing, to find those factors in growth and development which, under lack of overall planning, had been disruptive and antisocial, and those which had led to low standards and a dearth of 'community spirit'. The planning was based on the argument that social facts are primary, and the physical organization of a city, its industry and its markets, its lines of communications and traffic, must be subservient to its social needs.

These ideas were also operative in the design for a new Nemours, put forward in 1934 by Le Corbusier[20] on the basis of the 'Athens Charter' of the International Congresses for Modern Architecture.[21] The scheme was for a town of 50,000 to be erected in 'echelons' of either 2,500 or 1,250 residents. These units were furnished with common services and show one solution to the problem of supplying adequate space for communal activities: by exploiting the possibilities of 'the vertical city'. Although there is no real variety in the housing provisions, the layout has the great advantage of combining social concentration with openness. It was a compelling experiment in new urban design.

Later, the figure of 5,000 or 10,000 as a suitable number of people for a 'neighbourhood unit' was adopted in many plans, largely based on the provision of schools.

Specialist Viewpoints

To the geographer, the study of the social units is a logical develop- ment of the ideas of regionalism. R. E. Dickinson, for example, says that the community unit is a geographical area with a considerable measure of unity in its services and organization, surrounding and including a focal settlement or sub-centre, given unity by the services emanating from foci: an area of common living with common features of social and economic structure.[22] This definition has been useful in planning patterns of location to achieve a better distribution of service buildings than was achieved in the past by cruder systems of analysis.

While geographers have been interested in the spatial aspects of small urban regions, sociologists have used similar techniques to locate associations, communities, and neighbourhoods. Ruth Glass states that: 'The concept of the neighbourhood unit . . . implies con- siderable localization. It assumes the tendency for, and the desirability of, social integration on the level of the small territorial group'[23] and a neighbourhood is defined as 'a distinct territorial group, distinct by virtue of the specific physical characteristics of the area and the specific social characteristics of its inhabitants'.[24] In this sense neighbourhoods exist in many degrees of social integration, in all urban settlements, and can be located. A test of the level of integration is found by the concentration of social services. This gives a guide to the priorities of planning.

Thus to a sociologist, a neighbourhood unit becomes the flexible shell for a territorial group, the members of which meet on a common ground within their own area for primary social activities and for organized and spontaneous social contacts, and this type of planning is a method of aiding the social integration of the district communities within our conurbations and of remedying their defects. The fact that social life goes on in 'fields' not at all coincident with the boundaries of district territorial groups militates against the conception of a standard unit. Existing communities can be defined by comparing vital statistics, facts of environment and social rank and their effect on living conditions, institutional equipment, and degree of integration (i.e. the extent to which a particular group use their own institutions) as well as actual geographical demarcation.

Real communities can only be created if the planning is backed up by sympathetic socially and politically conscious people working in association. Thus, the contributions of the social theorists and political writers are of interest.

Lewis Mumford has pointed out that in order that people shall be able to play their proper part in the greater associations and larger cooperations 'upon which the very fate of mankind as a whole now depends',[25] the barriers between classes, groups, sects, and people of different financial and social status must be broken down. He advocates conscious planning of our cities to produce active citizens, so that we can have 'the conscious practice of democracy in small units' and to avoid a state of only 'conditioners, and conditioned'.

NOTES

1. W. Segal, *Home and Environment*, London, Leonard Hill, 1948.

2. Sir Thomas More, *Utopia*, trans. R. Robyson, New York, Heritage Press, 1935.

3. See *The Republic of Plato*, trans. F. Cornford, New York, Oxford University Press, 1945.

4. Robert Owen, *A New View of Society and Other Writings*, New York, E. P. Dutton & Co., 1927, first edition 1813.

5. See *Selections from the Works of Fourier*, trans. J. Franklin, London, S. Sonnenschein, 1901.

6. Peter Kropotkin, *Fields, Factories and Workshops*, London, T. Nelson, 1912.

7. Sir Charles Fawcett, *The English Factories in India*, Oxford, Clarendon Press, 1936.

8. William Morris, *News from Nowhere: an Epoch of Rest, Being Some Chapters from a Utopian Romance*, New York, Vanguard Press, 1927 (first edition 1891).

9. John H. Forshaw and Patrick Abercrombie, *County of London Plan* and *Greater London Plan*, London, Macmillan, 1943 and 1944.

10. Ebenezer Howard, *Garden Cities of Tomorrow*, London, Faber & Faber, 1946 (originally published in 1898 under the title *Tomorrow: A Peaceful Road to Real Reform*).

11. See Clarence Stein, *Toward New Towns for America*, New York, Reinhold Publishing Corp., 1957.

12. Octavia Hill, *Homes of the London Poor*, London, Macmillan, 1883.

13. Edward J. Ward (ed.), *The Social Center*, New York, D. Appleton & Co., 1913.

14. Clarence Perry, 'The Neighborhood Unit', in *Regional Survey for New York and Its Environs*, Vol. VII, 1929.

15. Clarence Perry, *Housing for the Machine Age*, New York, Russell Sage Foundation, 1939.

16. H. Kampffmeyer, 'Town Planning in Soviet Russia', *Wohnen und Bauen*, 1932.

17. Royal Institute of British Architects, *Rebuilding Britain*, London, 1943.

18. Frank Pick, *Britain Must Rebuild a Pattern for Planning*, London, Kegan Paul, 1941.

19. John H. Forshaw and Patrick Abercrombie, *County of London Plan*, London, Macmillan, 1943.

20. Le Corbusier, *Oeuvre complète 1934–1938*, Zurich, Girsberger, 1953.

21. 'The C.I.A.M. Charter of Athens, 1933', *Ekistics* 92, p. 263.

22. R. E. Dickinson, *City Region and Regionalism, a Geographical Contribution to Human Ecology*, London, K. Paul Trench, Trubner & Co., 1947.

23. Ruth Glass (ed.), *The Social Background of a Plan, a Study of Middlesborough*, London, Routledge & Kegan Paul, 1948, pp. 17–18.

24. ibid.

25. Lewis Mumford, 'Britain and Her Planning Schemes', B.B.C. talk, 1948.

21. Sociological Aspects of
Urban Structure

MARGARET WILLIS

Town Plans and the Neighbourhood Unit

The neighbourhood unit was originally conceived as a means of fostering the growth of community spirit, and to this end it was considered desirable to delimit the area by physical barriers. This social function of a neighbourhood was put forward in the Dudley Report, *Design of Dwellings 1944*, and was more or less adopted in the immediate postwar new towns. Since then sociological inquiries[1] into neighbouring and social contacts have shown that the neighbourhood unit of between 5,000 and 10,000 persons is not a significant area for social relationships and this has been generally accepted in current town planning proposals.

The neighbourhood unit was discarded completely in the plans for Cumbernauld and, more recently, in Skelmersdale, where the consultants point out that 'the increase of car ownership has resulted in people becoming more mobile and able to satisfy their interests over a wider field'.[2] In support of this there are several studies to show the relatively limited amount of recreational activity now taking place inside the neighbourhood.[3]

The residential unit has, however, reappeared in most of the master plans for the more recent new and expanded towns. It would seem important, therefore, to consider what role these units play in the plan, how they are conceived and what determines their size. In so far as sociological assumptions are made on residential groupings, how far does existing research support them? The various master plans approved or submitted have been analysed and Table 1 sets out in comparative form the residential unit and facilities proposed and the densities required.

Provision of Amenities and Services

In the earlier neighbourhood units a much wider range of services and facilities were planned for a population of about 10,000 than is proposed in the current plans for residential units. This reduction has occurred as a result of the trend towards specialization of services, the economic advantages of larger catchment areas and the realization that strong neighbourhood centres detract from the town centre.

There has also been an increasing awareness of the variation in demands made on the local area. Instead of providing for the whole community it is now recognized that any individual's needs 'in regard to the neighbourhood vary tremendously according to sex, age, and family status'. P. H. Mann in his book defines more fully what these needs are in relation to the different stages in the life cycle.[4] The small child's contacts are limited to those people living virtually next door, extending as he gets older to families 'along the pavement'. When the child is of school age he becomes part of a wider geographical group and at the secondary school this extends further. The teenager and young unmarrieds choose their activities from beyond the neighbourhood, but after marriage the first child restricts the mother to the local area. At this time the neighbourhood can have real meaning for her, especially where there are other young mothers also facing the problems of child-rearing and home-making. The middle-aged with less family responsibilities may take part in local organizations but with the car they can travel further afield. In old age there is a return to greater dependence on local shops and neighbourly help.

Some recognition of different patterns in the use of facilities by social class and car ownership is to be found in a number of the new town proposals. The Redditch report[5] says 'the more dispersed car-orientated families could be located towards the outer edge', and the Washington report[6] states: 'Because of their higher car ownership rates areas of owner-occupied housing can be further away from the centres'. But most of the plans are anxious not to segregate the social classes and state that the separate areas of owner-occupied housing

TABLE ONE
Companion of Residential Grouping proposed in Master Plans

Publication*	Residential Unit	Sub-Division	Factors Determining Size	Net Housing Density
Greater Peter-borough. Draft Basic Plan, 1968	Each township houses 30,000 persons. No further division	Up to 250 houses (village streets) Up to 20 houses (a close)	High degree of mobility and flexibility of location of facilities if no division of town-ship. 90 per cent of houses within five minutes' walk of bus stops and schools	48 p.p.a. (average)
Runcorn New Town Master Plan 1967	8,000 persons (a community)	2,000 people (a neighbourhood) 100–200 persons (30–60 houses, a residential group)	Five minutes' maxi-mum walking time to public transport system and local centre	61·5 p.p.a. To contain 8,000 within area of 162 acres
Central Lancashire, study for a city. Consultants' new town designation proposals, 1967	4,000–5,000 (a neighbourhood)	No figure given	Can support local facilities at economically viable levels within con-venient walking distance	30–60 p.p.a.

Redditch New Town Planning proposals, 1966	No figure given	Residential districts subdivided by topography, planting, buildings 200–600 dwellings (a 'place') 50 dwellings (a group)	Walking distance to local facilities (half mile maximum)	50 p.p.a. ranging between 25 and 75 p.p.a.
Washington New Town Master Plan and Report, 1966	4,500 persons (a village)		Relates to two-form primary school	43·5 p.p.a. average, ranging between 30 and 55 p.p.a.
Skelmersdale New Town: Planning proposals report on basic plan, 1964	None planned		Concept of the town as a 'compact urban centre'. A large proportion of the town within walking distance of central area	60–75 p.p.a. (most of town) 45 p.p.a. (remainder)
Hook: London County Council's proposed new town, 1961	4,000–5,000 persons (super block residential unit)	100–400 dwellings (length of cul-de-sac and studies of 'real community')	Related to population required for two-form entry primary school	70 p.p.a. (45 per cent of population) 40 p.p.a. (38 per cent of population) 30–120 p.p.a. (population constant but size of area ranges 482–168 acres)
Dudley Report Design of Dwellings, 1944	Not exceeding 10,000 persons (a neighbourhood)	100–300 families (social grounds of homogeneity)	Allow full growth of community spirit and comprehensible entity	

* For details, please see notes and references at end of chapter.

should be relatively small and that they should be interspersed in such a way that the occupants use the same facilities as other groups. However, if these people tend to prefer central or non-local amenities, this could result in less use of local facilities. This suggests that either larger residential units are needed, if these are to be based on the provision of facilities, or that less facilities be provided, if economic viability is to be taken as a criterion, with a consequent greater 'inconvenience' for the elderly, mothers with children and without cars, and the poor.

Catchment Areas and Changing Demand

Because of the unbalanced age structure of new towns the demand on local services will vary considerably at different times. For example, a survey of the use made of meeting rooms in new towns[7] showed that the present high number of children results in about a third of all 'meetings' being concerned with this group in the population, and the emphasis was, therefore, placed on the provision of local accommodation to suit their needs. Later, when the children become teenagers, this use of local facilities will be much less.

Primary schools are, in the consultants' reports, frequently a key factor in determining the size of the residential unit. But the numbers of such children are not static and can be affected, as the Washington report points out, by variations in the age structure, the stage in different population cycles, natural variations from the average, the proportion of children going to Roman Catholic or other schools of choice, and so on. The research work by Levin and Bruce at the Building Research Station[8] on the location of primary schools points out that school accommodation cannot easily be matched to such a variable and mobile demand, and the aim should be to distribute it more or less evenly over a wider area than the proposed residential units. Each area, it is suggested, should contain enough dwellings to support five or six county primary schools thus sharing out and absorbing fluctuations in demand and spreading out the benefits of new supply. The implications in terms of traffic or density, accepting a half-mile radius from the dwelling to two or more primary schools, are not, however, worked out. The South Hampshire Study pointed out that 'to conceive of the primary school as the nodal point of an actual fixed physical area is to restrict the natural tendency to overlap and merge of different areas'; while discussing the secondary school system it says: 'To embed each school in a fixed catchment area is to restrict its capacity for change.'[9]

Accessibility

A number of the master plans draw attention to the need for access *between* residential areas, and the plan for Peterborough[10] points out that the townships (30,000 population) should not be subdivided into self-contained communities 'so that a high degree of mobility is possible between all housing areas'. The need for greater accessibility of facilities is shown from the results of a survey carried out in existing new towns. Among the adult clubs and societies there was considerable demand for premises for hire in the town centre, although the present distribution of facilities is based on the neighbourhoods. As most clubs had members from all over the town, and the more specialized from outside the town as well, the meeting place they required was one which was convenient of access and a focal point of public transport routes. The report continues: 'In some respects the neighbourhood pattern in new towns exaggerates the difficulty of cross travel and emphasizes the importance of a central location.'[11]

In another survey among sports clubs (excluding junior clubs) the results showed that 'sportsgrounds are increasingly not expected to be within walking distance of their users. . . . Good accessibility, therefore, becomes important and sportsgrounds need to be related to the transport network of a town.'[12]

The urban structure in the master plans shows various ways of increasing accessibility and choice. Cumbernauld and Skelmersdale have concentrated facilities in the town centre, which is accessible by foot. Other plans, like Redditch, have the residential areas along a route of communication either using public or private transport, or as in Peterborough where 'the structure of the township is based on a simple organization of elements along a central linear spine [which] directly links all communal facilities'. Central Lancashire[13] proposes to disperse some of the major city-scale functions, in order, amongst other reasons, to level out traffic flows. Washington foresees its 'present centralized and hierarchical character giving way to a looser and freer structure'. This could be following the American pattern, described by Foley, resulting from 'increased affluence and increased reliance upon cars and telephones, with the corresponding tendency towards low-density community development and an ever loosening spatial patterning of trips to work and trips for services and social contacts'.[14]

'Convenience' as a Basis for Urban Planning

Although the size of a residential unit and the housing density is, in many new towns, related to 'convenience', few studies have been made into this factor as a planning measurement. D. Chapman defines convenience as 'a quality of the relationship between the home and other places'; it is not a fixed factor, but one that 'varies over time and differs from place to place' and is affected by personal characteristics like age.[15]

There are many factors other than distance that affect 'convenience'. The Building Research Station report continues by saying: 'At intermediate distances the level of accessibility for a child of a given age will depend on local conditions.'[16] The use of the car to take a child to school, for example, although fairly consistent for distances over one mile, varied according to other factors for distances between half a mile and one mile.

A further point made by the B.R.S. study was that the relationship of one facility to another also affects considerations of convenience. Assessments on the convenience of the school by mothers depended 'not only on the location of the school with respect to the home but also on the ease with which other activities, especially shopping, may be combined with escorting a child'.[17]

The quality of the facility also affects the extent people will travel. For example, the Council for Children's Welfare[18] found that rather more than three quarters of the children in their survey will travel up to 660 yards to an equipped playground, but this proportion will only go up to 220 yards where there is little or no equipment. P. J. Ambrose, in his work on shopping behaviour in the built-up area between Littlehampton and Seaford, found that there was a greater willingness to travel further than the nearest possible outlet when purchasing personal goods such as clothes – no doubt to achieve a greater choice – than when purchasing food, and 'more than one third of all purchases were made at points beyond the nearest outlet'.[19]

The type of facility makes a difference as to what distance residents expect it to be. A pilot study in Reading[20] suggested that whereas the bus stop, to be convenient, should not be more than a quarter of a mile away, and local shops, school, and pub not more than half a mile, other facilities such as the railway station, work-place, or relatives could be much further away and still be regarded as 'convenient'.

Finally, car ownership has a considerable effect on distances regarded as convenient. In Bracey's comparison of English and American housing estates[21] he found that, in contrast to the English demand for shops within ten minutes' walk, a visit to a peripheral shopping centre some twenty minutes' drive away was considered 'convenient' to American housewives. But even when households possess a car, the use they make of it is related to social class, at least in England. For example, the Kent County Planning Department[22] found that the higher status families made more use of their cars and shopped at greater distances from their nearest centres than the lower status households with cars, the latter making more use of public transport. In the Reading study[23] the authors suggest that in many households at present the car is used by the head of the household to travel to work and few second cars are owned by wives, so they still wish to be as near to the shops and bus stops as anyone else. However, there was some decline in the demand for proximity to the town centre among car owners, no doubt because the car is available on Saturday for the weekend visit.

Residential Sub-Units

Most of the newer master plans not only divide the town into larger units of 4,000–9,000 persons, but also suggest smaller sub-sections which are given some social significance (see Table 1). A number of the reports propose sub-groups of 300–600 dwellings, either resulting from the physical layout, or the size in which it was felt the same type of housing could be provided. This size of cluster of dwellings was felt to be large enough to provide a choice of social contacts but not too large to be a separate entity and foster class distinctions.

There is some evidence that the majority of people can define their 'neighbourhood' or 'home' area on a map and distinguish it from surrounding areas by consideration of physical appearance, although some informants referred to a specified set of people in status or other terms. This geographic area could vary considerably in size of population although Lee[24] suggests that the actual area remains fairly constant at about 75 acres. (The Runcorn plan suggests neighbourhoods of 2,000 people[25] and Lee puts forward a figure of 2,500 at modern density standards.)

However, some reference is made by sociologists to the 'large residential groups', 'whose physical unit is the street and which contains 60–100 families. . . . Its main objects are to socialize the children and to give help to needy members.' The authors, Morris and Mogey, point out that although the street has been an object of strong loyalties in working-class areas, 'such groups develop very slowly on most estates', and there is a 'surprising lack of reference to such residential groups',[26] although it could be the unit within which children's play groups function.

Whenever the consultants propose the smallest residential groups the encouragement of social contacts is implicit. The Washington report suggests 12–50 dwellings defined as 'the group' – 'house groupings of this size could aid in the formation by residents of a variety of overlapping social relationships'. The Runcorn plan suggests groups of 30–60 houses which 'would allow a reasonable choice of contacts to be made'. On the whole, sociological research suggests that the layout of small groups of houses can affect social contacts but only when other factors are also present such as immediate neighbours being homogeneous, particularly in social class and family type and when they are positively interested in developing relations with each other. Morris and Mogey's findings at Berinsfield suggested that this interaction, where it developed, was among 10–15 families; Willmott's studies at Dagenham[27] found a 'distinctive social atmosphere' in the culs-de-sac of about twelve houses.

Conclusions

The neighbourhood in sociological terms is a small group of people who have a direct relationship with each other and there are social controls operating over the members. Obviously the cohesion varies according to the amount they have in common and only where people want to get together will the physical characteristics of the layout affect the amount of contacts made. Most of the master plans recognize the existence of these sub-groupings but not all suggest numbers small enough to make them effective primary groups.

The larger residential unit, however, into which most plans have been divided, is sociologically not a feature of urban structure. This structure can be described as a 'series of local areas which overlap with each other and are different for different people'[28] of whom the 'different sexes, different ages, and different social classes have different types of interests and different physical areas within which interests are pursued'.[29] These varied and overlapping areas are not so much entities in themselves but parts of a town or city that make up the whole. In direct contrast to the physical delimitation of the Dudley Report's neighbourhoods,[30] the problem today is to facilitate movement and fluidity between physically separated areas, and this is of particular concern in the changing provision of amenities.

In drawing up their plans most consultants have made a number of social assumptions which scarcely seemed questioned, although there is little evidence on which they are based and they may not, in fact, be in line with 'popular preferences'. For example, the assumption is made that people will value 'convenience', that is, a short distance from home to services and amenities, more than lower densities. But surely the preferences often quoted for an 'open aspect' or 'larger gardens' ought to be equally considered.

Secondly, there is an implicit assumption that the 'aim in new town design is to promote social intercourse within the community at various levels' (Washington, p. 13). But how far does this meet the needs of 'customer orientation' planning? Neil Wates, of Wates the builders, says 'our customers chose freedom rather than neighbourliness'[31] while the more socially orientated report, *The Needs of New Communities*,[32] points out that 'families may wish to use their opportunities to live a family-central rather than a community-central life'. The planners' aim to achieve sociability is often seen as a consequence of higher densities: 'One advantage of a relatively high residential density is the greater opportunities it provides for casual social contact; this can be an important factor in establishing community spirit in a new area.'[33] But there is no evidence that people are particularly concerned about sociability of this kind and may in fact prefer privacy or space round their home.

A final criticism is more general and concerns the master plan concept and method itself. The narrow and restricted approach of what is primarily a physical plan, and one that is devised for the most part independently of the agencies that actually build and administer a town, shows the limitations of this type of planning in trying to meet social realities. Willmott, while working on town expansion schemes, says 'a general lesson for city planners' is to understand 'the importance of management', pointing out that 'if city planning is to respect social criteria, it must increasingly concern itself not only with physical design but also with the policies that will enable the design to work'.[34] Getting a more balanced age structure or a higher proportion of owner-occupiers depends on housing management policies, industrial policies, and so on. *The Needs of New Communities* stresses the importance of having a social development plan based 'on planning and administration and on services and activities rather than just buildings'.[35] If this is accepted and more emphasis in the future is to be on coordination and development of services, then the need is for more attention to be given to the *means* by which this is done, the type of organization required, the social policies to be effected, and so on.

Too much physical concern with the urban structure by emphasizing residential units can prove not only sterile but harmful, for more emphasis needs to be given to the patterns of social relations and 'the quality of family and social life which (the plan) permits and encourages'.[36] This analysis would seem to make it necessary to consider more effective ways of linking areas physically separated by roads, etc. and to look at accessibility of, and choice available among, the facilities and services provided. At the same time a greater understanding is desirable of the demands made on the local area by different groups in the population and the influence of their means of transport. These needs may conflict with other considerations, financial or physical, or even be irreconcilable within themselves. This was reflected in some of the plans. A physical plan for a new town needs to be part of a social program of implementation which adapts to change as time and demands require.

NOTES

1. See examples quoted by P. Willmott in 'Social Research and New Communities', *Journal of the American Institute of Planners*, November 1967.

2. Hugh Wilson and Lewis Womersley, *Skelmersdale New Town Planning Proposals. Report on Basic Plan*, Skelmersdale Development Corporation, 1964.

3. D. Waldorf, 'Neighbourhood Unit Assessments – Simple or Complex', *Official Architecture and Planning*, March 1967. Ministry of Housing and Local Government, *Meeting Places for Hire in New Towns*, 1966.

4. P. H. Mann, *An Approach to Urban Sociology*, 1965, p. 165.

5. Hugh Wilson and Lewis Womersley, *Redditch New Town. Report on Planning Proposals, 1966*, Redditch Development Corporation, 1966.

6. Llewellyn-Davies, Weeks, and Partners, *Washington New Town Master Plan and Report, 1966*, Washington Development Corporation, 1966.

7. Ministry of Housing and Local Government, *Meeting Places for Hire in New Towns*, 1966.

8. P. H. Levin and A. J. Bruce, 'The Location of Primary Schools: Some Planning Implications', *Journal of the Town Planning Institute*, February 1968.

9. Colin Buchanan and Partners, *South Hampshire Study*, Supplementary Vol. 2, p. 10.

10. T. Hancock and J. E. Y. Hawkes, *Greater Peterborough. Draft Basic Plan, 1968*, Ministry of Housing and Local Government, London, H.M.S.O., 1968.

11. Ministry of Housing and Local Government, *Meeting Places for Hire in New Towns*, p. 2.

12. Margaret Willis, 'Siting of Sportsgrounds', *Town and Country Planning*, April 1968.

13. Robert Matthew, Johnson-Marshall, and Partners, *Central Lancashire: A Study for a City*, Ministry of Housing and Local Government, London, H.M.S.O., 1967.

14. D. L. Foley, 'Planning for Social Change', paper in *Alcan: Universities Conference Programme*, April 1968.

15. D. Chapman, 'Convenience: The Measurement of a Desirable Quality in Town Planning', *Human Relations*, Vol. 3, No. 1, 1950.

16. Levin and Bruce, op. cit.

17. ibid.

18. Council for Children's Welfare, *The Playground Study: Preliminary Analysis*, 1966.

19. P. J. Ambrose, 'An Analysis of Intra-Urban Shopping Patterns', *Town Planning Review*, January 1968.

20. Ministry of Housing and Local Government, *Home and Environment: A Pilot Study in Reading*, 1966.

21. H. E. Bracey, *Neighbours: Subdivision Life in England and the United States*, 1964, p. 39.

22. Kent County Planning Department, *The Influence of Car Ownership on Shopping Habits*, 1964.

23. Ministry of Housing and Local Government, *Home and Environment: A Pilot Study in Reading*, 1966.

24. Terence Lee, *Psychology Applied to Town Planning*, paper to Scottish Branch of British Psychological Society, 1962.

25. Arthur Ling and Associates, *Runcorn New Town. Master Plan*, Runcorn Development Corporation, 1967.

26. R. N. Morris and John Mogey, *The Sociology of Housing: Studies at Berinsfield*, 1965, p. 146.

27. P. Willmott, *The Evolution of a Community: a Study of Dagenham after Forty Years*, 1963, p. 75.

28. P. Willmott, 'Housing Density and Town Design in a New Town', *Town Planning Review*, July 1962.

29. P. H. Mann, *An Approach to Urban Sociology*, 1965, p. 154.

30. *Design of Dwellings, 1944* (The Dudley Report), Ministry of Health, Central Housing Advisory Committee, H.M.S.O., 1944.

31. N. Wates, 'A Physical Framework for a Social Structure', *Alcan: Universities Conference Programme*, April 1968.

32. Ministry of Housing and Local Government, Central Housing Advisory Committee, *The Needs of New Communities*, 1967, p. 49.

33. Shankland, Cox Associates, *Expansion of Ipswich. Designation Proposals*, 1966.

34. P. Willmott, 'Social Research and New Communities', *Journal of the American Institute of Planners*, November 1967.

35. Ministry of Housing and Local Government, *The Needs of New Communities*, p. 50.

36. ibid., p. 49.

37. *Hook: The Planning of a New Town*, London County Council, 1961.

22. Neighbourhood Concepts in Sociological Perspective

SUZANNE KELLER

Both in physical planning and in sociology the term neighbourhood has been widely, variously, and often inconsistently, used. At times it seems to refer to an area having certain physical properties, at times to a set of human activities or relationships, and then again to an area in which such activities or relationships may, but need not, occur. C. H. Cooley, the American social theorist, considered the neighbourhood, along with the family and playmates, to be a primary group, and many physical planners similarly confound the spatial and the social dimensions of neighbouring. Before one can properly assess the current state of knowledge of neighbourhoods in modern urban settings, therefore, one must first clarify the various conceptions and assumptions contained within that ambiguous term.

The existing confusion is the result of at least three factors:

1. Conceptual ambiguity, particularly the failure to distinguish between three essential, yet separate, elements: that of the neighbour as a special role and relationship, of neighbouring as a set of socially defined activities, and of neighbourhood as a delimited area in which neighbouring and other activities involving neighbours may occur.

2. Contradictory evidence based on research, whose ambiguous assumptions have been incorporated into ambiguous research tools. So we are told, for example, that there is little sense of neighbourhood in community X because few people indicated that they were friends with their neighbours. But even the most impeccable research findings regarding friendly ties among neighbours cannot supply the needed information on *neighbourly* ties among neighbours if these two are, as appears to be the case, distinct relationships. If most neighbourly relations are in fact not relations of friendship, then to ask only about those that are, makes us miss the large majority that

are not. In addition, without having clearly defined the phenomenon, it is next to impossible to distinguish its essential from its accidental aspects and so to discover genuine rather than spurious empirical variations in neighbouring activities and relationships. Moreover, ignoring the conceptual distinction between friend and neighbour has led to unwarranted inferences about the alienation of modern urban man and to unwarranted idealization of the friendly neighbours in small towns and peasant villages. The failure of planners to recreate such 'friendly' neighbourhoods may thus be due less to any professional shortcomings than to their being ill-advised as to the conditions making for friendship and for neighbourliness in village and city.

3. The problem of rapid social changes which upsets the traditional balance between neighbours, neighbouring, and neighbourhoods, and leaves in its wake a residue of incoherent fragments of such neighbourhoods. When relatively compact and easily identified sub-areas of small towns and stable cities disintegrated under the impact of the industrial-urban tidal wave, often only the broken bits of such neighbourhoods remained. Studies of these partial neighbourhoods then showed them to be not only areas with variable and vague boundaries, but also areas of incoherent sets of activities and relationships. Instead of more or less unified social and spatial entities there emerged sprawling, seemingly formless, rapidly changing aggregates, within which the mobile urban multitude was forging the personal and social relations of its period. This posed great difficulties to a study of the problem. Even in the most distinctive natural areas of cities (with homogeneous populations, a historic identity, strong social traditions, and considerable stability), a continual back and forth movement of people and goods, responding to the ceaseless play of diverse social and cultural forces, transforms these neighbourhoods into hybrid creatures between past and future. In the absence of clearly defined concepts it is not even possible to form correct impressions of these events, not to speak of recording and measuring them precisely.

Empirical Studies

Our understanding of any phenomenon depends on the nature and the interpretation of available evidence. Interpretation consists of logically connected inferences drawn from observed data whose quality and utility is in turn dependent on the sources of information and the techniques used to obtain it. Two of the chief sources of information on neighbouring and neighbourhoods are knowledgeable or representative samples of informants and collected (tabulated or mapped) statistics.

Investigations of the Existence of Neighbourhoods

To locate distinct neighbourhoods, investigators have used two main methods based on objective and on subjective indicators. In the first, the investigator identifies and locates physically distinct neighbourhoods on the basis of statistical and census data, physical reconnaissance of the area, and information supplied by selected informants especially knowledgeable about the area. For example, Ruth Glass, in her pioneering efforts,[1] plotted the distributions of selected indicators of such area characteristics as net population densities, age and condition of dwellings, ethnic and religious composition of the populations, occupational distributions, and figures on school attendance, and then noted where these overlapped. By tracing boundaries around these areas of concentrated and overlapping distributions, twenty-six potential neighbourhoods were identified. Twenty years later, a study in West Philadelphia, seeking to locate sub-areas for more intensive analysis, asked twenty-one well-informed local persons to 'name the areas which they thought of as neighbourhoods'; newspapers, historical accounts, and organizational records provided supplementary information, and eventually yielded sixteen identifiable areas ranging in population from 10,000 to over 40,000 persons.[2]

Another method draws on information about where people in a given area shop, work, and play, and the spatial distribution of these phenomena then provide the basis for the tracing of boundaries around them. For example, in early investigations of village neighbourhoods, areas were marked off according to the uses of village centres; usually this left some marginal areas unaccounted for and therefore unclassifiable. Instead of asking adults where they shop or work, one may ask schoolchildren attending particular schools where their parents go for particular services and then plot their answers in relation to their individual residences. A variant of this technique is to obtain the addresses of clients, members, or customers, from village stores, schools, weekly newspapers, and churches, and then plot these service areas to see whether and where they overlap.[3]

A further method is to ask respondents themselves to indicate the boundaries and extent of their neighbourhoods.[4] Often this method is used in conjunction with the first and serves as a check on its utility.[5]

Assessments of the Functioning of Neighbourhoods

Even the most ardent partisans of the neighbourhood as a purely spatial phenomenon would agree that the location of geographically demarcated areas is as yet no proof of the existence of actual neighbourhoods. Some additional information is usually considered necessary to ascertain whether the residents in such physically distinct areas perceive these areas as distinct social and symbolic units. Thus, Glass, having identified twenty-six distinct territorial groupings, then went on to consider whether these also exhibited a given concentration of social activities. This involved a comparison of the geographic units with the 'catchment areas' of the following facilities and services for degree of boundary coincidences: the catchment areas (i.e. the spatial distribution of members) of all elementary and secondary schools, of youth and adult clubs, of post offices, and of greengrocers and shops for sugar registration.[6]

In an intensive study of three West Philadelphia sub-areas previously identified as possessing some neighbourhood potential, the following dimensions were studied further to see whether this potential was being realized: identifiability of the area, identification with the area, presence of friends and relatives within the area, use of local stores, churches, and recreational facilities, attitudes towards the area, and presence of organized local groups for the handling of local problems.[7] Another investigator participating in this broad inquiry into local neighbourhood life selected twelve sub-areas by means of social area analysis, a technique used to locate distinctive sub-areas of larger census tracts, and asked 100 randomly selected respondents in each of these to identify the sub-area by name and boundaries and to evaluate the area as a place to live.[8] This study, in not preselecting its neighbourhoods, has an advantage over those that do, in not inadvertently concentrating on areas of known neighbourhood potential. As a result however, this, as well as the study by Glass which it resembles in some respects, found very little overlap between potential neighbourhoods and actual neighbourhood identity, use, and participation.[9]

A knowledge of the predominant social character of an area, as tapped by various indexes of living conditions, residential stability, and population characteristics, may be used as clues to its neighbourhood potential. If we know, for example, that a given area has a high concentration of home owners of particular income and educational levels in skilled manual occupations, we might estimate their neighbouring activities to be low on the basis of what we generally know about neighbouring in such groups. Or, the presence of certain facilities may reveal the sort of population we are dealing with. Pawnshops or second-hand stores may signal the presence of low income groups; selected churches and schools, that of high income ones. In fact, Baltzell suggests the presence of certain schools and churches as a convenient way to trace the neighbourhood migrations of fashionable society and thereby the rise and decline of fashionable upper-class neighbourhoods.[10]

Information about boundaries, use of facilities, or relations among neighbours do not tell us how adequate, suitable, or desirable such local areas are. For this, objective standards or yardsticks are required. Since such standards are lacking, relative comparisons and subjective judgements are most frequently used, though this whole matter has been least systematically studied so far. Neither relative comparisons, such as ranking areas according to the presence of certain facilities or activities in relation to one another, nor unstandardized subjective judgements permit us to make valid generalizations.[11]

Some Problems in the Empirical Study of Neighbourhoods and Neighbouring

Trying to locate neighbourhoods via identification of boundaries founders on the fact that the most clear-cut physical and symbolic boundaries go hand in hand with clear-cut neighbourhoods, of which the boundaries themselves are only indicators. Where neither tradition nor relative isolation help forge precise neighbourhood boundaries, accurate boundaries apparently cannot be drawn. Thus, Riemer points to the danger of studying a delimited and contiguous 'patch of the urban fabric and recording activities sustained in such areas' since thereby, important social activities that do not take place in these areas remain hidden and are treated as nonexistent.[12]

Most studies, confined to small areas of local communities or to limited samples, emphasize only a few of the relevant dimensions of this complex subject. There is considerable ambiguity in the terms themselves and this conceptual confusion is often matched by confusing research evidence based on arbitrary definition of terms, inadequate samples, and unreliable instruments. Thus, by confounding the distinction between neighbour and friend, studies often report less neighbouring in cities than would be shown to exist were other definitions of neighbouring used. Nor is the meaning of replies always fully explored. If people are asked whether they like their neighbourhood, they usually say yes, but without knowing where they draw the boundary lines or which aspect of the neighbourhood they may be thinking of – the people near them, the shops and cinemas, access to the centre, or the reputation of the area as a smart place – it is virtually impossible to make sense of their answers and thereby to accumulate valid and reliable knowledge.

If we do not as yet have scientifically valid knowledge of the formation and functioning of neighbourhoods it is probably due to the conceptual difficulties involved in designing studies to yield such knowledge. To help develop such designs it is necessary to collect and classify the existing evidence based on personal impressions and fragments of existing studies. By thus piecing together the many varied bits of evidence gathered in as many varied ways, a fairly consistent set of relevant dimensions may be specified. This method, tedious, time-consuming, and cumbersome though it be, is useful as a preliminary approach to the problem to help guide more systematic research efforts in the future.

And in truth it is astonishing that respondents in different contexts answering, perhaps unreliably, lists of unsystematic questions yield as consistent findings as they do regarding, for example, rural and urban differences in neighbouring, the role of physical design in neighbouring, and the like. Of course, their consistency and agreement is in part a function of the investigator's demands, since facts rarely tell their own story. However, armed with a few concepts, primitive and preliminary though they be, the exploration of existing data provides at least a reasonable beginning, a reasonable approximation of what we know and do not know about the role of neighbouring and neighbourhoods in the cities and towns of our era.

Evidence on Neighbourhoods

Where neighbourhoods are clearly distinguishable by their geographic boundaries or by their distinctive ethnic or social characteristics, their identification presents no problem. However, where, as is true in rapidly changing urban areas, neither geography nor culture presents a reliable guide, how can one know whether one is dealing with a neighbourhood or not? Three separate alternative ways have been utilized:

1. To see how the people themselves identify an area.
2. To see how a given group uses the facilities in an area.
3. To assess how people feel about an area.

These three dimensions – the cognitive, utilitarian, and affective – overlap primarily in the geographically or physically well delimited areas that are clearly marked off from others by some physical barrier – be it distance, a highway, a ring road, an open space, or a railroad track – or in the closed milieus of certain ethnic, occupational, or social status enclaves. As these are rare in changing urban areas it is extremely difficult to locate coherent neighbourhoods in them. And since there is little consistent overlap between these three dimensions the question arises as to which one or what combination of them to use as a yardstick.

The extent of neighbouring in an area would seem to be of little help here, since not all people rely on neighbours and if they do they have contacts with very few of them. If neighbourhoods were to be defined by people's attachments to neighbours, the areas delimited thereby would be too small and variable to provide either general standards or areas sufficiently large for systematic planning purposes. Moreover, person-to-person neighbouring is at best only a partial datum. People may not engage in neighbouring and yet make use of local areas in other ways. Most investigators and planners would therefore implicitly include a wider area in their conception of neighbourhood. But how wide? And if it is possible to have neighbourhoods in which little or no person-to-person neighbouring occurs then how are these neighbourhoods to be demarcated?

Neither subjectively identified boundaries, concentrated use of area facilities, neighbourly relations, nor sentiments permit us to locate and classify distinctive urban neighbourhoods. The most distinctive urban neighbourhoods today are either poor and relatively isolated or extremely wealthy and exclusive so as to be equally isolated from the mainstream of urban life. The lack of overlap between neighbouring, use of facilities, and social attachments means that these cannot be used as indexes for consistently subdividing a larger urban area satisfactorily from both the physical and the social point of view.

On the basis of the admittedly sparse data on how people use given local areas, where they draw boundary lines, and whether they are attached to a local area, we can only conclude, while pleading for more and more systematic data, that the local area is no longer (or perhaps not as yet) of primary importance. With the exception of shopping – and the daily, grocery-store variety at that – and perhaps of primary schools (but this varies according to income and other values), there are very few facilities that must be located close to home for everyone. And as regards neighbourhood attachments, some urban residents are strongly involved, others only minimally. At best this is a subjective phenomenon greatly dependent on perceived and actual alternatives for friends, facilities, and dependence on a wider urban area. The economically better off are more mobile and less tied to their neighbourhoods than the poorer urban residents but even here personality factors may make some men urban in orientation despite limited means. Expanded or narrow local horizons seem very much dependent on opportunities for mobility and on personal selectivity. Thus, though physical neighbourhoods may be identified, social change in the family, work, and mass entertainments and amusements have displaced these from their leading positions as providers of information, identity, and social relations.

Concentration on the local area, no matter how imprecisely defined, seems to be most strongly correlated with a lack of alternatives, as when town centres are too distant, too costly or not appealing due to unfamiliarity or ignorance, and with isolation due either to local self-sufficiency or to strong ideological and social pressures. That is, where a solid local network of close economic, cultural, social, and physical ties already exists, there local loyalties and activities will be strong. This does not, however, mean that the provision of local services will by themselves stimulate the desired local loyalties and sentiments in areas lacking the social and historic preconditions for such solidarity.

Today it seems that local self-sufficiency and self-reliance are everywhere diminishing. Even remote villages are linked to the urban-industrial world via mass transport and mass media of communication, local branches of national associations, and personal use of urban centres for amusement or learning. The utility of the neighbourhood conception has in consequence been re-examined by many planners who increasingly find it wanting.

Conclusion

Two main questions have guided this inquiry:

1. According to existing evidence, how much and what kinds of neighbouring occur in different types of settlements and what factors account for the patterns found? and

2. What is the evidence for the existence of neighbourhoods in modern urban settings?

To answer the first question we had to consider the varying definitions of the role of neighbour, for it is this role that helps clarify the meaning of manifest neighbouring activities. Despite wide variations in practice, in principle this role assigns to neighbours a place intermediate between friends and relatives as regards their duties towards and feelings about one another. Neighbours are expected to assist each other during emergencies, to be sociable in a delimited way, and to do their part in maintaining common standards of conduct and physical upkeep in a given space.

Neighbouring activities, more diffuse and difficult to grasp in their complex entirety, may be analysed according to several different dimensions, each of them capable of independent variation. These are: the frequency of neighbouring, its priority, intensity, extent, formality, locale, and the occasions for it. These were found to vary by setting, by group and class affiliations, and by personal inclinations. Neighbouring activities and relationships are more fully integrated with social and economic life in small towns and villages or in special cultural and occupational enclaves in cities than in big urban centres, where friends tend to replace neighbours as sources of assistance and sociability. As individuals and groups become more self-sufficient and as the capacity of local institutions to meet current crises wanes, the need for neighbourly assistance diminishes. Fewer crises, more alternatives for dealing with them, increasing individuality and selectivity, and more mobility and fluidity, all make neighbouring less compulsory and also more variable.

Traditions of place and of social class seem to exert a general determinative influence on patterns of neighbouring within which personal characteristics and physical design play their particular parts. The rise of new values and institutions, the shift from an extended to a conjugal, companionate, family system, and the availability of alternative sources of amusement and employment, also change the content and meaning of neighbouring. It is not so much a decline in interpersonal neighbouring that we observe here as a change in the organization of life itself accompanied by new values, priorities, and preferences.

Neighbouring, in dynamic urban areas, is no longer part of a tight network of interdependent activities and obligations concentrated within a small physical and social space, but simply one more segmentalized activity. Only the most isolated, poorest, most immobile segments of the population continue to rely on the local area and its inhabitants – though not even they do so exclusively, taking for granted a degree of choice and change that would have been inconceivable in a less dynamic era.

The consequences of spatial mobility on neighbouring have often been observed though not always correctly assessed. The immediate rise in observed sociability following a move to certain suburbs or housing estates led to certain hasty and premature conclusions about the favourable effects of suburbs or better housing as such. But while such increased sociability among newcomers accompanies the early period of adjustment to a strange environment, it is by no means a permanent feature of their lives. Neighbours do turn to one another for assistance and fellowship during a period of stress and strangeness difficult for all, but once things get settled and familiar again, individuals become more selective in their neighbouring and specialized in their interests. This is true both for working-class and middle-class groups, for individuals who came from areas high in traditional neighbouring as well as for those who have moved from areas where more segmentalized neighbour relations prevailed.

In all of this, the role of age, personal temperament, and individual taste must not be neglected but neither are these among the primary determinants of neighbouring. It is true that children and adolescents may neighbour more, or closer to home, or that extroverts may do so more than introverts, but these cannot be considered apart from the broader context shaped by social traditions and the dynamics of social change. Similarly for the design of houses and dwellings. Under certain social conditions of like-mindedness, common footpaths, shared utilities, or shared spaces may help promote pleasant social encounters. But if these common facilities are to be shared by mutually antagonistic groups then the common footpaths may well turn into warpaths. The mixing of different social groups is a complex and delicate matter requiring a great deal of skill not yet contained in any existing formula.

As regards the existence of neighbourhoods, we confront a number of unsolved problems. Using the existence of boundaries or the use of local facilities as indicators works very well where boundary and functioning neighbourhood are in fact joined, each being an expression of the existence of the other. A problem arises when we try to use these indicators as independent measures, as 'proofs' of the presence of neighbourhoods; or worse, when we try to use them as promoters of neighbourhood formation. There we usually, and perhaps necessarily, fail. For it appears that such phenomena as clear-cut boundaries, concentrated use of local facilities, and strong local loyalties are only the expressions of neighbourhood cohesion, not their causes. By identifying physical boundaries, therefore, we have not yet taken more than a faltering first step in the location of neighbourhoods, even though most functioning neighbourhoods usually have either natural or man-made boundaries.

Moreover, the very same forces that have altered and in part eroded neighbourhood activities and relations have also eroded neighbourhoods. 'Where one resides,' Merton once wrote, 'is not necessarily where one lives.'[13] And this is by and large true not merely for the small town to which Merton referred but for urban aggregates in general. Generally, these neighbourhoods that are in fact neighbourhoods in the traditional sense, that is, clearly marked by physical and social boundaries, are also somehow atypical in being isolated or outside the main stream of urban life — economically, as in extremely wealthy or extremely poor districts, socially, as in slums or suburbs, and culturally, as in racial or immigrant ghettoes. To duplicate only their surface configurations without duplicating the conditions which gave rise to them is as unfeasible as it would be ineffectual.

The boundaries recognized or demarcated by individuals themselves may facilitate their subjective orientation to their environment but can hardly serve as more than that, since they are usually much smaller than those of political precincts, religious parishes, or planning units, as well as quite variable, hence unreliable, as an objective basis for demarcating neighbourhoods. Moreover, there is as yet no evidence that these subjective boundaries coincide either with special attachments to or concentrated use of local areas.

Satisfaction with one's local area is no better criterion for identifying the existence of separate neighbourhoods. First, because people are not quick to admit dissatisfactions or to find fault with the particular neighbourhoods they live in, and it is only by means of careful and explicit probing that their tendencies towards a blanket endorsement of existing conditions may be pierced to uncover more meaningful discriminations. Second, because, paradoxically, it is not difficult to obtain complaints if one makes an effort to do so, for if people are prodded they will readily catalogue the negative features of their neighbourhoods which may in no way, however, alter their overall favourable assessment of them. This whole problem of the relation between subjective judgements and objective inadequacies of neighbourhoods has been all too little explored. Finally, many people may actually be greatly attached to their neighbourhoods and yet leave them. The young and ambitious, the highly status-conscious, and certain personality types are generally more critical and more mobile irrespective of the objective characteristics of their environment. But even older, more stable settled residents may not hesitate to move from neighbourhoods they like in order to take advantages of better opportunities elsewhere. Thus, liking an area – at least in urban places – is not necessarily indicative of establishing permanent roots there. Local attachments are, of course, greater among long-term residents of a neighbourhood, among 'block' rather than 'city' dwellers as one classification would have it, and among those satisfied with or resigned to their current social status. But in a dynamic urban setting, these groups, no matter how empirically prevalent, do not typify the inherent tendencies of the urban-industrial age with its pressures for movement and variety. This does not, of course, imply that their particular needs and problems should be ignored or overlooked but it does urge that they be considered in the proper perspective. The dynamic forces of urban-industrial society are not concentrated in them or realized through them, since isolation and immobility are, perhaps unjustly, considered peculiar anachronisms or undesirable, and if possible temporary, marks of deprivation. More typical of the realities of this century are those individuals and families seeking to find more space, better jobs, higher status, or greater amenities, for whom local areas or neighbourhoods are but stepping stones – not necessarily devoid of sentimental value – in the pursuit of happiness. Perhaps future research will tell us that twentieth-century urban man had a utilitarian rather than a sentimental attitude to the areas in which he resided. Perhaps, today, sentiment is itself a specialized emotion attaching itself to selected points in a wider area – to a particular street, perhaps, or a favourite dwelling, or an ancient monument – but not to the entire sub-area in which one happens to live. Like urban man himself, ever in pursuit of actual or imagined opportunities, his emotions and sentiments are not fixed but travel along with him, staying where he stays and moving as he moves, in the varied course of his dynamic life.

NOTES

1. Ruth Glass, (ed.), *The Social Background of a Plan: A Study of Middlesbrough*, London, Routledge & Kegan Paul, 1948.

2. Mary W. Herman, *Comparative Studies of Identification Areas in Philadelphia*, City of Philadelphia Community Renewal Program, April 1964, Technical Report No. 9.

3. Roland L. Warren, *The Community in America*, Chicago, Rand McNally, 1963, p. 24.

4. Svend Riemer, 'Villagers in Metropolis', *Brit. J. of Sociol.*, Vol. 2, No. 1, March 1951, pp. 31–43.

5. Mary W. Herman, op. cit.; Donna M. McGough, *Social Factor Analysis*, City of Philadelphia Community Renewal Program, October 1964, Technical Report No. 11.

6. Ruth Glass (ed.), op. cit.

7. Mary W. Herman, op. cit.

8. Donna M. McGough, op. cit.

9. See also Bell, in Marvin B. Sussman (ed.), *Community Structure and Analysis*, New York, Thomas Y. Crowell, 1959, pp. 61–92.

10. Digby E. Baltzell, *Philadelphia Gentlemen*, Glencoe, Illinois, The Free Press, 1958, pp. 182, 194.

11. Ruth Glass (ed.), op. cit., pp. 41 ff.

12. Svend Riemer, 'Hidden Dimensions of Neighbourhood Planning', *Land Economics*, 26 May 1950, pp. 197–201.

13. Robert K. Merton, 'Patterns of Influence: Local and Cosmopolitan Influentials', in *Social Theory and Social Structure*, ed. Merton, Glencoe, Illinois, The Free Press, 1957, p. 393.

23. Neighbourly Relations and Ethnic Problems in Israel

DAN SOEN

Ethnic Clustering in Slums in Israel

In an article that appeared in the *Economic Quarterly*,[1] Dr Erik Cohen shows the existence of an 'orientalizing' process in the under-privileged urban quarters of Israel. This is demonstrated by the fact that inhabitants originally from Europe gradually abandon these quarters, and are replaced by inhabitants originally from Africa or Asia. Based on a statistical survey made in six of the problematic slums of Tel Aviv, Dr Cohen reached the conclusion that if no change occurs in the trend noticed, the slums will undergo a gradual homogenizing process (see Table 1).

TABLE ONE

Population Movement in Some Selected Neighbourhoods in Tel Aviv in 1962 and Comparison with the Composition of the Neighbourhoods in 1961*

Selected Neighbourhoods	Migration Balance of People Originally from Europe	Migration Balance of People Originally from Asia and Africa	Percentage of People Originally from Asia and Africa 1961	Percentage of People Originally from Asia and Africa 1962	Difference in Percentage of People Originally from Asia and Africa in 1961 and 1962
Manshieh	−288	−45	46·7	47·2	+0·5
Jaffa† West	−313	+226	59·3	61·4	+2·1
Jaffa† East	−189	+221	26·5	28·2	+1·7
Shapiro Quarter	−268	+90	33·6	34·8	+1·2
Hatikvah Quarter	−100	+124	89·5	90·2	+0·7
Kfar Shalem	−38	−64	85·0	85·7	+0·7

* These data were obtained from the Tel Aviv Master Plan.
† The two parts of Jaffa were taken here as one quarter.

We noted a similar trend in our study of the Jerusalem South-East neighbourhoods: Talpioth-Arnona and Geulim-Makkor Chaim.[2] An analysis of the findings of the survey made there showed, beyond doubt, that the relative weight of the population originating from oriental countries has increased during recent years, while migration of population of European origin into the area – considered today a backward area – is decreasing constantly.

On the basis of what has been said till now, it can be concluded, somewhat cynically, that if the present trend prevails, the ethnic problem will find its solution, in the not too distant future, within the slums, whereby the area of conflict will be transferred to the delimitation line separating the neighbourhood from the rest of the city. This segregation trend, on ethnic and social grounds, can be noted in Figure 1 where the ethnic clustering in Jerusalem is depicted. But the subject the author intends to discuss here is the inter-ethnic relations *within* heterogeneous neighbourhoods.

An examination of the dwelling patterns from the ethnic point of view shows that where settlement is voluntary and the result of individual initiative, not directed by some central organism, definite clustering trends based on ethnic considerations exist.

An excellent example can be found in the case of the Migdal quarter of Ashkelon, where settlement was voluntary and the settlers simply took over houses evacuated by the Arab owners during the War of Independence. The result of this voluntary settlement is primarily a picture showing two sectors of different ethnic composition: one in the North and another in the South. In the northern section, the number of settlers originating from Islamic countries is predominant, accounting for 89 per cent of the population: whereas in the southern section they represent only 56 per cent of the population. To clarify this matter further, we can analyse the composition of the population according to housing blocks. Although we cannot speak of numbers in absolute terms, we can at least isolate the general trends.

The following picture emerges from the finding of our survey of the Migdal quarter of Ashkelon:

Two blocks are 'Asian' in character.

Three blocks are purely Yemenite.

Five blocks are 'African' in character.

Three blocks are 'European' in character.

Two blocks are heterogeneous in the full sense of the word.

Differences relating to the degree of ethnic 'openness' also emerge from another type of examination, which consists in cross-checking the local ethnic concentrations by ethnically homogeneous neighbours, i.e. the homogeneity of a person and his two next-door neighbours, one to the right and one to the left.

Figure 1. Ethnic clustering in Jerusalem.

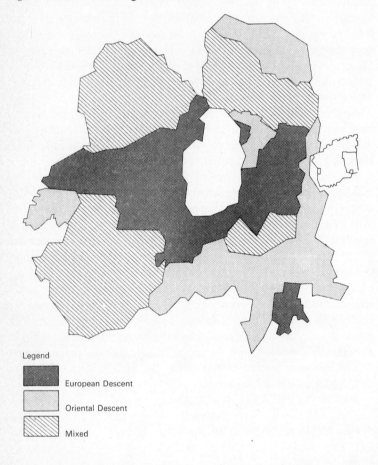

Legend

■ European Descent

▫ Oriental Descent

▨ Mixed

Here the strongest tendency for ethnic aggregation was again found amongst the Yemenites, 59 per cent of whom live in three blocks, where they are the majority, constituting 91 per cent of the families in these blocks. A less marked tendency for aggregation, although still strong, was found among the North Africans, 64 per cent of whose families are concentrated in specific blocks. There they constitute a somewhat smaller majority than the Yemenites in their quarters – 68 per cent of all the families in the blocks. In the case of the Europeans, their ethnic scatter is much greater: only 24 per cent of the European families are gathered together in three blocks which may be called 'European concentration', and where they constitute 58 per cent of the families. Among settlers of Asian origin there is a similar tendency for scatter – 26 per cent of the families are gathered in two blocks, where they constitute 49 per cent of all the families.

The percentage of *partial homogeneity*, i.e. the percentage of persons who, at least on one side, are 'backed' by a fellow member of their ethnic group, is of course much higher, although the order of intensity of homogeneity is similar in many ways to that of full homogeneity. That is to say, the Yemenites come first on the scale, followed by the North Africans, the Europeans, and the Middle Easterners. It seems that the Europeans' need for a 'secure backing' of fellow members of their own ethnic group is also strong, as is shown in Table 2, which examines the character of next-door neighbours in their ethnic concentration.

TABLE TWO

Homogeneity of Next-door Neighbours: A Comparison Between Percentage Found and that Expected According to the Local Concentration Found in Migdal

Group of Origin	At Least One Neighbour of the Same Origin		Two Neighbours of the Same Origin	
	Expected (%)	Found (%)	Expected (%)	Found (%)
North Africa	75	74	31	28
Yemen	72	76	52	54
Asia	46	43	10	19
Europe	55	70	15	6

The calculation was carried out in the following manner: N equals the population of a particular area; A is the number of settlers of an ethnic group in the area; Pa is the probability that the settler from group A will have at least one neighbour of the same ethnic group; Paa is the probability that both his neighbours will be of the same origin. If the number of settlers in the area is relatively large, we can make a rough estimate:

$$Paa = \frac{(A-1)(A-2)}{N^2}$$

$$Pa = 1 - \frac{(N-A)(N-A-1)}{N^2}$$

Ethnic clustering is a natural process in Israel. The apparent motivation of ethnic segregation is the preference of the individual to live within his own group. The need for moral security and the desire to save oneself unpleasantness or enmities encourage the clustering tendency. In a certain sense, it can be said that the ethnic cluster serves as a 'shock absorber' of a sort, by freeing its member from social solitude and enabling a gradual adaptation to the cultural environment.

Neighbours as a Factor for Encouraging Ethnic Openness

Ethnic clustering is a very common occurrence in Israel and the contact between the various groups usually results in intensified openness and increased liberality. This contention was examined in the survey of Migdal.

The following question was presented to the subjects: 'If you could choose the settlers of the suburb, from which country would you like them to be?'

Two other questions, which were analysed together, were also designed to render our conclusions in this field more clear cut: 'From what country do you think most of the settlers of the suburb come?' and: 'What do you think of the fact that most of the settlers come from the country you mentioned?'

The answers to the first question point to several conclusions. The first is that most settlers in the suburb are indifferent as to the ethnic group to which their neighbours belong. The second is that the more heterogeneous the living quarters, the more 'open' the settlers are to groups which are strange to them. In other words, settlers whose neighbours do not belong to their own ethnic group display more liberality towards groups of foreign origin. The same conclusion arises also from the answers to the remaining questions.

TABLE THREE

Choice of Neighbours in Migdal, According to General Ethnic Groupings

	Sephardis Homogeneous		Sephardis with Ashkenazis		Ashkenazis Homogeneous		Ashkenazis with Sephardis	
	No.	%	No.	%	No.	%	No.	%
Want to live with Sephardis	66	*35*	11	*12*	0	0	2	4
Want to live with Ashkenazis	18	*10*	12	*13*	2	*(28)*	9	*16*
Want to live with native of the country	6	3	3	3	0	0	1	2
Do not care with whom	96	52	64	72	5	(71)	43	78
Total	186	100	90	100	7	99	55	100

It appears from Table 3 that among Sephardim, for instance, living between homogeneous neighbours, only 25 per cent are liberal from the ethnic point of view, while 35 per cent prefer to live within their own ethnic group; among Sephardim with heterogeneous neighbours, 72 per cent have a liberal approach, while those preferring to live within their own group represent only 12 per cent.

Dr Judith T. Shuval,[3] in a study of Jerusalem neighbourhoods, reached a similar conclusion. She found that the experience of living among neighbours of European origin increases the willingness of oriental Jews to continue to live on a heterogeneous ethnic basis and weakens their inclination for neighbourly relations with members of their own group. She adds, however, that this reflects a certain degree of 'self hate' among those of the oriental community who voluntarily abandoned neighbourhoods with an oriental majority and moved to neighbourhoods of European character which enjoy a higher status. In any event, Table 4, also taken from Dr Shuval's study, would confirm the contention that ethnic heterogeneity may encourage ethnic openness, by stressing the fact that the rate of those preferring a mixed population is higher in the mixed neighbourhoods than in the homogeneous ones.

TABLE FOUR

Ethnic Preference Patterns According to the Origin of the Interviewed

| Objective Ethnic Composition of the Area | Number of Inhabitants Preferring: | | | | Total | |
	Oriental Majority	European Majority	Majority of Born in the Country	Mixed Population	%	No.
Areas of Oriental Majority	24	15	17	44	100	1,548
Mixed Areas	8	16	20	56	100	804
Areas of European Majority	2	26	28	44	100	1,466

Finally, the pioneering and most interesting research made in Israel of the importance of heterogeneous neighbours as a factor encouraging ethnic openness was made by Dr Shuval in Kiriat Gat, where a series of interesting conclusions were reached.[4]

The four most relevant points with regard to our subject are:

1. Stereotypes and prejudices are strengthened among a population of European origin when they have homogeneous neighbours on both sides.

2. The concentration of inhabitants originally from Middle Eastern countries in ethnic homogeneous neighbourhoods increases the aggressiveness of the other inhabitants towards them.

3. The negative attitude prevailing among the North African group towards the Europeans is intensified when they live between homogeneous neighbours.

4. All these confirm that heterogeneous neighbours are an important factor in the encouragement of ethnic openness.

Summarizing

The statement that the ethnic factor is important in the variables system that determines the satisfaction of the inhabitants with their residential environment finds confirmation in Israel.

The conclusion with reference to the planner is that sensible and careful planning in full awareness of the material previously discussed may not only achieve a higher satisfaction of the inhabitants, but also encourage ethnic openness, or what is commonly called 'integration of the exiles'. On the other hand, planning that ignores these points may fail on both counts.

NOTES

1. Erik Cohen, 'Problems of Development Towns and Slums', *Economic Quarterly*, 49/50, pp. 123–4.

2. South-East Jerusalem Master Plan Team, *South-East Jerusalem*, Institute for Planning and Development, 1968, p. 54.

3. Dr Judith T. Shuval, *Social Research in Jerusalem Neighbourhoods*, Institute for Applied Social Research, Jerusalem, May 1968, pp. 161–2.

4. Dr Judith T. Shuval, *Social Research in Development Towns: Social Problems related to the Planning of an Experimental Neighbourhood in Kiriat Gat*, Institute for Applied Social Research, Jerusalem, 1959.

24. Sociology of Urban Redevelopment Areas: A Study from Czechoslovakia

JIRI MUSIL

This study is partly based on official statistical data but mainly on a series of special investigations done in four Czechoslovakian cities: 360 households in a renewal area of Ceské Budejovice, 829 households living in blighted areas of Kladno, 196 households in Plzen, and 400 households in Prague. In all cases, standard questionnaires for random sampling of households in typical city areas were used. Social surveys were followed by structured interviews with sixty randomly chosen households in the renewal area of Kladno. These interviews gave us a better understanding of the population living in this locality, of their environment, attitudes, ideas, and wishes. All studies were done from 1963–5.

The redevelopment area in Kladno (51,000 inhabitants) was a mixture of one-family houses and small tenements; in Ceské Budejovice (68,000 inhabitants) there was a larger proportion of tenements; in Plzen (140,000 inhabitants), and in Prague (1,000,000 inhabitants) there were large blocks of tenements.

Rehousing Attitudes

As to the satisfaction with housing, three different answers could be given: satisfied, not completely satisfied, and dissatisfied. 40 to 60 per cent of households answered that they were satisfied with their housing and only 15 to 25 per cent were dissatisfied, as can be seen in Table 1. This means that, in spite of unfavourable physical conditions, most people living in blighted areas are satisfied with their housing; this fact was confirmed by other surveys. According to our survey, most households satisfied with their housing were living in the worst conditions. This result is not really paradoxical, since the oldest and least mobile population is housed in these parts of blighted areas, so that the answer 'satisfied with housing' must be explained very cautiously. On the one hand, it means that people are afraid of changes connected with rehousing, and, on the other hand, the aspiration level of some households living in these areas is actually lower than the average.

TABLE ONE

Satisfaction with Present Housing Conditions and Desire to Move Away from Renewal Areas

Satisfaction with Housing	Redevelopment Areas in Kladno %	Redevelopment Areas in Ceské Budejovice %	Desire to Move Away from the Area	Redevelopment Areas in Kladno %	Redevelopment Areas in Ceské Budejovice %
Satisfied	58·3	38·8	Yes	34·0	45·8
Not Completely Satisfied	26·2	36·9	No	65·0	51·4
Dissatisfied	15·5	24·3	No Answer	1·0	2·8
Total	100·0	100·0	Total	100·0	100·0

The degree of contentment no doubt depends on many factors, but a more detailed analysis has shown that the most important are the inhabitant's age, length of residence in the same place, and home ownership.

Social Organization

The study was especially aimed at problems such as the importance of kinship in the local social organization, forms of relations between relatives, role of neighbourhood, intensity of relations between neighbours, degree of isolation and stability of local communities, and forms of spending spare time.

Many features of social organization in redevelopment areas can be deduced from data about their population structure and from general ecological processes determining the population distribution in Czechoslovakian cities. Lowered mobility and a certain isolation of these localities can doubtless be explained by the concentration of a large number of old people and small households. Moreover, the social organization of clearance areas is determined by the fact that the 'modified large family' is still of great importance: it is a modified extended family system accommodated to conditions of an urban society. It becomes manifest in the following ways:

1. a high concentration of mutually related persons;

2. mutual help among relatives, including financial help, presents, household help, and looking after the children;

3. social contacts and activities, visiting, and spending spare time together.

Our survey in four cities of various sizes showed that relatives lived either in the same house or within fifteen minutes' walking distance (see Table 2).

TABLE TWO

The Percentage of Households with Near-by Relatives

Area	Relatives in the House	Relatives Within 10–15 Minutes' Distance	Relatives Living Near by: Total
Kladno	33·9	15·4	49·3
Ceské Budejovice	19·4	40·6	50·0
Plzen	11·6	55·6	67·2
Prague	8·4	45·1	53·5
New Housing Estate	1·6	25·6	27·2

In localities formed mostly by small homes, relatives were concentrated directly in the home, but where the area consisted of tenements, relatives lived in neighbouring houses or streets. A high concentration of relatives in redevelopment areas was found in a comparative study in one of the new Prague housing estates, where 27·2 per cent of households stated they had relatives within fifteen minutes' walking distance.

The tendency of families to live in close proximity becomes manifest especially in households in the first phase of the family cycle (young couples with small children) and also in its last phases. This is explained by the fact that young families are mostly formed by splitting of old families living in the same place. To preserve the advantages of mutual help, the newly formed households seek dwellings situated near their parents. In the later, medium phases of the family cycle, these families become independent from the economic and social, as well as emotional, point of view and they move away. Similar families in the medium phase of development replace them, but they are without any family ties with other people in the locality. This is also explained by the fact that people who have been living in the locality for a long time have a greater number of relatives in the proximity.

In order to find to what extent this space proximity is being utilized, we asked whether households needed help from their relatives and, on the contrary, whether they were helping their relatives. Three degrees of help were distinguished: often, sometimes, and never.

20 to 30 per cent of households in redevelopment areas stated that help was needed often or sometimes (see Table 3). Statistical analysis

TABLE THREE

The Percentage of Households That Need Help from Their Relatives

Needing Help	Redevelopment Areas in:			
	Kladno	Ceské Budejovice	Prague	Plzen
Often	5·7	5·8	12·7	12·6
Sometimes	13·1	20·0	16·5	20·8
Total	18·8	25·8	29·2	33·4

showed that need of help from relatives depended on the age of the people questioned. Such help was especially needed by young families, somewhat less by older families, with the exception of very old people, of whom 50 per cent depended on relatives.

The limited social significance of neighbourhood relations in everyday household life does not mean that the neighbourhood is completely without any function and that people living in the same place do not have the feeling of a certain solidarity. From interviews in Kladno, it was seen that almost half of those interviewed knew other people by name who lived on the same street; there was not a single family that did not know at least one person on the street, more than 25 per cent always went to the funeral when somebody died who had been living on the street, almost 25 per cent of families regularly met their neighbours as friends, and only 10 per cent of those interviewed reported unpleasant relations with their neighbours.

It seems that neighbourhood relations are considered as something given, something not much sought; they do not form – with only very rare exceptions – a very important part in the network of social relations; as good neighbours are considered people who are easy to get along with, who are willing to help in case of need and to whom one should also give help, but who do not intrude too much into family privacy. No other important economic or emotional relations between neighbours were mentioned. This was most evident in answers to a question about whether families living on the same street would like to be rehoused in the same house. Only eleven households out of sixty said they would like to live in the same house as their neighbours, thirty did not want to live with their neighbours, and nineteen were indifferent.

Practically all households in Kladno and Ceské Budejovice did their shopping in local shops and leisure activities were also concentrated at home or in the close proximity. Men's four favourite activities during their spare time were the following, in order of preference: reading, attending sports events, television, and walks in the neighbourhood; women preferred, in order: reading, needlework, walks, and television. When asked what they did last Sunday, men usually answered in this order: visit to relatives, walk, work around the house, television. Women answered: visit to relatives, work around the house, walk, television.

Rehousing Preferences

We have already mentioned that most households did not want to move from the site in which they had been living. In case their district were to be pulled down and renewed, 15·4 per cent of households would like to get a new dwelling in the same site as their old one, 63 per cent do not insist on the same site, but they do not want to leave the district to which they are accustomed, 16 per cent of households are willing to move into another part of their city, and only 1 per cent wish to leave the city and move elsewhere.

25. Social Values and Housing Orientations

CHESTER W. HARTMAN

In the course of studying the effects on mental health of forced re-location from Boston's West End, we have tried to clarify the prevalent values and patterns of a stable and vital urban working-class neighbourhood. The West End, a forty-eight-acre neighbourhood located in the centre of Boston, was demolished in 1958–9 as part of the city's urban renewal program. At the time of land-taking about 2,700 households – 7,500 persons – were living in the area. The population was predominantly working-class, with a scattering of students and professional people, the latter for the most part associated with the adjacent Massachusetts General Hospital. The inhabitants were primarily first and second generation American, and the predominant ethnic groups were Italian (42 per cent), Jewish (11 per cent), and Polish (10 per cent). Most of the data in this paper are taken from a two-to-three-hour interview conducted with a sample of 473 female household members. This represented roughly one out of every five families living in the West End.

Housing Attitudes

The people of the West End in general were very strongly attached to their neighbourhood.[1] An overwhelming proportion of the sample (78 per cent) also reported that they liked the apartments in which they were living, while very few (13 per cent) expressed unqualified dislike. In the light of more generalized conceptions of so-called slum areas, this is indeed a remarkable finding. It must inevitably lead us to question whether the usual descriptive criteria of substandard living conditions are adequate indicators of either objective physical standards or subjective value preferences.

Since West End rents were extremely low – average monthly housing costs, including heat but not utilities, were $42 – most persons were spending a very low proportion of their incomes for housing. 63 per cent of the sample devoted less than one sixth of their total income to housing, and 20 per cent less than one tenth. However, financial reasons were rarely mentioned by West Enders as motives for living there, and the rate of housing satisfaction is no higher among persons paying lower proportions of their incomes for housing. While there were many persons for whom the low rent levels, both in absolute terms and proportionate to income, must have been important sources of satisfaction with the West End, the desire to economize on housing cannot stand as a general explanation of the fact that nearly four fifths of the population in an area of ostensibly substandard housing liked their apartments. The most obvious question to ask initially is whether the description of the West End as a slum is an accurate one.

Housing Conditions

According to a pre-location survey of housing conditions, only 36 per cent of all buildings and 25 per cent of all apartments were in poor or very bad (dilapidated) condition, while 23 per cent of all buildings and 41 per cent of all apartments were in good or excellent (sound) condition.

One of the most striking features of housing conditions in the West End is the frequency with which apartment quality was superior to the building condition. In the majority of cases (61 per cent) condition of dwelling unit and condition of building were at approximately the same level. In only a small group (7 per cent) was building condition better than dwelling unit condition. But for almost one third of the sample (32 per cent) dwelling unit condition represented an improvement over building condition. This alerts us to the fact that, in some sense, good physical living conditions were highly valued in the West

End. Despite structural limitations, a great many West End apartments showed evidence of considerable care and attention; their inhabitants improved and maintained them, undaunted by the physical shabbiness of the immediate and general environment.

The difference in quality of interior and exterior residential spaces is a vital factor to be considered in evaluating slum areas. It evidences the importance of good dwelling units for a large proportion of slum inhabitants and the motivation to achieve this, within the limitations of the physical environment. Residential attachment and the significance of housing attitudes can be expressed in a variety of ways, and it would be a mistake to conclude from the external attributes of a dwelling or neighbourhood alone the prevalent values and orientation towards housing.

Social Values and Housing Attitudes

One of the most important social values we must consider is that 'people do not live only in houses, and this is most strikingly true for working-class people'.[2] The apartment proper can play quite different parts in the residential patterns of different people. For some, it is home and every movement away from this central area is temporary and carried out for a specific purpose. But in the working class, external areas are far more extensively and casually used, and by comparison, the surrounding neighbourhood is a far more important component of the residential 'life space'. If the apartment is considered as a connected part of an entire residential context, it may be that feelings about the residential situation as a whole are likely to 'rub off' and affect many discreet residential and housing experiences which, considered by themselves, might not be intrinsically satisfying.

A number of factors strongly suggest that feelings about the area as a whole markedly influenced attitudes towards the apartment. Certainly there was an extremely high rate of global satisfaction with the West End as a residential neighbourhood. The great majority of people living in the area (76 per cent) expressed quite unreserved positive feelings about the West End, and only a small proportion

(10 per cent) expressed unqualified negative feelings about the area. Several studies have also pointed to the deep attachment that many slum dwellers develop for their homes and neighbourhoods.[3] A review of some typical responses reveals the depth of feelings experienced by West Enders in considering their local neighbourhood. The following examples are selected from responses to the question, 'How do you feel about living in the West End?'

It's my home to me, because it's the place I've lived in all my life. It's nearest to my heart – just home to me – a wonderful thing.

I love it. I was born and brought up here. I like the conveniences, the people, I feel safe . . . I'm going to miss it terribly.

Good. Lovely. I'll never find any better than the West End. I love the West End.

Wonderful. We had such lovely times as kids. Wonderful memories.

I loved it very much. It was home to me. I was very happy. Everyone was so nice. All my relatives live here.

I enjoyed it. I liked it very much. People were wonderful. Everyone was so nice. Stores are very convenient and it was like a big family.

I feel so badly. I've got the blues about leaving here. Have lived here so long. It's really my only place.

You're asking an old-timer who loves it here. Do you think I can get used to any other place? I don't think so.

I love the West End – this is my country.

I love the West End. I love America, the people. I pray to God that they'll let me stay here.

I loved it. I don't know no other place. I loved it.

As these responses suggest, the West End was a place to which people were deeply committed and in which they were rooted by an abundance of interpersonal ties and attachments to meaningful places. There were strong feelings of belonging, of being 'at home'. Most of these responses have a diffuse, generalized quality which communicates a sense of total embeddedness, the feeling that the area was the setting for their entire lives. Under these circumstances, the evaluation of discrete places or experiences is likely to be dominated by the more general sense of satisfaction and meaningfulness of the total environment, of its dominant values, and of the life-styles characteristic of the people living in the area. Housing will be perceived in a quite different way in this case, compared with the more usual situation in which the dwelling unit itself is of predominant importance.

In the West End, the apartment was merely one aspect of residential life. Its functions and significance were, to a large extent, defined by the broader personal and social setting and the attitudes of people towards their housing situation. If we examine attitudes towards the dwelling unit, we find that: (1) feelings expressed about the apartment were quite pallid and unemotional compared with comments about the West End; and (2) the responses frequently by-passed the actual question and alluded to factors extrinsic to the apartment itself, such as neighbours, relatives, view, contact with the street, general accessibility. This becomes quite apparent when we consider a series of responses from the same persons whose comments about the neighbourhood are reported above, in answer to the question, 'What do you like about your apartment?'

Within my means, clean and nice-looking – I like the cleanliness and heat and hot water.

A good-sized kitchen. It's airy. I can look out on the street. Friendly neighbours.

It's just because I stay here a long time. It's just that I haven't found anything wrong.

It's all okay.

The neighbourhood.

Steam heat. First floor.

Convenient to everything. Large rooms, heat supplied. Large bathroom.

The rooms are laid out nice and I have a hall.

Convenient. Nothing wrong. Found refrigerator here. Warm, cosy rooms.

Nothing special, I'm just used to it here.

Nice rooms, friendly location.

Well, once it's cleaned up, it's cosy. It's got enough room for what I have.

It's clean. One flight up. It's nice, that's all.

These responses convey both the limited affective tone in their orientation to the apartment and the sense of the apartment as part of a larger world with many other dimensions. It is also notable that there was a considerable amount of intra-West End mobility – moves from one apartment to another within the neighbourhood. Of the 295 residents who lived in the West End at least fifteen years and thus indicated their deep commitment to the area, 50 per cent had changed apartments within the last ten years, and 17 per cent had moved more than once. Thus, for many residents, the basic sense of residential satisfaction and continuity was not necessarily tied to a specific dwelling but was inherent in the larger residential context. Dwellings were often replaceable; the area seems, for a very great many, to have been utterly irreplaceable.

Housing Conditions, Housing Attitudes, and Social Values

It is quite clear from the data that if one had strong positive feelings about the West End one also had positive feelings about the apartment. Under these conditions objective housing quality was almost irrelevant as a determinant of housing attitudes. Among those who liked the West End very much, almost everyone with good housing (98 per cent) liked his apartment, and only a slightly smaller proportion of those with poor housing (86 per cent) liked their apartments. As feelings about the area itself became less positive, however, rates of satisfaction with apartments of comparable quality decreased. And only then did objective quality of housing appear to affect attitudes towards the apartment.

People who had frequent contact with neighbours or a large extended family living in the same neighbourhood were highly likely to be satisfied with their apartments, almost irrespective of objective apartment quality. These data again demonstrate that, in varying degrees, the experience of social and personal satisfaction in the local area markedly limits the effect of objective housing qualities on attitudes towards the apartment. Only in the absence of these meaningful experiences does the objective physical quality of the dwelling become an important determinant of housing satisfaction.

For many people, particularly the working class, the social and personal satisfactions that derive from the total living situation may be of primary importance. It is inevitable then that conflict will frequently arise between the desire to retain these critical features of life style, personal meaning and continuity and their desires for physical housing quality, whether these are based on the intrinsic significance of a good apartment or on status aspirations related to housing. When this conflict occurs, some compromise is necessary in order to retain the maximum benefit within the limits of the physical reality.

It cannot be denied that the West End was characterized by many shoddy-looking buildings, lack of light and air and green space, considerable dirt, and street patterns inadequate for many aspects of urban life. But the primary satisfactions connected with West End living were able to flourish within this physical setting. Implicit was a compromise: to accept the external space as it was and to restrain desires for physical quality, applying efforts to achieve this within the more easily controlled area of the apartment. Thus, apart from any ideal desires regarding the physical habitat, overall physical quality of the living space necessarily assumed a secondary place in the hierarchy of residential values.

From the point of view of physical planning, it would be of considerable importance to know if some of these interrelationships also hold for other population groups. It is, at the very least, a reasonable hypothesis that if urban planning were to create large-scale physical spaces for all socio-economic groups with a greater potentiality for becoming meaningful personal and social settings, the traditional primacy of the dwelling unit might diminish considerably.

Residential Density

The West End was a high-density area, and overcrowding, both internal and external, was one of the putative evils that led to the neighbourhood's condemnation. The streets were noisy, narrow, and crowded, and there was virtually no internal open space, although the Charles River and its parks formed the western boundary of the area and the Boston Common was within walking distance. According to the Boston Housing Authority's Declaration of Findings: 'Almost all [of the 798 residential structures in the West End] cover 90 per cent of the lot on which they are situated, and almost all of these structures have no setback from the streets.' Compared with several other Boston neighbourhoods generally considered to be crowded, and with the city as a whole, housing densities were also relatively high.

When the residential situation is characterized by considerable choice and minimal restriction, as was generally true in the West End, density patterns are likely to be a product of certain critical features of living patterns. Thus, density cannot be regarded as a discrete variable and evaluated without reference to the larger residential context provided by other physical and social variables. In the West End it is clear that residential stability and the ways in which living space was organized with reference to a range of important physical spaces and social relationships were key determinants of the observable density patterns.

The West End population was highly stable. 71 per cent of the sample had been living in the area nine years or more and fully 56 per cent had been living there at least nineteen years. During this time, moreover, many of these same families experienced major shifts in family composition due to life-cycle changes. Thus, many West End families were living at densities higher (or, in some cases, lower) than those which *ceteris paribus* they would have preferred and for the most part were able to afford. However, rather than disrupt personal ties, attachment to places, and a general sense of continuity in the area, the minor discomforts which resulted from changes in spatial needs and desires were adjusted to and absorbed as alternative costs.

In discussing the determinants of housing attitudes, it was apparent that the residential patterns in the West End and in similar high-density working-class neighbourhoods could be understood only in the context of the central importance of widespread associational networks of local kin and friends and an abundance of near-by places which were part of the daily life-pattern. This would imply that the individual apartment and individual household tend to function less clearly as discrete units than is characteristic for the middle class. In the West End, and in most urban working-class communities which have been reported in the literature, there was considerable inter-action with the surrounding physical and social environment, an inter-action which formed an integral part of the lives of the people. This has important implications for the entire notion of residential densities, for it meant that the West Ender had available more living space than within his own apartment.

Among a population for whom sitting on stoops, congregating on street corners, hanging out of windows, talking with shopkeepers and strolling in the local area formed a critical part of the *modus vivendi*, the concept of personal living space must certainly be expanded to include outdoor as well as indoor space. Likewise, a high level of intimate and casual social interaction with immediately surrounding neighbours means that other dwelling units may be used as extensions of or escapes from one's own apartment. In other words, if the prevalent life style is such that the street scene, hallways, and the apartments of others are the locus for a considerable part of the day's activities, measures and standards of residential density must be revised to include a realistic assessment of available living space as well as consideration of the preferred pattern and intensity of interpersonal contact.

A further consideration in evaluating the effects of housing conditions generally and of density specifically relates to conceptions of privacy. A good deal of our thinking about optimum amount and type of living space is based on an explicit or implicit regard for the virtues of privacy and the ways in which privacy permits and encourages orientation towards individual responsibility and achievement. However, this orientation, generally associated with the middle class in our society, is not universal and there still remain large segments of the population for whom kinship ties, interpersonal relations, identity, and a sense of belonging in an area are critical orientations. For groups like this, 'apartments' connotes something quite different from its meaning for the middle class. For the middle class, 'housing' is an apartment contained within walls – the quantity and quality of its internal space, apart from its adjacent setting – and the 'home life' refers to the interpersonal contacts that take place within the confines of the apartment. By contrast, working-class housing is not so clearly oriented around an 'apartment' (the word itself is quite revealing) defined or conceived of in this discrete way; it represents a constant interplay between 'inside' and 'outside', both in a physical and social sense. It is not that distinctions between the interior and exterior are non-existent, but they are less rigid, less important. Apartment walls, windows, and doors are relatively 'permeable', in terms of sights, smells, sounds, and persons from the outside entering the apartment, as well as the 'insiders' moving out, a high degree of informal socializing, an intensive use of the street.

Density must be regarded in terms of overall spatial use and organization. Fried and Gleicher have used the term 'territorial' to describe the organization of space in the West End, and, more generally, in many working-class neighbourhoods.[4] That is, the space immediately surrounding one's dwelling is regarded and used as a stable, meaningful locus for interpersonal contact, leisure time activities, shopping, and services. It is a particular, non-interchangeable, contiguous territory to which an individual belongs and within which he feels 'at home'. Since this territory is readily and immediately available, it is in fact one's personal living space, even though it is not exclusive or private, and therefore must in some way be included in the evaluation of density. In contrast, organization of space among the middle class is far more selective and exclusive, defined in terms of a far-flung network of chosen relevant points, connected by a series of functional paths.

Conclusion

This paper has attempted to show that for certain people the accepted standards of housing quality and quantity may be of secondary importance in determining residential satisfaction or dissatisfaction. More generally, it suggests the significance of social values and the ways in which they can modify attitudes towards and use of the physical world. Traditionally, physical factors alone have been stressed in the evaluation of housing conditions and in planning for improved residential areas. Physical factors are important, but they have no invariant or 'objective' status and can only be understood in the light of their meaning for people's lives – which in turn is determined by social and cultural values. The tendency to regard the physical environment as having independent meaning and significance is in part related to middle-class values of individuality. But in part, too, it may reflect a failure of existing neighbourhoods and communities to provide the kinds of settings wherein meaningful communal life can take place.

British experience with housing estates has led some observers to a similar conclusion. Vere Hole writes:

> So far, however, the ideological emphasis in rehousing has been on the dwelling rather than the estate where it is located. In spite of protestations to the contrary, estates are still being planned as dormitories rather than as communities, and the tenants moving on to them have had neither the expectations, the incentives, nor the opportunities that would be necessary if genuine communities are to be created.[5]

The extreme 'apartness' and inward quality of so much of today's housing, the exclusive personal involvement in one's own home, may in fact be a function of limited alternative choice. It is quite possible that a great many features of working-class residential life could have far wider appeal and applicability. In studying working-class residential orientations, the importance of the larger residential experience within a meaningful physical area is revealed. While the nature of this relationship may be quite different for the middle class, greater attention to a meaningfully designed neighbourhood might have wide-spread significance and offer an opportunity for different conceptions of residential life. Certainly within the working class, the interaction of inner and outer space and the effect of social values on housing behaviour is a critical consideration. Only with a deeper understanding of working-class orientations and life styles and of the familiar or unfamiliar alternatives which can be meaningful in working-class perspectives may we hope to design housing which is more gratifying than the slums we wish to eradicate.

NOTES

1. Marc Fried, 'Grieving for a Lost Home', in Leonard J. Duhl (ed.), *The Urban Condition*, New York, Basic Books, 1963; Marc Fried and Peggy Gleicher, 'Some Sources of Residential Satisfaction in an Urban Slum', *J. Amer. Inst. Planners*, 1961, 27, pp. 305–15; H. Gans, 'The Human Implications of Current Redevelopment and Relocation Planning', *J. Amer. Inst. Planners*, 1959, 25, pp. 15–25.

2. Marc Fried, 'Personal and Social Deprivations and Family Roles', unpublished paper delivered before the National Conference on Social Welfare, New York, May 1962.

3. Marc Fried, in Leonard J. Duhl (ed.), *The Urban Condition*; Marc Fried and Peggy Gleicher, op. cit.; Peter Marris, *Family and Social Change in an African City*, London, Routledge & Kegan Paul, 1961; Michael Young and Peter Willmott, *Family and Kinship in East London*, Glencoe, Illinois, The Free Press, 1957.

4. Marc Fried and Peggy Gleicher, op. cit.

5. Vere Hole, 'Social Effects of Planned Rehousing', *Town Planning Review*, July 1959, 30, 2, pp. 161–73.

*Part Four. Shell: Priorities in
Designing the Human Habitat*

Introduction

The underlying concern of the author of every article in this section is not simply the urgent problem of producing huge quantities of mass housing *now* – though this is a critical issue – but of providing mass housing that can respond to the individual needs of each man.

Their main emphasis in this context is upon two overriding priorities: the provision of a variety of communal spaces and the possibilities for each family to shape their own community. The approach to each is from a universal point of view. As Aldo Van Eyck, a member of Team 10, notes, 'Man is always and everywhere essentially the same. He has the same mental equipment though he uses it differently . . . according to the particular life pattern of which he happens to be a part.' Whether the examples are drawn from the slums of Calcutta, housing blocks of Boston, or *barriadas* of Peru, the two priorities continue to hold.

The authors pay relatively little attention to some other well-known problems, such as the mechanics of house building on a large scale, internal planning of dwelling units, the questions of high-rise versus row housing, and optimum housing densities. Furthermore, there is assumed agreement with the statement of Lewis Mumford that 'minimum housing is obsolete from the moment it is built', and 'the only cheap housing is good housing . . . one must overcome the illusion that equates cheapness with first costs'.[1] Thus, there is little discussion on this point, although Elizabeth Wood does elaborate on the benefits of good housing, stating that it enables a family to 'achieve or sustain feelings of personal dignity'; permits the family to stay together (or does not force separation); allows the family to perform all daily functions in accordance with its rising aspirations; and makes the family feel the dwelling to be 'theirs'.

Priority One: Provision of a Variety of Public Spaces

The provision of public spaces involves a recognition and interpretation of the many coexisting uses of a single space. The sidewalk may actually be a storage place for construction materials, play area for three to nine year olds, visiting area for housewives, delivery area for a variety of goods and services, as well as being a pedestrian concourse.

A theoretical approach to understanding the interrelationships between spaces and activities is set forth in the final article by Professor Christopher Alexander. He shows how the urban structure is made up of many complex interactions of sets of activities which may be organized into a semi-lattice.

Some sets of activity-spaces are recurrent and have been found in a variety of empirical studies to have positive effects on the community. Elizabeth Wood, with the backing of long practical experience in managing large-scale integrated public housing projects in Chicago, emphasizes the importance of 'built-in' gathering places that are self-policing. Such areas include places for planned opportunities to get on terms of nodding acquaintance with one's neighbours, without being thrust into perhaps unwanted intimacy with them; places located and designed so that casual social interaction and 'loitering' can be both agreeable and acceptable; and places that can encourage the formation of informal gatherings of each age-group. These places listed by Elizabeth Wood are not mutually exclusive nor do they have a standard relationship to each other or to the dwellings, but several such places should be readily accessible to the different members of each family.

Other authors provide additional support for the importance of such areas. Aldo Van Eyck pleads for the development of what he calls the 'in-between realm' or 'doorstep area' between house scale and city scale. Chester Hartman, in the foregoing section on Society, brought out the importance of casual meeting places outside the house, associated with the sidewalk and the street. Christopher Alexander gives a vivid description of the interaction of a newspaper stand on a street corner and the working of the traffic lights: 'the money going from people's pockets to the dime slot, the people who stop at the light and read headlines, the traffic light, the electric impulses which make the lights change, and the sidewalk which the people stand on, form a system – they all work together'.

A similar notion from the Eastern cultural orientation is brought forward by N. Kurokawa. Eastern countries have always considered the street as an extension of man's dwelling space, a place where man meets man and where different functions and activities can coexist. Kurokawa then cites a comparable example from the West: the plan for the extension of the city of Toulouse by Candilis, Woods, and Josic, in which all community facilities are located along a pedestrian community spine. Shadrach Woods (Team 10) calls this the 'stem' and the dwelling the 'cells', and he states: 'the stem is considered not only as a link between additive cells, but as the generator of habitat. It provides the environment in which the cells may function.'

Priority Two: Possibilities for the Family to Shape Their Own Environment

Man must be able to define in space his personal opinion of life, as J. B. Bakema says in the Team 10 article. G. Candilis adds: 'We must provide a framework in which man can again be master of his home.'

A belief in the ability of 'the average family' to fashion their own dwelling is implicit in the two preceding statements. And evidence is now accruing, particularly from the squatter settlements of Latin America and North Africa, that this belief can be verified.

John Turner draws a clear distinction between families living in old and unsuitable dwellings, which become urban slums, and families living in squatter settlements – which may be called shanty towns, bidonvilles, or *barriadas*. Professor de Maisonseul of the University of Algiers once put it more dramatically: 'The urban slum is the refuge of the urban failure – a man overcome and rejected by the city – but the bidonville is the expression of an attempt to make a new life by bold and gallant men.'[2]

It often seems absolutely incomprehensible to any public official that order and architectural unity can be created in unregulated situations; yet the ability to give a 'natural' order to a site and to build up a community seems to be a potential inherent in a group of human beings, provided they are given enough time and enough security to identify themselves with a given place. However, this is where the administrators become anxious and ask: How can we give security to the squatters without encouraging anarchy? How much time do squatters need to create an orderly community?

Some answer to the last question is given by John Turner who has made a long-term study of the situation in Peru. In many countries a rush of squatters to occupy government-owned land could be expected to result in a complete pell-mell of buildings, with no coherent layout or provision of public spaces or places where public services could develop. In Peru it is different. Even the most illiterate peasants of Peru have a tradition of urbanism that goes back long before the Spanish Conquest and the building codes set up by the Law of the Indies in 1573. Automatically the advancing hordes of Peruvian squatters take it for granted that they should establish their plots in squared 'quadras', leaving one or two unbuilt upon by mutual agreement, so that these can serve as public open spaces. The image of an organized urban settlement is already present in their minds, and so – even though they start off with makeshift huts and no public services at all – the initial layout permits these to be installed reasonably economically and efficiently when the time comes. John Turner outlines the fifteen-year sequence in which a full complement of community facilities are demanded and installed. During the first few years all efforts are concentrated upon land acquisition, transportation facilities, and the provision of local shops and schools; after five or six years the demand is for piped water and electricity; sewers and paved roads appear in the third and final stage.

Team 10 – a small international group of architects – is keenly interested in the possibilities of mass-produced dwelling units, capable of variation by their inhabitants. They willingly concede that these are unlikely to be as orderly in appearance as many large-scale housing projects, which are kept swept clean of all traces of humanity by the 'civic vacuum cleaner'. At the same time they realize that it is barely possible for metropolitan cities to submit to long periods of chaos while the slow upgrading of squatter settlements takes its natural course. An acceptable level of facilities — adjusted to the needs and way of life of each locality — must be insisted upon for the basic elements of shelter and community services. Inevitably they must be provided by the municipality.

As new mass housing projects almost automatically lack the supportive relationships individuals find in established neighbourhoods and are usually at long distances from existing sources of work, Elizabeth Wood emphasizes that institutional arrangements to meet both these needs must accompany their development. Three things that can serve to make the new structures more immediately habitable are: the provision of programs of employment expansion and vocational training parallel to the building program; a policy of allowing dwellings to be used initially for small businesses such as hairdressing, dressmaking, or shoe repair; and a good overall plan that includes appropriate communal spaces.

All articles state, or imply, that housing (and this means mass housing) together with its immediate environment should somehow express and encourage a rich family life and create possibilities of community involvement. The Smithsons (Team 10) state: 'The shell that fits man's back looks inward to the family and outward to society, and its organization should reflect this duality.' An architect and a sociologist, Brent Brolin and John Zeisel, decided to interpret a fairly elaborate social study by Herbert Gans of a well-established community in the West End of Boston, Massachusetts, in terms of a housing program, giving (as far as possible) a physical form to each social finding. The result of their efforts showed that, for an architect to be able to give a meaningful interpretation of social data, he needs to know three things: the character of the 'primary actor' and the nature of the activity in which he is engaged; who else is involved in the situation; the relationship between the 'primary actor' and the others. The type of statement they could interpret read: 'While the teenage groups were sexually segregated, girls' groups in the West End met near the corners where the boys hung out' (Program: Adolescent girls' areas to be visible to boys' areas).

Planning according to such social analyses, however, does not necessarily mean that the needs of the people are being provided for if the people are not themselves participating in the shaping of their environment. What is really needed is a possibility for the people to discover ways of using places (that have been provided by the architect) that can satisfy their own social needs, as well as other places, probably on a more modest scale, where they can leave their own mark : places where they can give some physical expression to their own notions. Such places and activities can occur only if the possibilities exist in the design of the architect and if there is good will on the part of the authority. As Margaret Mead said at Delos Five: 'People are not cement, though cement may get in the way of people.'

NOTES

1. L. Mumford, 'A New Approach to Workers' Housing', *International Labor Review*, February 1957, Vol. 75, pp. 94–103.

2. P. A. Emery, 'Creative Aspects of Shanty Towns', *Ekistics* 70, May 1963, pp. 268–71.

26. Housing Design: A Social Theory

ELIZABETH WOOD

Part 1: A Social Theory of Housing Design

What has been completely lacking is a study of design based on a theory of what kind of social structure is desirable in a project and how to use design to get it. Such a theory would be expressed almost exclusively in the design of the space outside the dwelling units. It would be expressed in the design of public spaces; corridors, lobbies, grounds, and the non-dwelling facilities and buildings on the project. The design of these aspects of public housing projects expresses a social philosophy whether designers have one in mind or not.

Most housing projects seem designed to minimize or to prevent accidental and casual communication between people and the informal gathering of people, and to provide minimum facilities for the formal gathering of people. Their design prohibits these activities *within* residential buildings, except in very few cases. Their design also sharply limits the variety and kind of activities outside the residential buildings.

This paper propounds the theory that the rich fulfilment of the needs of people, as individuals and groups, is in itself a suitable design objective. Design to serve this objective serves also a larger purpose: it makes possible the development of a social structure, by means of which people can create their own social controls, and do their own self-policing.

The suggestions for such design are made in full recognition that even the ideal design can be made useless by management practices that grow out of failure to understand the design. I visited a high-rise building that had exterior corridors last spring. The corridors were being used exactly as intended. Babies in pens and buggies were out getting the sun. Mothers were hanging out baby clothes on small racks. Neighbours were passing the time of day. It was exactly the 'sidewalk in the sky' or 'backyard in the sky' that had been intended. The manager going with us was obviously disturbed by the clothes racks. We asked if they were against the rules. They were. We asked if they damaged the floor. They did not. We asked why they were against the rules. They spoiled the appearance of the project.

The Needs of People

Without making any pretence at an analytical inventory of the needs that must be served outside the dwelling, we suggest the following five categories:

1. There is the need for active exercise. This is a need felt by all children, most teenage and adult males, and maybe a few teenage and adult females. The more limited the space within the dwelling the more acute the need.

2. There is the need for sunshine and fresh air. This need is felt by children, all mothers and babies, all old people, and a lot of others including adults.

3. There is the need to get 'out'. This need is felt by all housebound people, especially mothers with pre-school children, all other children and the old. This need is felt no less when getting 'out' cannot mean getting 'outdoors' because the weather is cold and stormy.

4. There is the need to go somewhere; to shops, to church, to movies, to buy sodapop – the list is endless. It is felt by every human over the age of three or thereabouts.

5. There is the need to do some household chores which are much better done outdoors, or which cannot be done indoors: washing the car, sunning the woollens, repairing the bike, drying the baby's clothes.

Design for Social Fabric

The first goal of housing design is to satisfy 'with richness and imagination' the needs of people for activities outside their dwelling units.

The second goal is to so design for people-in-aggregate that out of the fulfilment of these needs there can come into being this thing called social fabric.

People begin life in a housing project as an aggregation of strangers with diverse habits, culture, and background. If design is based on the theory that they want privacy above everything else, they remain strangers. Then if nasty incidents occur, if one individual misbehaves (as may well happen), the good people tend to think that everyone but themselves is bad. They are not able to tell how many or which families are good like themselves. They distrust the community.

Design should help this aggregation of strangers become less strange, more familiar to each other. Out of this familiarity can come the informal communication, the informal groupings that constitute fabric. This second goal has relevance for all kinds of people. As has been said, it has relevance to management, to general tenant morale, to tenant self-direction. But it has particular relevance for families with children.

The basic evil of high-rise apartments for families is the distance they place between the mother and her children when they are playing outside the dwelling. She can keep them in the apartment with her except when she goes down with them to the playground, she can find paid supervision for them, or she can trust them to informal supervision by the people who are downstairs in the playground: janitors, groundsmen, other mothers, older children. To the degree to which she does this, the children will be raised by these other people. This is one of the things the critics view with alarm.

As a matter of fact, most mothers, even the most conscientious, trust their children to the supervision of others, including other parents they do not know personally. They trust the unknown when they have reasons such as 'the neighbourhood is very nice', 'the school has a good reputation'.

Design for social structure is for the purpose of making it possible for mothers to entrust their children to their community. We suggest four principles to guide the architect in design of social structure:

1. First, the architect must design for visible identification of a family and its dwelling. This characteristic is to be found in every street of free-standing houses and in row house developments. It is not found in high-rise buildings with interior corridors.

2. Second, the architect should design so as to make association and loitering easy not only on the building floor, but at points away from it; that is, in lobbies and on the grounds.

3. Third, the architect should design so as to make the formulation of informal groups easy. This is effectuated by facilities that call for group use and by purposeful arrangements of benches and grounds equipment.

4. Fourth, the architect should locate the facilities and equipment in such a way that they provide and are provided with social controls.

The first three guides – design for visibility, for loitering, and for the formation of informal adult groups – are intended to create physical situations within which there is a maximum opportunity for people to fulfil their needs as social beings. This kind of design should make for wider nodding and speaking acquaintances on the part of those who want them, and for more informal groups. This does not mean that the solitary or the individualists will be swept up against their will into group activities, or that the persons who want to perform their outside-of-the-dwelling activities in privacy or solitude may not do so to the extent they are able. It simply means that if the aspirations and needs of the socially minded are truly served, the stuff of the social fabric will be created.

The Building Floor

It is at the building floor that the architect designs for visibility. He secures this visibility by designing corridors so that activities will take place in them.

The exterior corridor (balcony corridor) offers the best enticements and excuses for activities, with the greatest protection against noise inside the dwelling units. It gives the people upstairs a chance to get outdoors without going downstairs, a very desirable and fulfilling thing. I have seen women playing bridge out on these corridors; couples sitting out watching the sunset; mothers drying baby clothes and airing woollens; babies sleeping in perambulators or playing in baby pens; small children working off their energy riding kiddie cars, their mothers watching them through the kitchen window in traditional suburban style.

Exterior corridors which are not designed generously enough so that they can serve these social purposes have no excuse for existence. When so narrow that they can function only as corridors, they are less comfortable than interior corridors, and will be subject to the same nuisance as interior corridors. Not only should they be generously sized, but the space abutting the corridor should be designed so that the windows (preferably kitchen windows) not only allow the mother to keep an eye on the children, but will serve as symbolic social controls.

Anyone who has seen Scandinavian housing remembers it chiefly for the colour that appears on the balconies. This comes partly from the brilliantly coloured canvas screens, and partly from the flower boxes overflowing with flowers. Although the buildings may be as plain as shoe boxes (and often are) they don't look it, so beautiful and lively is the effect of these two elements.

Lobbies: New Functions, New Design

Almost universally, lobbies are trouble spots. They are apt to be grim and institutional looking by virtue of minimum size, ugly colour, no windows, and total lack of adornment. But they also look scarred and beat-up from heavy traffic and misuse. As in the case of corridors, the architect must find a design that will generate good activities and assure the presence of people who will prevent vandalism and misuse.

Some of the needs which people would like to have served in the lobby are known. People on welfare need to wait for the mailman on the day their cheques are due — because they need it so badly, or because it might be stolen. Mothers loaded with babies and shopping bundles would like to be able to sit down while they are waiting for the elevator. There are old housebound people who need a place to go on stormy days.

But these are mostly daytime users; there is a need to generate evening users. Facilities could include such things as chess tables or space for dart boards. If there are planned loiterers in a lobby, it should be possible to place toilets off the lobby for the use of children on the playgrounds. These should be locked at night, of course.

For social as well as aesthetic reasons, this new kind of lobby — greatly enlarged — should have no enclosed areas; its walls should be glass and it should be brightly lighted at night. The entire area should be visible from any spot outside the front door and within the lobby itself. Finally, there should be provision for future adornments such as flower boxes.

The Concierge in Public Housing

It would be a great advance in public housing management if a dwelling unit could be provided off the lobby for an employee who (in addition to other functions) would have a generalized responsibility for keeping an eye on the lobby. The mere fact of his presence and immediate availability would be of major importance in the success of this new kind of lobby.

Site Design

The genius of good urban residential planning lies in the skill with which non-residential services are used to enrich the architectural quality of the surroundings, and the human quality of day-by-day life.

There are two kinds of facilities that should be placed next to residential buildings: areas for mothers and small children, and playgrounds for the five to twelves.

Certain other facilities gain greatly from grouping away from the residential buildings, but within the site plan. Teenagers and adults want to go where there is life and liveliness. Most of these facilities and services cannot by themselves create either life or liveliness. Some churches and all shops want to be in the main stream. Grouping these services makes them function better for their own purposes, and as a social facility.

Mothers and Small Children

The play-sitting areas for mothers and pre-school children should be located close to building entrances. This is for practical reasons. Mothers don't want to go far with babies and their paraphernalia. A good place is a paved area in a bay off the main sidewalk to the building entrance. It should be paved to permit the use of the wheel-toys that pre-school children play with. It should have a small sandpit and steps for toddlers and climbers, but the equipment should be kept small in order not to interfere with the use of the area by other informal groups.

The Playground for the Five to Twelves

The playground for the five to twelves should be close enough to the building so that mothers can overlook it, and they will, and yell down to their children, though that is not the prime social control intended. It should be close to the front door, and reachable from it, by wide paved areas. Children of this age are apt to burst out of the building entrance and begin playing at once. They are not usually disciplined enough to walk or run (keeping off the grass) any distance to a playground.

Teenagers

If teenagers are interested in games (and sometimes teenagers in low-income families are not) they are interested in competitive games. For these they are dependent on facilities in parks and community centres where supervision is provided. Otherwise, teenagers are interested primarily in their own particular kind of loitering. Because this kind of recreation seems so pointless, if not actually bad, to adults, designers do not plan for it. But studies in London have shown that it is the one kind of recreation that the designer can count on their wanting. The problem is, to make it good.

Teenagers want to hang around where they can get soft drinks, and where there is no formal supervision. They like to be able to use a record player either for dancing or as a background to their talking. Because teenage loitering and record playing is noisy, it should be located away from residential buildings, but it should be located where there is a great deal of pedestrian traffic and activity.

Adult Recreation

Recreation for the male adult may include games, but the designer may not always know what kinds of games a particular population would like. He can, however, allocate space – in the proper locations –

for future game facilities such as bocci or shuffleboard courts. Adult males (and younger males, too) like to play chess and checkers, if one is to judge by the sights in small parks where new tables are provided. This facility constitutes one of the most useful vehicles for bringing 'bodies' — social controls — to areas that need them at night. Their users will go a distance to have a chance to use them.

The job of the mother in the low-income family is confining and lasts long hours. Outside of the recreation she gets in the organized activities of the community centre, school, or church, her recreation consists mostly of sociable visiting with the shopkeepers, the friends she meets at the shops or wherever she can sit and rest on a bench. The designer's obligation is to locate the benches where she needs them as she goes about her many chores, doing the laundry, airing the baby, going shopping; or when she can seize a few minutes to get 'out'.

Part 2: Social Aspects of Housing and Urban Development

Too often the slums of the world are all regarded as housing the same kind of people, whether the slum is a newly made *barriada* or an ancient bazaar or *bustee*. The characteristics of the people are interpreted on the basis of the physical conditions that surround them.

Historically, slums have been the nurseries of urbanization and have functioned as productive or not, depending on the opportunities for growth offered by the city and depending on whether or not the city permitted the slum dwellers to move out of the slums freely to have access to work and to the city's institutions. A slum that is a ghetto is not the same kind of 'nursery' as, for instance, a newly built squatter town.

The Economic Meaning of Slums to Slum Dwellers

If one is to attack the problems of slums from the point of view of their occupants, and prepare plans that meet their economic and social conditions, it is necessary to examine the benefits that slum dwellers derive from the very fact that they live in slums. These benefits arise from four conditions: lack of legal and social controls; the low rents or low housing costs; proximity to the heart of the city where job opportunities are concentrated; and recourse to the traditional security that exists where persons live in natural groups, whether these be the extended family, the same tribe, the same nationality, religion, or caste.

The lack of controls permits the slum dweller – all over the world – to do what he pleases in and with his dwelling. It permits him to build a makeshift dwelling. It permits him to use his dwelling as a shop or his shop as a dwelling. He and his family can sleep in the rear of the shop or, pushing aside the equipment, sleep in it. This arrangement, of course, reduces his rent.

In some cities, the man builds a platform across the front of his dwelling and thus gets a counter from which to sell food or goods. Or he builds a lean-to addition and goes into business with a forge, lathe, or glass-blowing equipment. He can minimize labour costs by using his grandmother and grandfather, his brother and his brother's wife, his children and grandchildren, when he needs them, and they do not have to be paid regularly. He can keep a pig or chickens or a cow and they can forage in the streets. He can tie them to his doorstep or let them sleep inside his dwelling so they will not be stolen. The whole family can crowd into half a dwelling and he can rent the other half for income, or he can let his wife's sister and her family move in when they have been abandoned and have no other place to go.

The lack of controls works just as constructively in the slums of the most prosperous cities. A woman can set up beauty parlour equipment in her living-room, hang a sign in the front window and earn a living without paying shop rent. A man can set up a radio repair shop or shoe repair shop in his basement or back room and supplement his insufficient earnings. Families can crowd together and lease a room or rooms to supplement their earnings.

None of these activities are allowed to take place in a proper housing project, a well-zoned residential neighbourhood or a planned resettlement in developed countries, or those which follow the same pattern. Yet the only way that these poor households can make ends meet is by taking advantage of the lack of controls.

Location close to job sources and the complex of sellers and buyers has importance in itself. It is not only that proximity minimizes or eliminates transportation expenditures, though that is a matter of some importance when one tram ride represents the cost of a meal. Usually, the bulk of lowest paid jobs is in the centre of the city. It is the best location for the bootblack, the errand runner, and the man who lives by picking up odd jobs. It is of great importance to the man who makes his living by hauling goods on a cart or pulling a rickshaw or performing other services that oblige him to get to work early. It is important to the man who runs a small business and must get supplies or deliver finished goods without losing too much time from a working day. It is important to the persons who work in small factories which take on workers only when the factory gets a contract. Such workers must live close to their potential employers so as to reach them before all the jobs are filled. Workers depending on makeshift or odd-job work must live close to as many possible sources of employment in order that their chances of finding a job are good.

Many slums throughout the world have been settled by groups of people from the same village or by members of the same extended family or members of the same nationality, caste, or religion. The economic advantage of this to the old and indigent and the unemployed, in countries where there is no public assistance program, no social security, no old age pension, or unemployment compensation, is self-evident.

The Urban Development Dilemma

To recognize the nature of the dependence of slum dwellers on the slums they live in is to be confronted with the urban development dilemma. Some countries, recognizing this dependence, have required that rehousing accommodation should be located within a prescribed distance (usually one to three miles) from the cleared site. Such land is often costly and is competed for by others. This competition results in a constant rise in costs stimulated by the very fact of urban development. Each urban development project increases competition and makes each subsequent project more difficult to acquire. Costs of land and competition for its use require that the architect minimize

land cost for dwellings and maximize use by building multi-unit buildings; high costs of construction require that he design units of minimum size. All such projects require at least a minimum management-
maintenance staff. The result is that even with subsidies running as
high as 90 per cent of capital cost, the rents are higher than those
which the slum dwellers are accustomed to pay. Furthermore, the type
of unit and building is alien and ill-adapted to their needs.

The result, in most developing countries, is that too many of the
units are illegally occupied – in one country, for instance, the illegal
occupancy runs to 90 per cent. Rights of occupancy are sold to higher
income households, at a high figure, and those legally eligible to be
occupants move back to the slums. Or, in some countries, the rents
are not paid; the projects look like slums because they are used in
ways that were not intended; they are abused and vandalized.

Where cities are not bound by legislation to rehouse displaced slum
dwellers close to the cleared site, the tendency is to move them to
cheap land, as far away as possible. Thus, whole communities have
been cut off from their job sources. Where job sources have been
provided, they had little relevance to the capacities of many of the
people, and they were not ready when the people moved into the
housing. Thus, in time, the resettled population had to move back into
the slums, thereby adding further to the overcrowding, or the people
scraped a miserable level of subsistence, with no opportunity for development.

In a few places, excellent and subsidized transportation has been
provided, and this has made it possible for a number of wage earners
to keep their jobs, though it could not help the people who did not
have regular jobs but depended on picking up odd jobs.

This also suggests a new approach to the dilemma of urban development and a sounder and slower approach to human development. Wherever it is necessary for the larger purposes of urban development that a slum be cleared, the initial approach should be an
intensive investment in the economic development of the people.
Concretely, this means: intensive investments to bring about the expansion and strengthening of the existing small industries; the stimulation of new small industries; the planned relocation of these industries
together with owners and employees to outlying settlements; the

introduction of vocational training for the jobs that the new and expanded industries will create, as well as training for existing large-scale
industries needing workers; planning of appropriate housing facilities;
vocational and other training for women in preparation for new
planned work opportunities in the resettlement areas.

What this approach seeks to do is to put together four fundamental
urban programs: urban planning (which designs the plans and land-
uses specifically for the displaced persons and industries); small-
scale industrial expansion (to provide the major job source);
vocational training for specific jobs as a preliminary to relocation and
a job; and the improvement and elimination of slums with minimum
hardship to people.

The possible benefits of such an approach are many: dependence
on the central city for work is diminished by the creation of jobs
elsewhere that are better from the point of view of the people; with
the use of cheap land and self-help labour and initiative, housing costs
are reduced; at the same time, the construction of housing that suits
the cultural and social requirements of the people is facilitated. The
benefits of such an approach will be realized only if the steps taken
by Government (from survey through motivation and technical assistance to final resettlement in the new community) are so well planned
and firmly *based on the desires and needs of the people* that the process is a continuum in which Government and people are at all times
working together.

The approach raises two questions. First, will it work for all
people? The answer is, no. There may be households where the wage
earner is not capable of using vocational training, or of holding the
new kinds of jobs. The number may be large or small. If it is small,
these households may still be moved to the new settlement, provided
that it is large enough to generate enough service jobs to give them
employment. If not, the conclusion will of necessity be that many
slums cannot, perhaps, be cleared for the indefinite future and that
there are people who are better housed, in the broad sense, in slums
than in distant places which have no economic meaning for them.

Second, where does this approach fit into national economic development programs? The contention of this report is that social
development is not nourished on a diet of health, education, housing,

and austerity; that the most economic investment is one which includes the equipment and opportunity for economic advance.

Slum Improvement: A Permanent or Interim Measure

There are usually three types of slums in the larger cities of the world: (1) inlying slums densely covered with makeshift or shanty structures; (2) inlying areas where conventionally built structures have been taken over for use by low-income people and are crowded, misused, and deteriorated; (3) outlying slums, found especially in Latin America and Northern Africa, often covered with makeshift shelters, occupied by squatters.

The method of slum improvement may be used for both interim and permanent purposes. If it is to be used for the development of a permanent residential community, it has as its objective the creation, over the years, of an urbanized citizenry and a community which meets minimum urban standards with regard to dwellings, their surroundings and their use, and community facilities. This is usually the objective in the case of squatter towns where the city can afford to have the area retained in single-family dwellings and where it can get the benefit of maximum use of self-help. Since the households are not cut off from their established sources of income, a special or intensive investment in their economic development is not a prime requirement.

If, as is often the case, the slum lies near the centre of the city and the land will, under the terms of the master plan, be needed sooner or later for some more productive use, the improvement may be designed as an interim program. In this case, it is not necessary to meet the modern urban standard that all dwelling units should be self-contained; public or common latrines and showers might be used; main sewer and other utility lines might be installed with reference to the future development of the land, not the present distribution of dwellings. There might be minimum requirements for improvement of shelter. But there must be an intensive investment in vocational and other types of education, preparatory to the relocation of the households when they are ready and equipped for new jobs and life in a modern urban community. It is probable that not every household has a wage earner capable of holding a regular job, but the process described above will reduce the size of the slum.

A scheme for a 'sanitary slum' was devised in one city in India, which illustrates the dilemma one faces if an interim slum improvement plan is designed without this special kind of investment. Occupants of an inlying slum were moved a very short distance to an area where the authority had installed utilities and built individual sanitary cores (water closet and shower). The families rented the land and, with the assistance of loans and materials, constructed dwellings according to plan. 'Interim' in this scheme meant twenty years. Two things happened: one group of families immediately started improving their property with paint, fences, landscaping, and additions to the dwellings. These families refused to believe that they only rented the land – they were certain they owned home and land. At first the authority forbade these improvements on the theory that any family that had made its home so attractive, with its own labour, would be quite impossible to move at the end of twenty years. The authority changed this regulation, in part because of what a second group of families was doing. This group, believing that residence was temporary, took no care of their property. Their buildings all but crumbled.

Slum improvement is economical in developing countries only if there is a substantial use of human resources. The commitments which a government must make as partner in this enterprise include the following: (1) the designation of the slum area as one properly used for slum improvement on either an interim or permanent basis, and if the former, designation of area or areas to which the families will, eventually, relocate; (2) the solution of land tenure problems in such a way as to clarify terms of occupancy, if an interim program; or assure security of occupancy, if a permanent program; (3) agreements between Government and the residents as to the division of responsibility for the installation of such public improvements as are necessary to meet acceptable standards of sanitation; (4) the agreement between Government and the people as to the financial or other resources that will be made available for construction of buildings, whether homes, community buildings, or utilities (though in some Latin American cities private entities are carrying this responsibility);

(5) the provision by Government of the technical, professional, and other staff necessary to the conduct of the program; (6) the provision of usual municipal facilities such as fire, police, refuse disposal services. In order to get the maximum benefits from this common activity, the terms of the understanding must be as clear as if it were a partnership contract between the interested two parties, the Government and the people.

Land Problems

The essential first step in a slum improvement program is the solution of land problems. Families must be given security of tenure if they are to invest their own labour in the improvement of the area; the land must be freed of complications that prevent the design of a proper site plan: well laid out streets, properly laid out utility lines, buildings oriented and arranged to fit the requirements of climate.

The Problem of Sanitation

The first objective of a slum improvement program is the improvement of unsanitary conditions: the provision of an adequate supply of pure water; provisions for drainage and disposal of human waste.

The simplest situation is one in which the size of the lot and the soil conditions permit the system to be wholly private. Then, each household can have its own well, and its own self-servicing sanitary system, such as a pit latrine or a septic tank. Later, as in the case of Maracaibo and other Latin American cities, the public services of such plotted land projects will be added and administered by the appropriate authorities.

In denser communities where water sewerage and drainage systems are needed, a public works department or other governmental agency must assume a larger responsibility. Usually, the owner will construct only the lines and facilities within his holding. However, in some Latin American cities, the residents of squatter towns built the main distribution lines up to the point of connection with the city system. In some cases, the people undertake these expenses; in some cases, they only contribute labour.

In many of the older inlying slums, the problem of a sanitary installation is complicated by the land pattern. Often the streets are not plotted; narrow lanes run crookedly between buildings and there are dense clusters of buildings with little space for a sewer or water line – much less a water closet or bathing facility. There is no possibility of achieving a desirable minimum standard of one water closet per dwelling. If the improvement is interim, not permanent, the plan may provide for communal latrines and bathing facilities. This will automatically require either paid staff to keep them sanitary – which is always expensive – or an intensive educational program, or both. If the improvement is to be permanent, it may begin with a skeleton installation with minimum outlets laid out in accordance with the new site plan. Additional outlets may be added as the area is improved. The ultimate standard is the water closet and bathing facility, and water, for each dwelling.

The Improvement of Shelter

The chief difference between an interim plan and a permanent plan is in the quality of shelter required.

One of the social goals in permanent slum improvement programs is to permit the families to stay on the site during the improvement process. This is the current pattern of the municipal program in Tokyo and of most of the programs in Caracas.

In some Latin American and African cities, the people in peripheral developments live in temporary shelters at the back of their lots while they build the permanent dwelling. In some areas, they live in the first completed rooms – or the core of the dwelling – while they build the additional rooms, as in the case with some projects under the direction of the State Housing Agency in Rio de Janeiro. In Cairo, a suburban village has a unique plan. It provides for the construction of sixty new dwellings on adjacent land, the demolition of the unsound buildings and the repair of the repairable buildings. The sixty new dwellings will be used by those whose buildings are to be demolished, either because they are unsound or because they are located in a needed right of way, and by families accommodated with others. The improvement plan will take place in three stages to permit loans, a practical schedule for demolition, and new housing construction.

Because unaided self-help housing takes so long to construct, several countries have introduced systems for expediting construction by loans, and provisions of materials or pre-fabricated units such as window and door frames.

The question of physical standards is not amenable to a universal answer, but the two basic guides, in the case of permanent improvement schemes, would seem to be the following: (1) in time, each dwelling must be self-contained, that is, have its own water closet, water supply, bathing and cooking facilities, and a method of sewerage disposal which meets modern standards; (2) the amount of dwelling space must be adequate to serve the household in its current composition (for example, if grandparents or indigent relatives live with the household in the slum dwelling, the rebuilt dwelling must be of a size to house the same family). This is easy to accomplish when building single-family houses on individual lots. Since the economy of this program lies in self-help, and since most if not all self-help housing is single-family housing, this is an achievable goal, implicit in the use of self-help.

Social Investments in Slum Improvement Schemes

The advantages of slum improvement as a method of urban development are many:

1. It keeps the families close to whatever jobs they had, including a large supply of low-grade jobs, while encouraging their desire for advance.

2. It does not destroy the social structure either of families or of larger groups.

3. It is the most intensive course in urbanization with regard to standards of urban living, relationship to Government and the way of finding an individual role in a vast and anonymous city.

4. It gives this course in urbanization to people living close to the sources of advancement, the stimulus and incentives for advance that are inherent in the city.

There are, however, some specific social investments that must be made to assure that full value will be received from the program.

There must be investments in social and educational services that will assure the good use and maintenance of the physical facilities. Chief of these is education in the use of the sanitary facilities for the disposal of human waste.

A second necessary investment is in vocational training.

Finally, the very fact that a slum improvement plan hypothesizes that all residents will remain in the area raises some further problems of social welfare. Relatively few squatter towns, and probably few or no old slums, have a population every member of which has demonstrated his physical capacity and willingness to participate in a slum-improvement, self-help program.

The Base for Physical Design

The social theory for physical design that will facilitate the creation of social community requires the existence of small groups of families, either natural groups existing by virtue of extended family, caste, tribe, nationality, or cultural ties or groups that come into existence because families have been given the opportunity to form relationships on their own initiative. In every community the way a social organization is created is by binding together such small groups into larger entities. A community will be organized only if these small groups exist. Therefore, it is essential for the planner to design physical settings where small groups – not more than twenty families – have this opportunity.

In schematic terms, the physical plan for a community begins with small intimate groupings with appropriate common spaces and facilities. In Zelengrad, in the U.S.S.R., this is accomplished by designing neighbourhoods on the 'cluster principle, the cluster consisting of several dwelling houses'.[1]

Everybody has to do some things outside his dwelling. If the dwellings are so arranged that people can see their neighbours doing these things, they can make a visual acquaintance and appraisal. If neighbours seem 'nice' to each other, then they will talk and get acquainted. If they do not seem 'nice', this will not happen.

It is not to be expected that in any artificially created group everyone will seem to be a potential friend of everyone, but a member of the community can be given the opportunity to form relationships on his own initiative. Design for visibility expedites the normal process of forming relationships. In multi-storey apartment buildings, visibility has been achieved in some housing developments by the construction of wide exterior corridors. They provide outdoors-upstairs areas for the convenience and pleasure of everyone: a place to sun the baby, dry clothes, get small children out from under foot without taking them downstairs, or a place for the adults to sit out in the fresh air. Single-family or row-house developments have achieved it by arranging the row of dwellings or the single family houses in the shape of a three-sided rectangle or around a *cul-de-sac*.

The principle of common use (as of a pump, a spring, a place for washing clothes) as a means of expediting acquaintance has been demonstrated since time immemorial. It is, of course, a two-edged sword − the facility is the scene or cause of quarrels, too. But these usually occur when there are too many users for the facility.

It is proposed here that the arrangement of the buildings should provide for a common open space, visible to all, which will be used all the time for the play of children, and on special occasions, by several or all of the members of the group. The space could be the site for an image around which a *puja* centres, or for a Christmas tree, or it might be used as an overflow for visitors to a wedding or other family ceremony. Studies of the behaviour of families in a heterogeneous slum in Calcutta have shown that the existence of usable common space encouraged first on-looking by neighbours of different caste or religion, then gradual participation.

The principle of design for beauty and enrichment is too seldom used in the design of housing for low-income families. This is because of poverty of imagination, not shortage of money. It is not always easy to know what constitutes beauty or decoration for people who have been ground down by poverty. In some countries the first outlet of a person wanting something 'more' or 'pretty' may be to plant flowers or vines. In other countries he may plant a fruit tree; or it may be that a flowering tree or a sacred tree has such meaning. In some countries delicate and elaborate designs are painted on the front of the home with rice flour paint. In Trinidad, local artists make murals and sculptures for buildings.

The process of planning should make articulate what it is that people want and need and what space provisions should be made. The pride and warmth of feeling that come when members of a community have beautified their own home are basic to the creation of social community.

Arrangement in the Larger Centres

There is one principle of arrangement that is universally applicable, whether designing space and facilities for the primary group, the grouping of primary groups or the town centre: the principle of clustering. From a social point of view, two activities placed side by side are much better than one isolated from the other. This is primarily because of people's love of the sight of activity.

Visiting places of activity is a recreation that people throughout the world can have without spending money. And this is not a pleasure confined to low-income families. All kinds of people go to the station to watch the trains pull in and out – the young mother with her little boy in a Long Island suburb, and the couple with a crowd of children in an Asian city. The bus station of Munich is the Sunday refuge of workers from Turkey and Greece. Courting couples stand enthralled in front of shop windows. Women in every country lean over a balcony rail or watch from behind curtains to see what goes on in the streets. Families drive out to the airport to watch planes come and go. Elderly couples sit on benches along busy streets to see the people and the cars go by. Hence, the livelier the heart or the centre of the town can be made by a concentration of facilities and services, the more social a purpose it serves.

But the major question of how to plan to give spirit, meaning, and pleasure can only be answered with the help of the people. Why are there so few shops and activities in centres of refugee settlements? Does no one want to be a small shopkeeper? Are small shops forbidden? Are there no buyers because of the universally low incomes of the people? Activity begets activity; how can it be increased so that the area comes alive?

What facilities, spaces, or objects would add to creature comfort in the centre and thus encourage people to linger? Trees to sit under?

Benches under trees, or, as in Norway, benches under the sun? A source of drinking water? A public latrine? More vendors selling cold drinks and sweetmeats? How and where does a planner do something about religious activities? Would a planned space for large-scale *puja* celebrations or fiestas be used? Would a few religious symbols – a sacred tree, a shrine, or a cross – give people a good feeling?

Housing Policy and Social Development

The net impact on a family of a government housing program is the product of the social policy expressed in each of the elements of that program: the method of tenure, the form of the subsidy, the terms of the loans, the physical standards offered, and the management policies. Each element is capable of functioning in a more or in a less constructive way, depending on how it fits the needs and aspirations of the people. The best combination of these elements will differ according to the income level of the people to be served, their cultural backgrounds, their social institutions, and the climatic conditions under which they live.

Thus, the problem of developing an effective formula for low-income groups in the urban areas of developing countries has been extremely difficult. Part of the problem has arisen because of the tendency on the part of the governments to use the public housing formula used by developed countries: multi-unit buildings, government-owned, subsidized, and managed. This is because there are few studies of the sociological or economic significance of this formula even though it is used so widely. Evaluations are not usually made on the basis of its relevance or significance to the people for whom it is intended; rather, evaluations tend to use real estate criteria: Are the buildings fully occupied? Are the rents paid? Do the tenants use the property well so that maintenance expenses are not too high? If there are vacancies the remedy sought is the real estate method: advertising, or trying to find people who fit the formula, not examining the formula in relation to the people. As long as there are plenty of poor people to draw from, the formula has been presumed to be right.

The formula is alien to a large number of rural newcomers to the city in both developed and developing countries. It calls for renting, not owning, and this does not appeal to one of the strongest forces for development to which low-income people are responsive. It calls for an urban, and therefore a disciplined, way of life, wholly different from that lived in rural or urban slums. From the day families move into the buildings they must become different. Garbage must be wrapped in a bag or tidy package, carried down the hall or down the stairs and put into a can or incinerator, and woe to the child and his family if the paper package bursts open and the contents spill on the ground on his way. Children must not write on walls or fences. Children must not play on the grass, they may only play in playgrounds. Children must not be nuisances. Mothers must not put bedclothes out of the window to air. Families may not keep a chicken or a Paschal lamb in the kitchen. Mothers may not accommodate a deserted sister and her children, or her newly widowed mother, without permission from the management, and then only for a limited period.

Such a body of rules, however necessary in a dense urban setting and however acceptable to middle-class people, is formidable to a family moving in from a village or urban slum where food and other waste is tossed into the yard for chickens to eat, where children are accustomed to relieve themselves wherever they are, where every place is a place to play, and where one of the reasons for having a home is to shelter the family's relatives when they are in trouble.

In developed countries, the transition and adaptation has been accomplished in public housing estates through tenant education and disciplinary measures – eviction, if the tenant proves too intractable. Thus, most of the families come, in time, to fit into the middle-class pattern and nobody, including themselves, knows what, if anything, is lost or damaged in the process.

Thus, although the newcomers to cities in developed countries have been able, by and large, to adjust themselves to the sophisticated public housing formula, one cannot be sure that newcomers in all developing countries can, or should be asked to, adjust to the same formula.

Space Requirements and the Family

The most significant trend in the design of urban housing in the last fifty years, from the social point of view, has been the steady reduction of dwelling space and the intensification of building use. The trend has been forced by the rising cost of construction and increased competition for urban land.

There have been some serious social consequences of this trend in developed countries that should be examined because the trend is being accepted as inevitable in the developing countries. The most important of these consequences are those affecting the family. The reduction of dwelling space has supported and expedited a trend which began for other reasons: the break-up of the three-generation household consisting of grandparents, parents, and children. The housing factor has added physical distance to a separation which began as a distance in attitudes and opinions.

The aged have gained and lost in the process. They have gained independence of responsibilities and, in the case of the poor, economic independence, but they have lost or are losing their place as members of the family and community. That such separation does not make for a good or healthy society is still admitted only grudgingly because the revolt of the younger generation against the older is still too recent. But both demographic trends and social considerations require that the elderly should not be deprived of their membership in the family and community. The family whose strengthening is the concern of this paper includes grandparents as well as the nuclear family.

Strengthening the family thus conceived begins with the removal of physical distance. This means that every community should provide housing both for nuclear families and for elderly persons and couples. It should be possible for family and grandparents to live near each other if they wish to; it is desirable that children should grow up in the presence of elderly people, if not their own grandparents.

The problem of the dependent aged may not be so widespread in developing countries as in developed countries but it exists, and on such a scale that housing programs and policies should take cognizance of it. This means that dwellings should be so designed, and rent policies so fixed, that a family with dependent aged parents can bring them into a housing development without being penalized with additional rents, or without being forced to abandon them outside.

The Dwelling as a Means of Strengthening Family Life

It may be safely averred that all housing legislation has had this objective. Unfortunately, not every government-aided dwelling functions automatically as a vehicle for strengthening family life, even when it is decent, safe, and sanitary. The capacity of people to make the best of almost any kind of shelter is extraordinary, and it is this very capacity that makes the analysis of housing-family relationships difficult.

The criteria used in evaluating the elements are these:

1. Does it enable the family to achieve or sustain feelings of personal or human dignity?

2. Does it permit the family to stay together, or does it force separations before the family wishes them?

3. Does it permit the family to eat, sleep, and perform all daily functions in accordance with the family's standard of decency and its requirements for privacy?

4. Does it stimulate and assist in the expression of the family's rise in aspirations?

5. Does the family feel the dwelling to be so much *theirs* (regardless of the method of tenure) that they adorn it, making it the outward visible symbol of an inner spiritual grace?

There is a long history in many countries of the basic desire of families to own their own home. It has been in many cultures and income groups a symbol of status: evidence to the community that the owner had prudence, stability, and love of family and home. By the same token, renters in some countries are assumed to be unstable, improvident and lacking in love of family and home.

The desire to own is instrumental in building up systems of savings, such as building, saving, and loan associations in Latin America, which increase loan sources for housing construction.[2] The social meaning of ownership has been recognized as so important that it is being used in a number of housing situations which were established on the basis of renting.

But ownership means more than status and security to the owners and their families. An owned house is a possession, regardless of the size of the mortgage. An owner and his family live in it as they want to; they can paint it as they want to, add a room, build in kitchen shelves, decorate it inside and out, as they please. The owner can make his own repairs and thus save money. From the point of view of both household and government, the home ownership pattern can be the most economical and most productive of all methods of tenure for the low-income family in developing countries, if the appropriate educational and management resources are used in the process.

In the modern urban world renting, as a method of tenure is, however, no longer a symbol of improvidence, lack of love of family or any other invidious characteristic. It is the prevailing and accepted pattern for all income groups. It is also necessary as land costs increase and competition for land requires increased density of use. This type of tenure is not inherently constructive or destructive, social or antisocial. It can be either.

Ownership in condominium and cooperative ownership permit some of the advantages of home ownership in multi-storey buildings, and also some of the advantages of rental, such as relief from duties of management and physical maintenance of a house. Both bring the advantages of lower costs due to large-scale construction. Both give the individual family more freedom within his dwelling, so far as decoration is concerned.

NOTES

1. *The Building of New Towns in the U.S.S.R.*, Moscow, 1964; also *Ekistics* 108, November 1964, p. 314.

2. Charles Abrams, *Man's Struggle for Shelter in an Urbanizing World*, M.I.T. Press, p. 223.

27. Architecture That Works

JOHN TURNER

Part 1: Lima's Barriadas *and* Corralones

Barriada is the Peruvian-Spanish word for an urban squatter settlement, the equivalent of the Brazilian *favela*, the Mexican *colonia proletaria*, the Venezuelan *rancho*. Each country has its own term, not only in Latin America but in all regions where the rate of urbanization has overwhelmed planning and building legislation and where cities are plunging into an even greater chaos than those of the already urbanized and industrialized world.

The image which the word *barriada* and its equivalents conjure up in the minds of the wealthier nations as a whole, or the wealthier classes of the poorer nations, is of the worst kind of slum: miserable shanty towns in which the poorest of the world's poor suffer miserable lives. In some areas this may be a true picture but, anyway in the Latin American context, it varies between a half-truth and an almost total untruth. In Lima, the capital of Peru, the *barriada* population grew from an estimated 100,000 in 1958 – then 10 per cent of the total city population – to an estimated 400,000 in 1964 – over 20 per cent of the total. The majority of the Lima *barriada* population are not, by Peruvian and even by Lima standards, very poor and the lives they lead in their *barriadas* are a considerable improvement on their former condition, whether in the city slums from which they moved to the *barriada* or in the villages from which they moved into the city slums. The *barriada* family has its own plot of land and at least part of a fairly well-built dwelling, which it will eventually complete and of which it is proud; even though it lacks many public utilities such as water and sewers, which may already be under construction, the family has a home of its own together with the security, status, and vested interest in social development and political stability which this represents.

To the casual observer in Lima an incipient *barriada* appears the same as a *corralon*: both seem to be a jumble of cane matting or adobe shacks. But, in spite of the superficial similarity, there is a world of difference between the two which in time becomes apparent, for the *barriada* will almost certainly develop while the *corralon* will stagnate or decay. To observe this process, however, is more difficult, requiring a lot of patience or a good deal of knowledge; requiring also direct personal contact with the people themselves. Neither the local well-to-do Peruvians nor the foreign reporters stray far from the residential and commercial areas of the city, and what they see from, or even in, these areas, as well as from the highways leading out of the city, are either *corralones* or *barriadas* in their early stages of development.

Such observers are almost certain to overlook some important differences between the incipient *barriada* and the *corralon*. The great majority of the *corralones* are situated on small plots near the city centre, market areas, or any other source of casual or unskilled labour. The majority of the *barriadas*, on the other hand, are situated at some distance from the city centre, along secondary roads, and they are much larger. Unless the observer has access to housing reports or can speak to the people, he is unlikely to discover that the majority of the *corralon* inhabitants are appreciably poorer than the majority living in the *barriadas*; also that the latter have lived in the city a good deal longer and that the *corralones* constitute the principal 'reception' or 'transit' camps for rural immigrants. *Corralon* 'rooms' or shacks are commonly rented.

They form the cheapest available accommodation located near centres of casual employment: thus the *carralon* is often the immigrant's or the destitute's best available solution for his housing problem.

The outlying *barriada*, on the other hand, is impractical for newcomers or the indigent, as their inhabitants have to pay for transportation and to buy water in order to go to work and to live there.

It will be clear from the above that though both types of settlement are clandestine and superficially similar, they have different origins and functions as well as different destinies. The typical *corralon* was previously, say twenty to forty years ago, a market gardener's smallholding. Then the owner – or tenant – found it more profitable to sell – or to rent – tiny plots to immigrants or to families evicted from city-centre slums. In the rare cases when the population of these shanty settlements has become relatively stable, all the families have been able to do to improve their condition is to turn their cane-matting shacks into adobe huts, as their tenancy of their extremely small 'plots' is too uncertain to justify the investment of any hard-earned savings that they may manage to accumulate. Obviously, sooner or later, these isolated slum settlements, often blocking the completion of city developments around them, must be demolished and their inhabitants moved elsewhere.

The typical *barriada* has a totally different origin. It is started by an organized group of families, some threatened with eviction from slums scheduled for demolition to make way for city improvements or new buildings, some unable to pay rents, others unwilling to go on living in slums or *corralones* and determined to build themselves a better house in more open and healthier surroundings. These families, often led by a small group interested in the chances of profit through the control of the distribution of the land, select and invade a suitable area of marginal desert land belonging to the state. The scale of such invasions and the political problems posed by attempting to frustrate them (without providing adequate alternatives) by either the public or the private sectors, have often guaranteed their success, and the *de facto* possession of the land they have occupied. On adequate plots, regularly laid out by the organizing group, and with their relative security of tenure, further consolidated through permanent construction work, each family builds as fast as its resources permit.

The *corralon* has no future. At best it crystallizes out into a labyrinthine complex of slum courts which can only deteriorate until, eventually, they are eradicated. The *barriada*, on the other hand, albeit slowly, as it will take the average family about twenty years to complete its house without credit assistance, will develop into a typical working- and lower middle-class suburb.

Part 2: Schedule of Barriada Development

Figure 1 shows one aspect of the social change that takes place: the *barriada* is established by young families with a high proportion of very young children; after passing through an intermediate stage when the ratio of infants has dropped, and the average age of the adults has risen, the local population structure is similar to that of the city as a whole. After ten or fifteen years, the *barriada* population is spread across the generations and is balanced between the sexes in the pattern typical of cities in rapidly urbanizing countries. These demographic changes, together with the changes of household structure, translate into changing demands for schools, health services, transportation, and so on, as well as for the volume and organization of domestic living space.

Figure 2 shows the changes of income and income distribution that commonly occurs during the *barriada* development period. Very young families who establish the *barriada* have low or very low incomes; they are upwardly mobile, however, and their incomes increase substantially over time. If the three different cases of the same type of settlement (at three stages of development) are as representative as I believe, the average household income trebles during the most rapid development period. As the majority of the permanently resident families enjoy rising incomes, the socio-economic spread or heterogeneity of the population increases, along with the density, intensity, and diversity of activities.

Figure 3 shows the changing demand and, by inference, the changing priorities for the basic components of the physical environment. Each column on the figure represents the percentage of the population, at each stage, that both demands and has the material means to obtain or to use the component. A study of the incomes and family structure of the incipient *barriada* in the context of Lima (which, for instance, has a very mild climate and virtually no rainfall) soon leads to the conclusion that the highest priorities are for building land, transportation, and local community facilities – all of which are cheap and all of which are essential for the low-income family moving from an inner-city, rented slum to a peripheral *barriada*. With these components, the family can live, and generally much better than in the worst kind of slum, erecting a provisional shack and buying water

Figure 1. Age–sex distribution in *barriadas*.

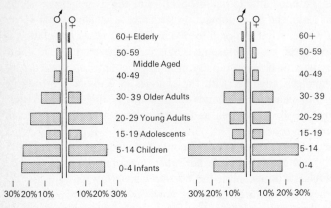

A1   Age-Sex Distribution: Stage 1
Source: El Ermintaño, U.N.S.M. Survey 1965

A2 Age-Sex Distribution: Stage II
Source: Manuel Prado, Areqiupa J.N.V. 1963

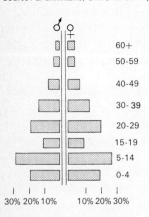

A3 Age-Sex Distribution: Stage III
Source: San Cosme, Lima, J.N.V. 1964

delivered by lorry. A decade later, however, the vast majority can afford the full complement of modern utilities; the increased density also makes their installation necessary, just as increased income levels

Figure 2. Annual household income in *barriadas.*

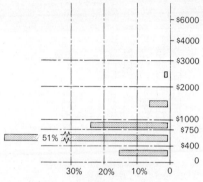

B1 Annual Household Income:
Stage I, Average $680
Source: El Ermitaño, U.N.S.M. Survey 1965

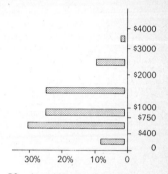

B2 Annual Household Income:
Stage II, Average $1092
Source: Pampa De Cueva Survey,
J.C.U.S. 1965

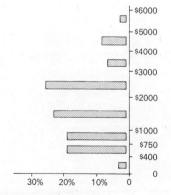

B3 Annual Household Income:
Stage III, Average $1930
Source: San Martin De Porres
J.C.U.S. Survey 1965

and status heighten the demand. It takes the average family at least ten years to complete the ground-floor, the first stage of their house, and it is only when the structure is well advanced that the full complement of installations is required. The demand for rental accommoda-

Figure 3. Sequence of development in *barriada* utilities.

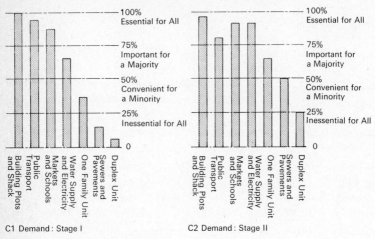

C1 Demand: Stage I

C2 Demand: Stage II

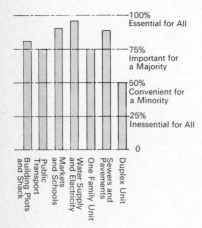

C3 Demand: Stage III

tion grows, at the expense of owner-occupier properties, as the area diversifies and as land values increase. Opportunities for local employment will also increase, especially for those with very low incomes who cannot afford to build or own a property at the level achieved and who, therefore, demand rental accommodation. This demand is met by original settlers seeking secondary sources of income who subdivide and sublet their property in part. Although this process often results in slums that really are a health menace, there is no intrinsic reason why this should be so; sensibly regulated, it provides an economic and socially viable answer to an acute problem.

The schedule of actual development (Table 1) is self-explanatory and confirms the environmental 'fit' or 'response' of the progressively developing *barriada*. It is not a perfect fit, of course, either socially or economically and the architectural form of the planned *barriadas* leaves much to be desired.

The squatter *barriada*-builder who chooses to invest his life's savings in an environment that he creates, forms himself in the process. The person, as the member of a family and of a local community, finds in the responsibilities and activities of home-building and local improvement the creative dialogue essential for self-discovery and growth. The *barriada* provides a basis for living that the housing units, marketed or allocated by mass-consumption society, do not provide.

The *barriada* in Lima (like the *geçekondu* of Istanbul or the *villes extra-coutoumiers* of Kinshasa) is one element of a typical, rapidly growing city in a transitional economy. It is a suburb and, like the suburbs of modern cities, the *barriada* represents a step *up* from the inner city – and the vast majority of squatter home-builders are ex-city slum dwellers.

The cities of the incipiently industrializing or transitional world, such as Lima, respond far more readily to the demands of the poor majority than cities of the industrial or post-industrial world, like Chicago or New York, respond to their poor minorities. Because the poor are the majority in Lima and because the government controls neither the material nor the human resources necessary for the satisfaction of essential housing needs, the poor must act for themselves – and if the official rules and regulations get in their way, these, along

TABLE ONE

Schedule of Barriada *Development at the Three Selected Points in Time (or Stages)*

Stage I: At 1–2 Years (Incipient)	Stage II: At 4–5 Years (Developing)	Stage III: At 10–12 Years (Completing)
Land Surface		
20–30-foot × 60–80-foot *plots* allotted to each participant family on condition that it is permanently occupied by them	No change	Some *subdivision of plots* in response to growing demand for rental accommodation and individual needs for capital and/or reduced space requirements as families shrink
Sites designated for anticipated community facilities; *public squares* serve as playfield, etc.		
Streets 30–60 feet wide with rectangular grid varying between 150–250 feet × 250–300 feet		
Communications		
Regular *omnibus services* are provided as soon as the land is occupied if, as is usual, the site is adjacent to an existing route; *communal taxis* (*colectivos*) often owned by residents provide additional service	No change	No change in transportation services (except for frequency with changing intensity of demand)
		Telephones for public use are generally installed at this stage and, if the area is large enough, a *post office*

Community Facilities

A local *market* and many small *stores* and bars are established at the time of occupation; *primary schools* are also organized and put into immediate operation (with volunteer or locally contracted teachers if necessary); a *chapel* or shrine is set up and neighbouring priests are invited to officiate

Commercial facilities are expanded and complemented by *artisan workshops* for domestic and building trades; TV sets with private generators provide local *cinema* services; a *parish centre* is often instituted providing many additional religious services; locally instituted primary schools are adopted by the state and *additional schools* are provided; *medical treatment* will be provided by visiting doctors and dentists and a local *pharmacy* will be established

More specialized commercial facilities are established if the population is large enough – for example, *commercial banks*, *specialized stores, cinemas, restaurants*, etc. Local workshops will develop into small industries, for example, for the manufacture of furniture, delivery tricycles, etc. *Day nurseries* are often set up with outside agency help and *clinics* fully installed; all professional services will be available locally

cont.

Stage I: At 1–2 Years (Incipient)	Stage II: At 4–5 Years (Developing)	Stage III: At 10–12 Years (Completing)
Structures		
Initially all structures are *provisional* but *starts* on permanent dwelling structures are made at the earliest possible moment in order to consolidate claims and invest savings before purchasing power diminishes	During the first years the *shell of a first floor* is generally completed enclosing an average of 1,100 square feet of roofed space; permanent *school structures* are built during the first years	After about 10 years the ground floor *one-family unit is completed* and a (potentially independent) *second floor is started*; commercial and public buildings will be completed or newly built to modern standards
Public Utilities		
Initially *water* for domestic and construction use must be brought by lorry and sold by the 50-gallon drum (at about 5p (12 cents) per drum); no other 'utility' is provided at this stage	Considered and occasionally successful efforts are made at a relatively early stage to obtain *water mains* and *mains electricity*; more frequently water continues to be brought by lorry but local electric generators are set up to supply immediate neighbours	*Water mains*, *mains electricity*, *sewers*, and the *surfacing of main roads* may be completed during this period

with any policemen who may be sent in to enforce them, are generally swept aside. Consequently, the very poor are able to find some corner for their private life, even if it is only a temporary shack in one of the interstices of the city – on an unguarded lot, in a ravine, or even under a bridge. And the somewhat less poor are able to choose between renting one or two tenement rooms and squatting on the periphery. The urban poor in wealthy and highly institutionalized mass-consumption society do not have these freedoms. At best, like the Algerian and Portuguese immigrants to Paris, they are able to set up very poor *bidonvilles* on the edge of the city; more commonly, like the ghetto inhabitants of the United States cities, the poor can only rent tenements, from slumlords or from public housing authorities. There they must stay until they can make the far higher grade of suburbia in one leap – unless, of course, they are an ethnically discriminated minority, in which case their environment will hold them down for ever, or until they burn it down.

The man who would be free must build his own life. The existential value of the *barriada* is the product of three freedoms: the freedom of community self-selection, the freedom to budget one's own resources, and the freedom to shape one's own environment.

The Freedom of Community Self-Selection

Barriada inhabitants, unlike institutionally or corporatively sponsored and controlled project 'beneficiaries', are self-selected. The *barriada* squatters have a homogeneity of purpose but maintain the heterogeneity of social characteristics vital for cultural stimulation and growth. The project beneficiaries, as one result of the perhaps inevitable political constraints, have a far greater homogeneity of social character but are rarely unified by common purpose – except in opposition to their 'benefactors'. Anyone, or any household, is free to join a *barriada* association as long as there is enough land to go round and as long as dues are paid – the only common rule is that the member must live on his plot. As dues are low (and not always collected) and as a family with a very low income can afford to build a shack and live in the typical *barriada*, the lower socio-economic limit is very low indeed. On the other hand, the *barriada* offers many opportunities to the small businessman, the (lower-echelon or excep-tionally unpretentious) professional or, even, to the aspiring political leader. It therefore attracts a wide range of individual interests and, naturally, the wider the range of its members, the better served the community, and the greater the opportunities of those who most need them.

The Freedom to Budget One's Own Resources

The outstanding difference between the *barriada* and orthodox modern housing is between the ways in which they are built: the squatter – when his tenure is secure enough to risk investment in permanent structures – builds by stages, in accordance with his priorities and budget; the modern housing development is completed, to 'minimum standards' at least, before it is occupied.

The traditional 'progressive development' procedure is essential for those with low and uncertain incomes who are using their property and environmental improvements as socio-economic bootstraps. Those who are constantly threatened with loss of income through unemployment, or because they have no health insurance and little free medical care, must depend for their security on relatives or on home-ownership. A new, largely young, immigrant population will have few relatives on whom to depend for food and shelter in time of need – both necessities are too scarce to share for more than very brief periods. The young low-income family obliged to spend one third or more of their cash income on rent for a slum tenement in constantly increasing demand is extremely vulnerable: as the landlord can get a higher rent when his tenants change he will have little patience with those in arrears. Eviction in time of domestic crisis is a sure way of destroying a poor man's home – without which he will never seek opportunities or progress. But if the family is the owner, or *de facto* possessor of their home, even if it is no more than a shack on a plot of undeveloped land, they have an excellent anchor for their hope. In time of need their cash expenditure can be reduced to a much lower minimum as they have no rent to pay; in addition to that vital advantage, the family (or the abandoned woman with children) can get income from their property by renting part (or attracting another man), by using it as a shop or workshop or, in the last resort, by selling it in order to move on to greener pastures. 'Property security' is a vital function of housing for the 'consolidating' masses in cities like Lima and it is eliminated by the 'instant development' procedure. The threat of foreclosure on the mortgage demanded by heavy initial capital outlay can be even greater than the threat of eviction. The family can lose a good part of their savings as well as their home. The disadvantages, so impressive from the point of view of the modern middle class – the necessity of living in provisional or incomplete structures and without all utilities for long periods – are small by comparison with the advantages. In addition to the incalculable value of securing their hope and sustaining their expectations through the steady improvement of their inalienable homes and local environment, the squatter families have far more space, light, and fresh air than in the rented slum.

28. Mass Housing: Social Research and Design

BRENT C. BROLIN AND JOHN ZEISEL

Since the beginning of the Industrial Revolution, mass housing has been designed for the worker, not by the worker, and has had a dehumanizing and degrading effect in imposing new ways of life on its tenants. This is in sharp contrast to unplanned housing built by the inhabitants themselves, changing over a long period of time, and serving social functions not apparent to architects who are not of that culture. Urban redevelopment and new town programs are often based on what the designer considers adequate for himself. Often when he consciously tries to build for those different from himself, he unconsciously imposes his own values.

Modern architecture asserted the principle of functional design, but the architect's concept of function has usually been limited to manifest functions: kitchens for cooking, stores for buying, streets for driving. He does not usually take into account the latent functions of behaviour required for social and psychological stability in cultures or subcultures other than his own: for example, driving a car as a means of demonstrating a certain status as well as a means of transportation.

In building for different cultures or subcultures, architects have introduced – along with modern sanitary standards – middle-class assumptions of privacy, comfort, forms of sociability, and community living. Western middle-class norms, as we can see, have often proved inappropriate.

1. The Brazilian government built apartment buildings in Pedregulhos for the inhabitants of the shantytown around Rio de Janeiro and then destroyed their primitive shacks. Several months later, the tenants of the projects rebuilt their shacks and moved back.

2. A modern low-income community was built by the Hungarian government in Budapest for families from a physically deteriorated

district in the city. Many of these people sold their new apartments to middle-class families from the old district and, exchanging apartments, moved back to their old but familiar physical slum.

3. Riots in Kingston, Jamaica, in the summer of 1966 reportedly 'were partly prompted by resistance to public housing proposed to replace familiar "slums"'.

Although the cause of these reactions is complex and demands investigation, the situation is partly encouraged by socially inadequate, though technically adequate, mass housing.

It is difficult to find examples of the successful integration of different cultures within a single city. The assimilation of ethnic groups was a challenge that the American city met with neither grace nor efficiency. In addition, cultural integration may not be felt possible, or desirable, by all minority groups. Instead of asking if America has lost its power of integration, we should ask whether America ever had that power.

Unfamiliar Cultures

When a person moves from the country or from a small urban neighbourhood into urban mass housing, one way of life is cut off for him and another begins. His new environment is often incompatible or hostile to his way of life. When traditional living patterns are denied him, it is always with the implication that they are wrong or inappropriate, and that he must now imitate the new way of life around him. But if left to his own choice, the urban migrant often seeks to retain his cultural identity.

For moral as well as for practical reasons, it is vitally important to respect the different customs of groups within our own society, and within urbanizing societies throughout the world.

The social parameters of housing are as important as the legal, economic, and physical. The architect and planner need detailed information about the living patterns of people who are of different cultures or subcultures. This information about the functional requirements of urban subcultures, or rural cultures in transition to urban life, can be provided by analysing the latent social structure and living patterns as they relate to the architectural environment. The architect must then be able to translate this information into a form useful in three-dimensional planning.

Observations

To determine what information about social behaviour is useful to the designer we have drawn freely from Herbert Gans's *The Urban Villagers* (New York, 1962), a perceptive description of working-class Italian life in the West End of Boston.

We have put part of Gans's material into guidelines for the designer. From these guidelines we have designed housing which might have replaced the physically substandard housing in the neighbourhood Gans studied without destroying the healthy, low-income community.

To demonstrate the method of using specific research for design, and to place our study in a relevant physical context, we chose an existing site in the North End of Boston. This area is physically, ethnically, and demographically similar to the old West End.

From Gans's report, which followed his living in the West End and studying it over a period of months, we chose statements about the social behaviour of the inhabitants.

Some samples of the original observations, and their translation into architectural requirements, follow:

1. Observation: 'Food preparation serves as an example of the woman's skill as a housewife and mother. When company is present, it enables her to display her skills to relatives and peers.'

Requirement: Area for cooking visible from where women visitors gather.

2. Observation: '. . . the normal tendency is for men and women to split up, the men in one room and the women in another'.

Requirement: Privacy between men's and women's social gathering areas.

3. Observations: 'While the teenage groups were sexually segregated, girls' groups in the West End met near the corners where the boys hung out.'

Requirement: Adolescent girls' areas visible to boys' areas.

We then grouped together the requirements that referred to behaviour taking place in the same physical areas: apartments, groups of apartments, areas of informal social activity, and commercial areas. The architectural design followed from this. Therefore, on each of the drawings, there is a set of observations as well as the requirements met by the drawing (Figures 1 and 2).

Relevance of Observations

We began with over 200 observations of behaviour, most of which described an activity taking place in a physical setting. Many of these, although telling us how the West Enders behaved, were not necessarily helpful to the architect: 'Girls from about age ten are expected to help with the household tasks. . . . Adolescents and young adults are frequent moviegoers.'

Whether or not young girls help around the house does not tell us about the preferred apartment layout or the size of rooms. Nor does the second observation, as it stands, guide the architect's work; he knows no better whether the movie theatre should be in the centre of the area or its outskirts, or whether the movies downtown are just as good. He must know who else is involved in movie-going. If he knew, for instance, that when going to the movies, teenagers were seen by other young people from the neighbourhood – and avoided adults – he would know that the social significance of this activity is related to its physical location in the area. The theatre should be visible to teenagers doing other things and not be easily visible from areas of adult activity.

In sum, the observations we found to be useful to the architect possessed the following attributes: (1) a primary actor and his activity; (2) the significant others in the situation; and (3) the relationship between the primary actor and the significant others. This relationship is the means of including or excluding the significant others from the realm of the primary actor.

In the example above, the movie-going teenagers are the actors, the

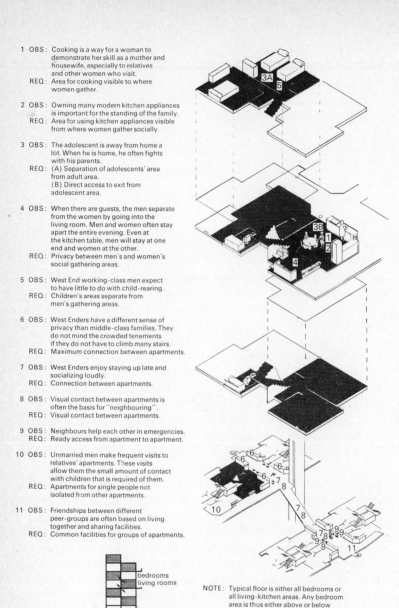

1 OBS : Cooking is a way for a woman to demonstrate her skill as a mother and housewife, especially to relatives and other women who visit.
  REQ : Area for cooking visible to where women gather.

2 OBS : Owning many modern kitchen appliances is important for the standing of the family.
  REQ : Area for using kitchen appliances visible from where women gather socially.

3 OBS : The adolescent is away from home a lot. When he is home, he often fights with his parents.
  REQ : (A) Separation of adolescents' area from adult area.
        (B) Direct access to exit from adolescent area.

4 OBS : When there are guests, the men separate from the women by going into the living room. Men and women often stay apart the entire evening. Even at the kitchen table, men will stay at one end and women at the other.
  REQ : Privacy between men's and women's social gathering areas.

5 OBS : West End working-class men expect to have little to do with child-rearing.
  REQ : Children's areas separate from men's gathering areas.

6 OBS : West Enders have a different sense of privacy than middle-class families. They do not mind the crowded tenements if they do not have to climb many stairs.
  REQ : Maximum connection between apartments.

7 OBS : West Enders enjoy staying up late and socializing loudly.
  REQ : Connection between apartments.

8 OBS : Visual contact between apartments is often the basis for "neighbouring".
  REQ : Visual contact between apartments.

9 OBS : Neighbours help each other in emergencies.
  REQ : Ready access from apartment to apartment.

10 OBS : Unmarried men make frequent visits to relatives' apartments. These visits allow them the small amount of contact with children that is required of them.
   REQ : Apartments for single people not isolated from other apartments.

11 OBS : Friendships between different peer-groups are often based on living together and sharing facilities.
   REQ : Common facilities for groups of apartments.

NOTE : Typical floor is either all bedrooms or all living-kitchen areas. Any bedroom area is thus either above or below another apartment's living-kitchen area.

Figures 1 and 2 (opposite). Observations and requirements.

12 OBS: After they are ten years old, boys
are generally unsupervised while
outside, and enjoy the freedom to roam
the neighbourhood.
   REQ: Many places for pedestrian movement.

13 OBS: Groups of teen-agers of different
sexes spend a lot of time "hanging·
around" or looking for something to
do. Often they do this with adults
or teen-agers of the opposite sex.
   REQ: (A) Connection between boys' group
and peer groups of other statuses.
(B) Connection between boys' and
girls' outside areas and apartments.

14 OBS: Teen-agers gather on corners near
small stores.
   REQ: Areas for informal congregating
outside and around commercial areas.

15 OBS: Although boys meet with boys, and
girls with girls, the girls meet near the
corners where the boys hang out.
   REQ: Adolescent girls' areas visible to
boys' areas.

16 OBS: Young teen-age girls take care of
younger children on the streets.
   REQ: Adolescent girls' areas near
children's play areas.

17 OBS: Both men and women use dress as a
means of self-expression, spending
much money on clothes.
   REQ: General visibility among pedestrian,
apartment, commercial, and
recreational areas.

18 OBS: Men wash their cars on the streets
as often as once a week. For men, the
car is important as a means of
expressing their identity.
   REQ: Visibility for areas related to
automobiles.

19 OBS: Bars and luncheonettes are places to
exchange news and gossip, as well as
message centres for regular customers.
   REQ: (A) Commercial area connected to
living areas.
(B) Commercial area visible from
street and other commercial areas.

20 OBS: Women socialize while shopping.
   REQ: Commercial areas visible to and
from streets.

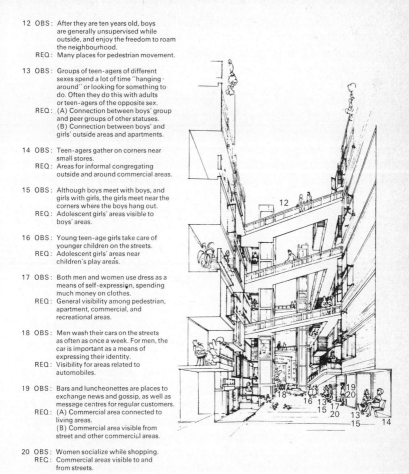

significant others are non-movie-going teenagers and adults. The relationship in the teenagers' case is visual and auditory connection, and in the adults' case, visual and auditory separation. The field observer, by asking: 'Who is doing what, including or excluding whom?' will most likely encompass all of the necessary sociological components in his observations.

Furthermore, in spelling out the relationship — the means of inclusion or exclusion — we get the 'requirement' to be fulfilled by the new physical form. This is the link between social behaviour and physical form, by which we can specify how an area in which a given activity takes place should be connected to or separated from another area.

From the sample list of observations and requirements we derive:

1. Area for cooking visible from where women visitors gather.
2. Privacy between men's and women's social gathering areas.
3. Adolescent girls' areas visible to boys' areas.

These requirements indicate the social connection that the designer can either break or allow to exist. If we see the design process in large part as putting up or leaving out different kinds of barriers, by defining where these walls are socially desirable, we can help the designer meet people's needs.

The Existing Environment

The requirements are the design implications of social behaviour. We must also see the social implications of the existing physical environment that is to be replaced.

Two things must be established: (1) Is the existing physical form compatible with the prevalent social patterns? (2) What patterns does the physical form make difficult or easy?

Some indicators of incompatibility between the existing physical form and social needs are: changes made in the original form — windows painted black, doors nailed shut, ramps built over stairs; aspects of the environment totally unused — playgrounds, balconies, park benches; and aspects falsely used — children playing in the street instead of a near-by park, dinner cooked on the fire escape, the car parked in the living-room.

Indicators of compatibility, on the other hand, will be the absence of these changes in form or use, as well as little destruction, much use, relatively low turnover, and conscious efforts at beautification by the inhabitants.

Avoiding Mistakes

To find out what patterns the physical form allows, we translate an observation of the existing physical environment into the requirement it seems to fulfil. If that aspect is compatible, the requirement is one to be fulfilled by new designs, while the requirements reflected in incompatible form are clearly to be avoided. By taking into account both the social implications of the environment and the indicators of conflict, we can avoid present mistakes.

The field observer could apply the method we have described in the following ways:

1. Looking at behaviour. He notices repeatedly that boys play ball in the street. Looking for the significant others in the situation, he finds that girls of the same age often sit around watching the boys, while adults stop to look and comment. The primary actors – the boys – are related visually to two groups of significant others – the girls and the adults. This complete observation is translated into the requirement: boys' play areas should be visibly connected to where the girls hang out and to where adults are. If other observations indicate a similar requirement, the designer might build a playground near the shopping area or subway station, as well as near the stoops where young girls get together.

2. Looking at the environment. A playground with basketball courts is far from both the busy life of the street and from the door stoops and shops where the teenage girls hang out. By asking, 'Who can play in the playground, including or excluding whom?' we translate this simple observation into the social pattern it allows: teenagers, mostly male, can play basketball there. While other boys, both younger and older, may be included, both adults and girls of the same age are excluded. Since this playground is rarely used by anyone, it is evident that we should avoid the separation of the boys' play area from that of the girls' and from 'where the [adult] action is'. More simply, we come up with the previous requirement: the boys' play area should be visibly connected to these other places.

This observation alone would, of course, not be enough to make a

374 Shell: Priorities in Designing the Human Habitat

final judgement. Both repeated observations and the use of other techniques — surveying attitudes, informal interviewing, counting how often people do things — are necessary to validate findings.

Appropriateness of the Method

Although it should be augmented with survey techniques, this observational method is very different in content. Most people will answer questions about a proposed plan in terms of what they have experienced or what they want. When the respondent is a potential buyer in a housing market, it is important to know his preferences. But this often has little to do with the latent functions of behaviour that are integral to the social stability of a group. We therefore distinguish these conscious wants from unconscious needs.

We must be aware that the designer has only limited control over the social lives of the people in his buildings. He can neither limit people's social behaviour nor force them to change by building a socially inhibiting environment. Their living patterns will stay the same or change regardless of the physical environment in which they live. If the designer does try to limit behaviour when change is imminent, or to force change when the inhabitants neither want it nor are ready for it, he can cause potentially harmful conflict. This conflict can have several consequences: the physical environment may be altered, misused, or not used at all, and the people may suffer social and psychological stress. To stop this we would have the designer understand the social behaviour of those who are to live in his buildings, and try to avoid putting up barriers to their way of life in the physical environment.

Design Freedom

The results of this type of research define a minimum set of social behaviour patterns which the physical structure should not prohibit.

The means that one designer uses to achieve this end as well as the number of non-conflicting alternatives he offers is in no way limited. For example, to separate the cooking area from the social area we use a folding partition. This allows the alternative of connecting these areas. Many different walls, both more stationary and more adaptable, could meet the same requirement.

The social parameters specified by these requirements are ideals; it is difficult to meet them all equally well. One essential next step is to determine the hierarchy of requirements, so that there is a basis for making choices when conflict occurs among the requirements. We must, therefore, determine the relative importance of the behaviour's latent function to the social stability of the group. We might also define the architectural means for separating or connecting the activities related in the requirements.

In applying this research-design method we must consider that the living patterns of those for whom we design will eventually change. But any change will have its starting point in existing social patterns. If the Italian community of Gans's research becomes more middle-class it will still retain many of its present social customs. In any case, to design now in a way that we know will not fit existing life styles is to make the hypothetical misfit of the future a reality of the present.

29. The Role of the Architect in Community Building

TEAM 10*

There was a time not so long ago when minds of men moved along a deterministic groove; let's call it a Euclidian groove. It coloured their behaviour and vision, what they made and did and what they felt. Then – it had to happen sooner or later – some very keen men, with delicate antennae – painters, poets, philosophers, and scientists most of them – jumped out of this groove and rubbed the deterministic patina off the surface of reality. They saw wonderful things and did not fail to tell us about them. Our unbounded gratitude is due to them: to Picasso, Klee, Mondrian, and Brancusi: to Joyce, Le Corbusier, Schoenberg, Bergson, and Einstein: to the whole wonderful gang. They set the great top spinning again and expanded the universe – the outside and the inside universe. It was a wonderful riot – the cage was again opened. But society still moves along in the old groove, in bad air, making only sly use of what these men discovered; worse still, applying it on a purely technological, and decorative level, not the essence but what can be gleaned from it in order to give a pretence of moving more effectively.

Now what is wonderful about this non-Euclidian idea – this other vision – is that it is contemporary: contemporary to all our difficulties, social and political, economic and spiritual. What is tragic is that we have failed to see that it alone can solve them.

Each period requires a constituent language – an instrument with which to tackle the human problems posed by the period, as well as

*Team 10 includes J. B. Bakema and Aldo Van Eyck, Holland; G. Candilis, France; S. Woods, U.S.A.; A. and P. Smithson and John Voeleker, England; O. Hansen and J. Soltan, Poland; Gier Grung, Norway; Ralph Erskine, Sweden; J. Coderch, Spain.

those which, from period to period, remain the same, i.e. those posed by man.

Architecture implies a constant rediscovery of constant human qualities translated into space. Man is always and everywhere essentially the same. He has the same mental equipment though he uses it differently according to his cultural or social background, according to the particular life pattern of which he happens to be a part.

A. Van Eyck (Netherlands)

Role of the Architect

Architecture and town planning are simply the spatial expression of human conduct. In past societies the relation between man and total space was shaped by: religion (medieval age) − to have faith; political economy (nineteenth century) − to possess; administration (twentieth century) − to manage.

First, man creates environment, then environment in its turn influences man. Environment is created by simple means: walls, and openings in the walls. It is of small significance what materials the walls are made of. But man's constructions include more and more variations in walls and in openings of walls. The vocabulary has enlarged and it is becoming more and more rich. During thousands of years man was living under trees immediately above the ground. Only in the last century has he been able to live above the trees in contact with the horizon (Figure 1).

So now the whole alphabet has to be used. We have to harmonize life on the ground and life which is in touch with the horizon. If one visits old towns like Amsterdam or Paris, one sees the built volume of the houses of those people who produced goods. One does not see the constructed volume of the dwellings of the anonymous population, because very often this population was not entitled to own a permanent home. They lived in transitory, improvised dwellings outside the fortifications of the city or under the roofs of those who had leading roles in society.

I believe that the reason so many architects are interested nowadays

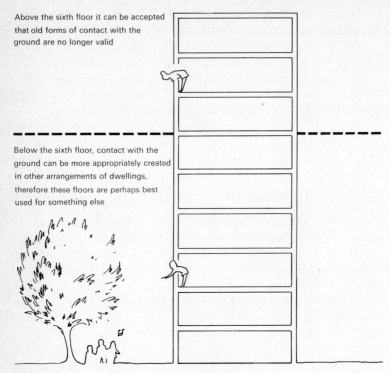

Above the sixth floor it can be accepted that old forms of contact with the ground are no longer valid

Below the sixth floor, contact with the ground can be more appropriately created in other arrangements of dwellings, therefore these floors are perhaps best used for something else

Figure 1. Man living in contact with the horizon.

in the habitat of the Pueblo Indians, or the Negroes in Africa, is that there one can still recognize the spatial expression of the whole population. We should not forget, however, that these populations are fighting fierce battles to be equipped with the modern techniques developed in other countries: in Western Europe, America, and the U.S.S.R. Here is the drama. In western societies we are attempting to enable the anonymous client to establish his own spatial expression of his own way of living. In primitive societies this way of living still exists, but it lacks the techniques which can help them to get rid of fear and to attain total life. Every day, there is taking place a confrontation between primitive societies with integrated habitats, whose members claim a right to be provided with modern techniques, and western society, disintegrated by these very techniques, whose members seek new disciplines of integration.

Our task is to introduce the play of volumes in space as a function of social life. The new society must enable the individual to express his personal opinion about total life. It is our task to transform a fear of total space into respect and confidence. These are the oldest and at the same time the most recent functions of architecture and town planning. Means are simple: walls, pilotis, windows, staircases, elevators, loggias, technical equipment, and the plan as a frame for a new freedom.

J. B. Bakema (Netherlands)

Can architects meet society's plural demand? Can they possibly substitute the present loss of a vernacular and still build a city that really is a city – a liveable place for a large multitude of people? The vernacular was always able to cope with plurality in former days. In what way are urban people to participate in fashioning their own immediate surroundings within a conceived overall framework? This is the first problem confronting the architect urbanist today. But if society has no form, how can architects build the counterform? I believe there is a paradox involved in this task.

A. Van Eyck

It is highly probable that the objects we are so painfully devising may be the wrong ones and it is a good thing every now and then to let other specialists into one's private world, to see if their specialization makes one's own irrelevant, or to produce a mutual modification of concepts. It is obvious, for example, in the case of cars and signs and roads and buildings, that the underlying concepts are wrong; and it is quite mad to think in terms of styling and not in terms of changing the total living pattern – not in any philosophical sense, but pragmatically because things affect the use of other things.

A. and P. Smithson (Britain)

What are the objections against architecture as we know it?

1. It has not solved the problem of quantity: the need for necessary accommodations and social amenities is constantly rising.

2. Contemporary architecture cannot be easily adapted to change and often becomes outdated, even before being completed.

3. Present architectural conception does not sufficiently take into account the personality of the inhabitants: it is too often much too inhuman.

4. Contemporary architecture is wasteful of the financial means at our disposal.

O. Hansen (Poland)

There are the problems of mass communication and the problems of the whole change towards a middle-class society with different sorts of drives – different sorts of status urges, and so on. But in addition you have the business of terrific complexity of actual physical communication – the cars and the motor-way situation – which seems to mean that we have got to evolve a completely new sort of aesthetic – a new sort of discipline – which can respond to growth and change.

The slum has gone but we have only to take a look at one of the new towns or a recent housing development, to recognize to what extent the spirit of spontaneity has also gone into hiding. Architects left no cracks and crevices this time. They expelled all sense of place. They were fearful of the unpremeditated event, the spontaneous act, unscheduled gaiety or violence, unpredictable danger round the corner. They made a flat surface of everything so that no microbes could survive the civic vacuum cleaner. To think that architects are given to talking devotedly about space while they are actually emasculating it into a void.

A. and P. Smithson

Urban Infra-Structure

Studies of association and identity led to the development of systems of linked building complexes which were intended to correspond more closely to the existing network of social relationships and self-contained buildings. These freer systems are more capable of change and, particularly in new communities, of mutating in scale and intention as they go along.

Although the roads system can be thought of as a triangulated net of varying density (no hierarchy of routes, equal distribution of traffic load over whole net, equal accessibility to all parts, only one decision at each intersection, etc., etc.), the realities of route findings and respect for (and wish to revalidate) the existing structure, as well as the desire to modify the town pattern, generally produce a road net which is not a pattern in the conventional formal sense, but is nevertheless a very real [system] to which the architecture must respond.

A. and P. Smithson

A city should embrace a hierarchy of superimposed configurative systems multilaterally conceived (a quantitative not qualitative hierarchy). The finer-grained systems − those which embrace the multiple dwelling and its extensions − should reflect the qualities of ascending repetitive configurative stages.

All systems should be familiarized one with the other in such a way that their combined impact and interaction can be appreciated as a single complex system − polyphonal, multi-rhythmic, kaleidoscopic and yet perpetually and everywhere comprehensible: a single homogeneous configuration composed of many sub-systems, each covering the same overall area and equally valid, but each with a different grain, scale of movement, and association potential.

These systems are to be so designed that each evolves out of the other − is a part of it. The specific meaning of each system must sustain the meaning of the other. The large structures − infra-structure − must not only be comprehensible in their own right, they must above all − this is the crucial point − assist the overall comprehensibility of the minutely designed intimate fabric which constitutes the immediate counter-form of every citizen's everyday life. They must not only be able to absorb reasonable mutations within themselves, but also permit them within the intimate smaller fabric they serve.

A. Van Eyck

The main case that is being made is that for a human agglomeration to be 'a community' in the twentieth century, it is not necessary – practically or symbolically – for it to be a dense mass of buildings; but that does not necessarily mean that a bigger overall area need be covered than is covered at present. It is essentially a matter for a re-grouping of densities. There is no need, for example, for low density family houses to be excluded from the central areas of the city, nor is there any need to think conventionally that housing nearer the country should be at low densities. It depends on the life pattern of the people who live there what sort of environment is needed and what sort of density results. The overall pattern of the community is of clusters of varying densities.

The intention of using the road system as the town structure is to keep the apparent level of mechanization under control. We are no longer in the position of needing to play up our devices, but rather to play them down, to channel mechanical noise and excitement, and to create 'pools of calm' for family living and regeneration.

Density and intensity will be related to the function of each zone, resulting in communities with a much greater genuine variation of living pattern. Somewhere there must be a place which not only allows for the contact of mind with mind, but also symbolizes it. This can only happen at the 'centre' (there can be only one place where the experience of the community reaches its maximum: if there were two there would be two communities). It is quite clear that in an ideal city at the present time, the communication net should serve (and indicate) places-to-stop-and-do-things-in.

A. and P. Smithson

The design process of 'recognized' kinds of buildings, as, for example, new headquarters for firms or government centres, has to start with the design of the program for the building because this program fixes how people can be alone – or can meet – while working in the building.

Buildings have to be more and more a kind of village and town, while towns have to be more and more like buildings. Neighbourhoods must be a kind of castle with towers, rooms, galleries, secret corridors, and surprising courtyards.

J. B. Bakema

Just as our mental process needs relatively fixed points to enable it to remain clear and sane while classifying and evaluating transient information, so the city needs identifying points, which have a long cycle of change, and by means of which things changing on a shorter cycle can be valued and identified. With a few fixed and clear things, transient elements – housing, drug stores, advertising signs, shops, and, of course, people and their extensions, clothes, cars, and so on – are no longer a menace to the sanity and sense of the urban structure, but can uninhibitedly reflect short-term mood and need. If this distinction between the changing and the fixed were observed there would be less need for elaborate control over things for which no good case can be made for controlling, and legislative energy could be concentrated on the long-term structure.

A. and P. Smithson

Today we are involved in mass production, mass distribution, mass consumption, mass housing, mass education, mass leisure. We are especially concerned with the relationships between these mass activities. We have to define the use of public and private transport, from rocket ships to bicycles, and to relate their different scales of speed to each other and to man. These problems are most acute where the mass is greatest, i.e. in our cities and urban regions. The constant and rapid evolution of our society cannot permit the stratification of cities. The question is not how to build flexible buildings but how to establish an environment in which buildings appropriate to their function may occur, and to encourage an interaction between these buildings and their environment. It is clear that no formal composition can provide an answer to this problem; for the nature of all formal composition is static, precise, and fixed. Buildings which formerly took fifty years to fail, now fail in five. Our problem is to seek a way to allow the five-year building to occur when and where it is needed. The object is not

to make the building flexible but to make the urban complex flexible
enough to foster short-life buildings as well as long-lived ones.

S. Woods (U.S.A.)

Grouping of Dwellings

It is impossible for each man to construct his house for himself. But
the architect must make it possible for each man to make his house
his home. Up to now the house is built down to the smallest detail and
man is pressed into this dwelling – which in spirit, is the same from
Scotland to the Gold Coast. Man is forced to adapt himself as best
he may to the life that the architect furnishes him with. We must design the 'habitat' only to the point at which man can take over. We
must provide a framework in which man can again be master of his
home.

G. Candilis (France)

The creation of non-arbitrary group spaces is the primary function
of the planner. The basic group is obviously the family. Traditionally
the next social grouping is the street (or square or green: any word
that by definition implies enclosure or belonging, thus 'in our street');
the next is the district; finally the city. It is the job of the planner to
make these groupings apparent as finite plastic realities.

In some suburbs and in most slums the vital relationship between
the house and the street survives: children run about, 'the street is
comparatively quiet', people stop and talk, dismantled vehicles are
parked. In the back gardens are pigeons and ferrets. The shops are
round the corner. You know the milkman.

The house, the shell which fits man's back, looks inward to family,
outward to society, and its organization should reflect this duality of
orientation. The looseness of organization and ease of communication
essential to the largest community should be present in this, the
smallest. The house is the first finite city element.

Houses can be arranged in such a way that a new finite thing, the
plastic expression of primary community, is created. The street is our

second finite city element. The street is an extension of the house. In it children learn, for the first time, of the world outside the family, a microcosmic world in which the street games change with the seasons and the hours are reflected in the cycle of street activity.

But in suburb and slum, as street succeeds street, it is soon evident that the district – the next level of organization – no longer exists. To maintain this looseness of grouping with easy access to other levels of communication, the density must increase, and with high densities, if we are to retain the essential joys of sun, space, and verdure, we must build high. In the past this has led to a form of vertical living in which the family is deprived of its essential outdoor life, and contact with other families is made difficult, if not impossible, along the narrow balconies and landings that are the sole means of intercommunication. Furthermore, the possibilities of forming friendships are made difficult by complete absence of horizontal communications between blocks, except at ground level, and the ineffectiveness of vertical communication.

The idea of 'street' has been forgotten. It is the idea of street, not the reality of street, that is important – the creation of effective group spaces fulfilling the vital function of identification and enclosure making the socially vital life-of-the-streets possible.

At all densities such streets are possible by the creation of a true street mesh in the air, each street having a large number of people dependent on it for access. In addition, some streets should be thoroughfares – that is leading directly to places – so that they will acquire special characteristics. Thus, the 'apartment block' can disappear and the freedom of vertical living can become a reality.

The question of the optimum density for various sorts of family life is tied up with the increased availability of personal transport, and the relationship of the car to the house. If the car is to be a convenience and a pleasure, it must be easy to use it. A family excursion with babies and baskets and buckets and spades, from the fifteenth floor of an access-balcony slab block via an underground garage, can be no picnic. Then there is the problem of the real space needs of family life, especially for children. Everyone needs a bit of sheltered outdoor space as an extension to his house and such a space can also serve the needs of children up to two or three years old. But older children need more and more space: space to play safely close by until seven years old or so, and space for wild running and little excursions until eleven, and then places to go and do things in until they are almost grown up. Maybe none of these requirements can be met simply and pleasurably at densities much above 70 persons per acre.

Of course, there are lots of people to whom 'hotel life' (by which is meant the maximum of privacy, anonymity, and simplicity of service) is suitable and pleasurable. This can even be 40 per cent of central city households, especially where the population is growing older. These people are in fact well served by conventional forms of high building, such as the Lake Shore Drive apartments in Chicago, or Swedish point blocks, where access is swift, secret and completely enclosed, and the windows look out over wide anonymous space. Such buildings, situated near city centres, give a maximum of convenience for students, single people, childless couples, and grown-up families. Their density can be very high indeed, up to 300 persons per acre. But families with children, except in exceptional circumstances, are best served by relatively low density development, whatever its location.

A. and P. Smithson

It has been found, in the planning of housing units, that the most effective way to proceed is to start with those elements which can first be determined and defined (entry, kitchen, bath, etc.) and to cluster the rooms around these services. This concept of planning by dissociation is general practice today. First the core is determined, then the cluster is formed. This is true for one-family houses as well as for blocks of flats, and as a planning process, it usually results in good and efficient design. Servant and served, as Louis Kahn puts it, are distinguished and the core brings clarity and organization to the cluster.

The idea of clustering the cells proceeds from the core. The core is usually expressed in the master plan as a fixed point in the general scheme, out of contact with the greater part of the homes.

In view of the failure of the traditional master plan to cope with the accelerated creation of habitat, it is proposed that planning be reconsidered as proceeding from stem to cluster (rather than from cell to symbol). In this way it is felt that a basic viable structure may be determined: this stem includes all the servants of the homes (all the *prolongements du logis*), commercial, cultural, educational, and leisure activities, as well as roads, walkways, and services. These are the factors which vary from place to place and from year to year; and if taken as determinants of a scheme can give it organization and identity of a higher order than that obtained solely from a sculptural arrangement of forms.

The stem is considered not only as a link between additive cells, but as the generator of habitat. It provides the environment in which the cells may function. The design of this basic structure influences the design of the cells it serves. If the structure itself incorporates, as it must, the ideas of mobility and growth and change, these characteristics will necessarily affect the design of the cells.

The validity of the stem – the servant of the community – is that which society gives it. It varies for the whole of the stem, and within the stem it varies from one function to another. It is felt that the stem will change constantly to reflect the mobility of society.

The plan of a housing scheme may be based, for example, on a pattern of movement valid today. In ten years the pattern of movement will almost certainly change. The plan will then tend to re-establish a new validity for the new pattern. This possibility must be conserved. The door to the future must be left open. The stem is conditioned by mobility. Its dimensions are given not in measures of length but of speed: $2 \cdot 5$ miles per hour and 60 miles per hour. It can provide the link between these measures of speed as it can between the measures of validity (the 25- and 5-year cycles of change). The process of planning from stem to cluster will tend to re-establish density and scale in habitat. The principle of equalization of spaces in the occupying of a given site will disappear and exterior space can again be small or large, crowded or empty. The street may be revalidated if it is considered as a place, as well as a way from one place to another. Its form or spatial content will be different from that of previous streets, but the idea of street (as distinct from that of road) is inherent in the idea of stem.

S. Woods

We propose:

1. To distribute ancillary activities throughout the domain of housing instead of localizing them in certain fixed places, to bring together as many activities as possible, to bring the sum of life to all

Figure 2. The linear organization of activities and the grouping of living cells around the linear centre.

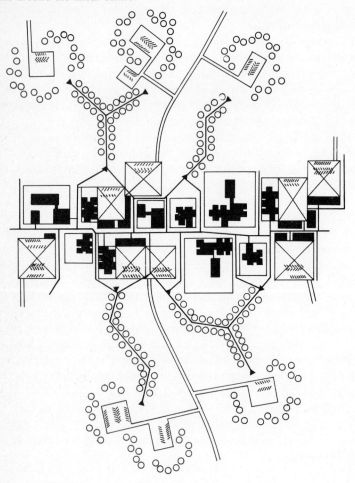

the parts. A linear organization (a line has neither shape nor size) is the truest reflection of an open society (Figure 2).

2. To define the use of the automobile, which, covering greater distances in shorter times, enables us to imagine a totally new organism in which vehicular and pedestrian traffic is entirely independent (Figures 3 and 4).

Figure 3. A synthesis of parking lots, pedestrian ways, and mechanical vertical circulation points becomes the generator of the urban element.

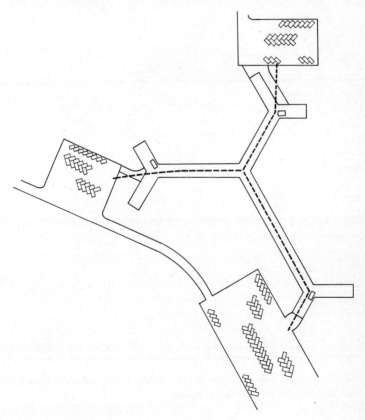

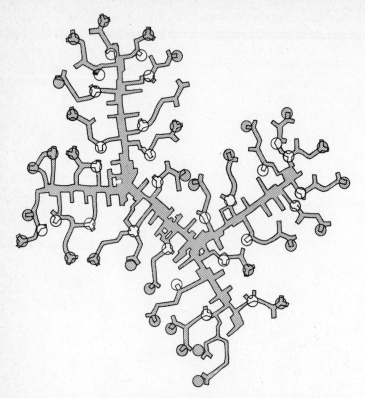

Figure 4. The linear centre is exclusively pedestrian and re-establishes the street as the primary feature of urbanism.

3. To determine points of contact between transportation and dwelling as a way towards the realization of a collectivity and hence to the identification of the individual (Figure 5).

4. To re-establish multiple access in collective dwellings, to have more than one way into one's house.

Candilis, Josic, and Woods

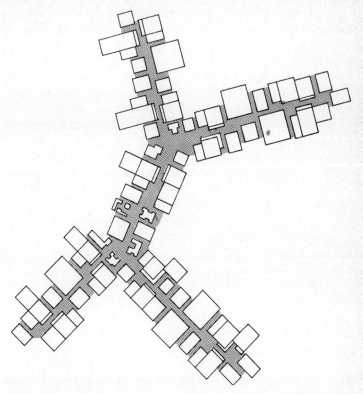

Figure 5. From the parking lot one moves into an independent pedestrian network. This operates at all levels, served by mechanical vertical circulation.

Doorstep

There's one more thing that has been growing in my mind ever since the Smithsons uttered the word 'doorstep' at the C.I.A.M. congress in Aix in 1953. It hasn't left me ever since. I've been mulling over it, expanding the meaning as far as I could stretch it. For example: the world of the house, with me inside and you outside, or vice versa. There's also the world of the street – the city – with you inside and me outside, or vice versa. Get what I mean? Two worlds clashing; no transition. The individual on one side, the collective on the other. It's terrifying. Between the two, society throws up lots of barriers, while architects are so poor in spirit that they provide doors two inches thick and six feet high: flat surfaces in a flat surface. Is that the reality of a door? Perhaps the greater reality of a door is the localized setting for a wonderful human gesture: conscious entry and departure. That's what a door is, something that frames you coming and going, for it's a vital experience not only for those that do so, but also for those encountered or left behind.

Take off your shoes and walk along a beach through the ocean's last thin sheet of water gliding landwards and seawards. You feel reconciled in a way you wouldn't feel if there were a forced dialogue between you and either one or the other of these great phenomena. For here, in between land and ocean – in this in-between realm – something happens to you that is quite different from the sailor's reciprocal nostalgia: you experience no landward yearning from the sea, no seaward yearning from the land, no yearning for the alternative, no escape from one into the other.

Architecture must extend this narrow borderline and persuade it to loop into a realm – an articulated in-between realm. The job of architecture is to provide this in-between realm by means of construction: i.e. to provide, from house to city scale, a bunch of real places for real people and real things: places that can sustain instead of denying their specific identity.

A. Van Eyck

City planning and architecture are parts of a continuous process. Planning is the correlating of human activities; architecture is the housing of these activities. City planning establishes the milieu in which architecture can happen. Both are conditioned by the economic, social, political, technical, and physical climate. Planning remains abstract until it generates architecture. Only through its results (building, ways, places) can it come into being. Its function is to establish optimum conditions in which the present becomes future. To do this it must seek out, explore, and explain the relationships between human activities. It must then bring these activities together so that the whole of life in the city becomes richer than the sum of its parts.

The important question is not 'how?' but 'why?' – or 'what for?' We have no quarrel with the past except when it is used to compromise the future. The past can guide us but past techniques are of little avail. Present techniques and present means must be used to open as many doors to the future as possible.

S. Woods

30. Architecture of the Road

N. KUROKAWA

The Road of Pikionis

I was stepping on something solid, walking against a current of sight-seers moving towards the Acropolis of Athens. I was walking in the direction of the hill of Philopappos, sensing with my whole body something unusual. This road by Pikionis had something to say to me.

Pikionis was an aged Athenian architect, who died in 1968. This road, two kilometres long, from the Acropolis to the Philopappos and the church of Demetrius Lombardiaris, which stands beside it, are among his many works.

Near the entrance to the Acropolis the road forms a symbolic open space, embracing a ruin of Doric and Ionic columns. Further down one comes across a parking lot, where the road has expanded like a calm pool of water in a stream. Still lower down, the stone-paved road forms a promenade which ceases abruptly when it meets a broad, asphalt-paved, automobile highway. Pedestrians then cross to the other side by stepping on stone islands, like a passage over a brook.

The ascent to the Philopappos starts here, and the road is bordered on both sides by steps, though the central part remains on a slope (Figure 1). Here and there marble benches are placed, making alcoves beside the steps and sometimes forming small enclaves. Rainwater flows down in concrete ditches or is caught in marble troughs before continuing its downward passage. The pattern of the concrete and stone pavement shows great variety, in some places designed as if to dam up the stream of cars, in others as if to wash it away (Figure 2).

Where natural rocks occur beside the road, the concrete pathway stretches out to engulf them, and a small church half-way up the ascent to the Philopappos is assimilated by the road, embraced by its pattern of stone pavement. If this road can be called an 'architecture for human movement', the little church should be called an 'architecture of the road'.

Figure 1. A stepped promenade borders the steep roadway.

Figure 2. The pattern of the rock and concrete road suggests the arrest and movement of cars and people.

At the top of the ascent, Pikionis' road comes to an end. When I looked back I saw a crowd of people unconsciously enjoying walking up the opposite slope to the Acropolis.

The Oriental Road and the Western Road

In India there are four types of ideal city pattern: Dandaka, Padmaka, Nandyavartha, Swastika. Each contains the Raj-Patha (King's Road) which runs east and west and the Mahakara (Main Street) which runs north and south (Figure 3). Community facilities and religious facilities are sited along both roads and a lime tree is planted at their crossing point. This tree is considered to have given birth to the sun, the moon, and the stars. It is not related to the life of the urban citizens, but is a symbol of the spirit which reaches into the cosmos.

The sun shines down upon the Raj-Patha and purifies it from morning to night, and the Mahakara is the pathway of the wind. Thus, both streets function as social spaces which relate the individual to the cosmos. After the long rainy season the Raj-Patha, road of sunshine, is filled with crowds of people. On the sleepless nights of high humidity people bring their beds out of the houses to catch the breezes along the Mahakara.

The city festival is performed on the two roads of the sun and the wind, which are then crowded with people. The processional religious festival also takes place on a road. In other words, ceremonies are related to significant urban spaces which link the life of the individual with the city.

This tendency to tie in activities of the citizen's life and the space of a road is even clearer in the plan of Hei-an-kyo (old Kyoto, Japan). The street pattern of Hei-an-kyo, which is on the Bojo system, distinguishes Ji, which is a traffic artery, from Michi, which is a street. As in India, the temple shrines and community facilities were not concentrated in a central area, nor did they form a square or a core, but were placed at intervals along a road.

Oriental festivals, in general, mainly consist of the movement of a procession rather than a gathering of people in an open space. There-

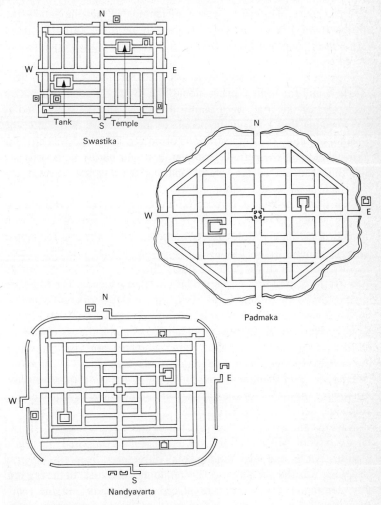

Figure 3. Three Indian ideal city patterns.

fore in Japan, ceremonial arches (Tori) are along the processional
way, and the temples, shrines, and community facilities are placed in
a linking arrangement along it rather than concentrated together in

a central place. Thus, it is easily understandable that the Sando (the approach way) to the Ise shrine is spatially more important than the shrine itself. It crosses over the Isuzu – a river – and is bordered by sacred trees.

The roads of Hei-an-kyo were passages for nobles riding in their coaches, and for festival processions. The rows of wooden houses on both sides of the road were family dwellings, and the road acted as a connecting link binding the people to the structure of the city, the ceremonies, and the demonstrations of power. The road was also the show-window of the period. However, it would hardly be true to say that this road played the role of uplifting the individual lives of the citizens to a sense of urban community.

Koji (small passages), Fukoro-Koji (cul-de-sacs) of the Mishijin in Kyoto, which is called Unagi-no-Nedoko (the bed of eels), run through the Machiya (old streets bordered by stores and residential houses). While arteries usually make edges between one district and another, or one town and another, the Koji passages penetrate through the district or are inserted into the house blocks. The Machiya have a semi-open architectural form, with lattice doors and windows on the house fronts. On summer nights residents come out into the Koji, to cool off in the breeze which blows along the narrow space of this passage, and the family entertainments are visible through the lattice windows. While the major roads were places of ceremony and power, and demonstrations of prestige, the Koji (narrow passages) were the places of the citizen's life and the spaces which bound individual activities together.

Have passages like the Koji existed in the western world? The old Greek city of Miletus in Ionia was basically composed on a grid pattern, but it had two fundamental differences from the Oriental city. One was the placement of its community facilities. In the oriental city community facilities were placed along roads and the roads themselves performed a civic function and acted as the public space of the city. The ancient Greek city had an *Agora* which was a centripetal public open space in the centre of the city. The streets of the grid became colonnades around the Agora, architecturally linking it to the city. In the old city of Miletus this open space became the link which bound the life of the citizen to the political activity of the city.

The other fundamental difference was the spatial structure of the road and the relation of the road space to the architecture along it. The houses of Miletus were based on a courtyard plan, which has an inner court on to which each room of the house opens. The citizen's private life was well established in this habitation unit focusing on the inner court, but was closed off from the public street. A drainage ditch about one to two metres wide was set where the backs of the houses came together, but there was no road on which the life of the citizens could mingle and coexist. Here, already, a functional organization of spaces was established which is quite different from the dynamic oriental urban space in which many functions coexist.

When the feudal city developed in the West, the character of the open space changed from something for the citizen to a demonstration of power and religious ceremony. Therefore, the square took on an even more centripetal structure and the street pattern became transformed from a grid of free communication to radial lines leading into the central square. Later, as the life of the people developed and power moved from high authority to the citizens, the original city square was increased in size and numerous new squares were established.

It was a pleasant surprise to me to recognize in Pikionis' road in Europe the formation of a spatial road in place of the functional street.

The Meaning of the Road in a Modern City

Duplication of the functional uses of paths, streets, and highway leads to confused and low quality traffic. Improving traffic quality does not only mean widening streets to make automobile highways, but more importantly, coordinating the essential communication systems with the rational functions of the city.

The French firm of architects, Candilis, Woods, and Josic, devised some interesting solutions in their plan for the extension of Toulouse. In this plan the pedestrian promenades are designed as the infrastructure of the new city. These roads, which are called stems, form an urban structural line along which all community facilities are located. The automobile highway and the system of utility supply lines are on the city's fringe. One side of the residential areas touches the stem road and the other borders these environmental service lines. The significance of the project is that the environmental service road and the spatial stem road are definitely divided, and the human-use road has become the main shaft of the city structure (see Figures 3, 4, 5, pp. 388–91).

31. A City Is Not a Tree

CHRISTOPHER ALEXANDER

The tree of my title is not a green tree with leaves. It is the name for a pattern of thought. The semi-lattice is the name for another, more complex, pattern of thought.

In order to relate these abstract patterns to the nature of the city, I must first make a simple distinction. I want to call those cities which have arisen more or less spontaneously over many, many years *natural cities*. And I shall call those cities and parts of cities which have been deliberately created by designers and planners *artificial cities*. Siena, Liverpool, Kyoto, Manhattan are examples of natural cities. Levittown, Chandigarh, and the British New Towns are examples of artificial cities.

It is more and more widely recognized today that there is some essential ingredient missing from artificial cities. When compared with ancient cities that have acquired the patina of life, our modern attempts to create cities artificially are, from a human point of view, entirely unsuccessful.

Architects themselves admit more and more freely that they really like living in old buildings more than new ones. The non-art-loving public at large, instead of being grateful to architects for what they do, regards the onset of modern buildings and modern cities everywhere as an inevitable, rather sad piece of the larger fact that the world is going to the dogs.

It is much too easy to say that these opinions represent only people's unwillingness to forget the past, and their determination to be traditional. For myself, I trust this conservatism. Americans are usually willing to move with the times. Their growing reluctance to accept the modern city evidently expresses a longing for some real thing, something which for the moment escapes our grasp.

The prospect that we may be turning the world into a place

peopled only by little glass and concrete boxes has alarmed many architects too. To combat the glass-box future, many valiant protests and designs have been put forward, all hoping to recreate in modern form the various characteristics of the natural city which seem to give it life. But so far these designs have only remade the old. They have not been able to create the new.

'Outrage', the *Architectural Review*'s campaign against the way in which new construction and telegraph poles are wrecking the English town, based its remedies, essentially, on the idea that the spatial sequence of buildings and open spaces must be controlled if scale is to be preserved – an idea that really derives from Camillo Sitte's book about ancient squares and piazzas.

Another kind of remedy, in protest against the monotony of Levittown, tries to recapture the richness of shape found in the houses of a natural old town. Llewelyn Davies's village at Rushbrooke in England is an example – each cottage is slightly different from its neighbour, the roofs jut in and out at picturesque angles.

A third suggested remedy is to get high density back into the city. The idea seems to be that if the whole metropolis could only be like Grand Central Station, with lots and lots of layers and tunnels all over the place, and enough people milling around in them, maybe it would be human again.

Another very brilliant critic of the deadness which is everywhere is Jane Jacobs. Her criticisms are excellent. But when you read her concrete proposals for what we should do instead, you get the idea that she wants the great modern city to be a sort of mixture between Greenwich village and some Italian hill town, full of short blocks and people sitting in the street.

The problem these designers have tried to face is real. It is vital that we discover the property of old towns which gave them life and get it back into our own artificial cities. But we cannot do this merely by remaking English villages, Italian piazzas, and Grand Central Stations. Too many designers today seem to be yearning for the physical and plastic characteristics of the past, instead of searching for the abstract ordering principle which the towns of the past happened to have, and which our modern conceptions of the city have not yet found.

What is the inner nature, the ordering principle, which distinguishes the artificial city from the natural city?

You will have guessed from my title what I believe this ordering principle to be. I believe that a natural city has the organization of a semi-lattice; but that when we organize a city artificially, we organize it as a tree.

Both the tree and the semi-lattice are ways of thinking about how a large collection of many small systems goes to make up a large and complex system. More generally, they are both names for structures of sets.

In order to define such structures, let me first define the concept of a set. A set is a collection of elements which for some reason we think of as belonging together. Since, as designers, we are concerned with the physical living city and its physical backbone, we most naturally restrict ourselves to considering sets which are collections of material elements such as people, blades of grass, cars, bricks, molecules, houses, gardens, water pipes, the water molecules that run in them, etc.

When the elements of a set belong together because they cooperate or work together somehow, we call the set of elements a system.

For example, in Berkeley, at the corner of Hearst and Euclid, there is a drug store, and outside the drug store a traffic light. In the entrance to the drug store there is a newsrack where the day's papers are displayed. When the light is red, people who are waiting to cross the street stand idly by the light; and since they have nothing to do, they look at the papers displayed on the newsrack which they can see from where they stand. Some of them just read the headlines, others actually buy a paper while they wait.

This effect makes the newsrack and the traffic light interdependent; the newsrack, the newspapers on it, the money going from people's pockets to the dime slot, the people who stop at the light and read headlines, the traffic light, the electric impulses which make the lights change, and the sidewalk which the people stand on, form a system — they all work together.

From the designer's point of view, the physically unchanging part of this system is of special interest. The newsrack, the traffic light, and the sidewalk between them, related as they are, form the fixed part of the system. It is the unchanging receptacle in which the changing parts of the system – people, newspapers, money, and electrical impulses – can work together. I define this fixed part as a unit of the city. It derives its coherence as a unit both from the forces which hold its own elements together, and from the dynamic coherence of the larger living system which includes it as a fixed invariant part.

Of the many, many fixed concrete subsets of the city which are the receptacles for its systems, and can therefore be thought of as significant physical units, we usually single out a few for special consideration. In fact, I claim that whatever picture of the city someone has is defined precisely by the subsets he sees as units.

Now, a collection of subsets which goes to make up such a picture is not merely an amorphous collection. Automatically, merely because relationships are established among the subsets once the subsets are chosen, the collection has a definite structure.

To understand this structure, let us think abstractly for a moment, using numbers as symbols. Instead of talking about the real sets of millions of real particles which occur in the city, let us consider a simpler structure made of just half a dozen elements. Label these elements 1, 2, 3, 4, 5, 6. Not including the full set (1, 2, 3, 4, 5, 6), the empty set (−), and the one element sets (1), (2), (3), (4), (5), (6), there are fifty-six different subsets we can pick from six elements.

Suppose we now pick out certain of these fifty-six sets (just as we pick out certain sets and call them units when we form our picture of the city). Let us say, for example, that we pick the following subsets: (123), (34), (45), (234), (345), (12345), (3456).

What are the possible relationships among these sets? Some sets will be entirely part of larger sets, as (34) is part of (345) and (3456). Some of the sets will overlap, like (123) and (234). Some of the sets will be disjoint – that is, contain no elements in common, like (123) and (45).

We can see these relationships displayed in two ways. In diagram A (Figure 1) each set chosen to be a unit has a line drawn round it. In diagram B the chosen sets are arranged in order of ascending magnitude, so that whenever one set contains another (as (345) contains (34)), there is a vertical path leading from one to the other. For the sake of clarity and visual economy, it is usual to draw lines only between sets which have no further sets and lines between them; thus the line between (34) and (345), and the line between (345) and (3456), make it unnecessary to draw a line between (34) and (3456).

As we see from these two representations, the choice of subsets alone endows the collection of subsets as a whole with an overall structure. This is the structure which we are concerned with here. When the structure meets certain conditions it is called a semi-lattice. When it meets other more restrictive conditions, it is called a tree.

The semi-lattice axiom goes like this:

A collection of sets forms a semi-lattice if and only if, when two overlapping sets belong to the collection, then the set of elements common to both also belongs to the collection.

Figure 1. Diagrams A and B.   *Figure 2*. Diagrams C and D.

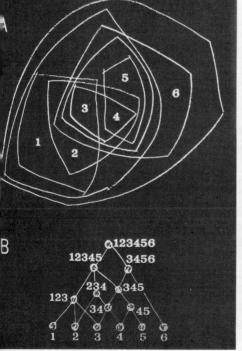
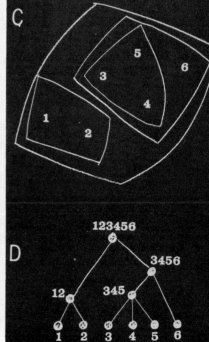

406 Shell: Priorities in Designing the Human Habitat

The structure illustrated in diagrams A and B is a semi-lattice. It satisfies the axiom since, for instance, (234) and (345) both belong to the collection and their common part, (34), also belongs to it. (As far as the city is concerned, this axiom states merely that wherever two units overlap, the area of overlap is itself a recognizable entity and hence a unit also. In the case of the drug store example, one unit consists of the newsrack, sidewalk, and traffic light. Another unit consists of the drug store itself, with its entry and the newsrack. The two units overlap in the newsrack. Clearly this area of overlap is itself a recognizable unit, and so satisfies the axiom above which defines the characteristics of a semi-lattice.)

The tree axiom states:

A collection of sets forms a tree if and only if, for any two sets that belong to the collection, either one is wholly contained in the other, or else are wholly disjoint.

The structure illustrated in diagrams C and D (Figure 2) is a tree. Since this axiom excludes the possibility of overlapping sets, there is no way in which the semi-lattice axiom can be violated, so that every tree is a trivially simple semi-lattice.

However, in this paper we are not so much concerned with the fact that a tree happens to be a semi-lattice, but with the difference between trees and those more general semi-lattices which are *not* trees because they *do* contain overlapping units. We are concerned with the difference between structures in which no overlap occurs, and those structures in which overlap does occur.

It is not merely the overlap which makes the distinction between the two important. Still more important is the fact that the semi-lattice is potentially a much more complex and subtle structure than a tree. We may see just how much more complex a semi-lattice can be than a tree in the following fact; a tree based on twenty elements can contain at most nineteen further subsets of the twenty, while a semi-lattice based on the same twenty elements can contain more than 1,000,000 different subsets.

This enormously greater variety is an index of the great structural complexity a semi-lattice can have when compared with the structural simplicity of a tree. It is this lack of structural complexity, characteristic of trees, which is crippling our conception of the city.

To demonstrate, let us look at some modern conceptions of the city, each of which I shall show to be essentially a tree. It will perhaps be useful, while we look at these plans, to have a little ditty in our minds:

> Big fleas have little fleas
> Upon their back to bite 'em,
> Little fleas have lesser fleas,
> And so ad infinitum.

This rhyme expresses perfectly and succinctly the structural principle of the tree.

Figure 3. Columbia, Maryland, Community Research and Development Inc.: Neighbourhoods, in clusters of five, form 'villages'. Transportation joins the villages into a new town. The organization is a tree.

Figure 4. Greenbelt, Maryland, Clarence Stein: This 'garden city' has been broken down into superblocks. Each superblock contains schools, parks, and a number of subsidiary groups of houses built around parking lots. The organization is a tree.

Figure 5. Greater London Plan (1943), Abercrombie and Forshaw: The drawing depicts the structure conceived by Abercrombie for London. It is made of a large number of communities, each sharply separated from all adjacent communities. Abercrombie writes, 'The proposal is to emphasize the identity of the existing communities, to increase their degree of segregation, and where necessary to reorganize them as separate and definite entities.' And again, 'The communities themselves consist of a series of sub-units, generally with their own shops and schools, corresponding to neighbourhood units.' The city is conceived as a tree with two principal levels. The communities are the larger units of the structure; the smaller sub-units are neighbourhoods. There are no overlapping units. The structure is a tree.

Figure 6. Mesa City, Paolo Soleri: The organic shapes of Mesa City lead us, at a careless glance, to believe that it is a richer structure than our more obviously rigid examples. But when we look at it in detail we find precisely the same principle of organization. Take, particularly, the university centre. Here we find the centre of the city

Figure 3. Columbia, Maryland.

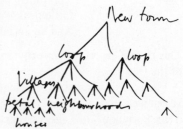

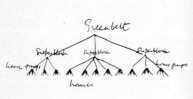

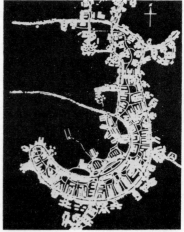

Figure 4. Greenbelt, Maryland.

divided into a university and a residential quarter, which is itself divided into a number of villages (actually apartment towers) for 4,000 inhabitants, each again subdivided further and surrounded by groups of still smaller dwelling units.

Figure 5. Greater London Plan (1943).

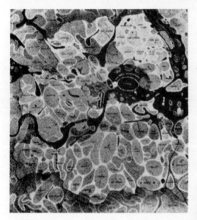

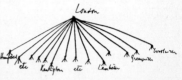

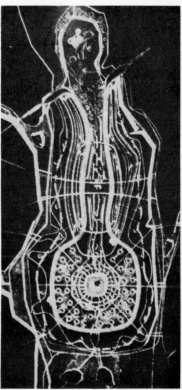

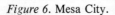

Figure 6. Mesa City.

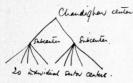

Figure 7. Chandigarh.

Figure 7. Chandigarh (1951) by Le Corbusier: The whole city is served by a commercial centre in the middle, linked to the administrative centre at the head. Two subsidiary, elongated, commercial cores are strung out along the major arterial roads, running north–south. Subsidiary to these are further administrative, community, and commercial centres, one for each of the city's twenty sectors.

Figures 8 and 9. The most beautiful example of all I have kept until last, because it symbolizes the problem perfectly. It appears in Hilbersheimer's book called *The Nature of Cities*. He describes the fact that certain Roman towns had their origin as military camps, and then shows a picture of a modern military encampment as a kind of archetypal form for the city. It is not possible to have a structure which is a clearer tree.

The symbol is apt, for, of course, the organization of the army was created precisely in order to create discipline and rigidity. When a city is endowed with a tree structure, this is what happens to the city and its people. The lower photo is Hilbersheimer's own scheme for the commercial area of a city based on the army camp archetype.

Figure 8. A modern military encampment.

Figure 9. Hilbersheimer's scheme for a city.

Each of these structures, then, is a tree. Each unit in each tree that I have described, moreover, is the fixed, unchanging residue of some system in the living city (just as a house is the residue of the interactions between the members of a family, their emotions, and their belongings; and a freeway is the residue of movement and commercial exchange).

However, in every city there are thousands, even millions, of times as many more systems at work whose physical residue does not appear as a unit in these tree structures. In the worst cases, the units which do appear fail to correspond to any living reality; and the real systems, whose existence actually makes the city live, have been provided with no physical receptacle.

Neither the Columbia plan nor the Stein plan, for example, corresponds to social realities. The physical layout of the plans, and the way they function, suggests a hierarchy of stronger and stronger closed social groups, ranging from the whole city down to the family, each formed by associational ties of different strength.

In a traditional society, if we ask a man to name his best friends and then ask each of these in turn to name their best friends, they will all name each other so that they form a closed group. A village is made of a number of separate closed groups of this kind.

But today's social structure is utterly different. If we ask a man to name his friends and then ask them in turn to name their friends, they will all name different people, very likely unknown to the first person; these people would again name others, and so on outwards. There are virtually no closed groups of people in modern society. The reality of today's social structure is thick with overlap – the systems of friends and acquaintances form a semi-lattice, not a tree (Figure 10).

In the natural city, even the house on a long street (not in some little cluster) is a more accurate acknowledgement of the fact that your friends live not next door, but far away, and can only be reached by bus or automobile. In this respect Manhattan has more overlap in it than Greenbelt. And though one can argue that in Greenbelt too, friends are only minutes away by car, one must then ask: Since certain groups *have* been emphasized by the physical units of the physical structure, why are just these the most irrelevant ones?

In the second part of this paper, I shall now demonstrate why the

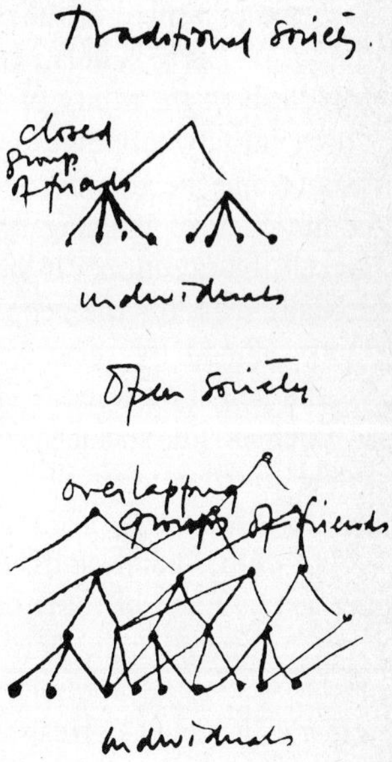

Figure 10. Grouping of friends.

living city cannot be properly contained in a receptacle which is a tree — that indeed, its very life stems from the fact that it is not a tree.

In simplicity of structure the tree is comparable to the compulsive desire for neatness and order that insists the candlesticks on a mantelpiece be perfectly straight and perfectly symmetrical about the centre. The semi-lattice, by comparison, is the structure of a complex fabric; it is the structure of living things; of great paintings and symphonies.

It must be emphasized, lest the orderly mind shrink in horror from anything that is not clearly articulated and categorized in tree form, that the idea of overlap, ambiguity, multiplicity of aspect, and the semi-lattice, are not less orderly than the rigid tree, but more so. They represent a thicker, tougher, more subtle and more complex view of structure.

Let us now look at the ways in which the natural, when unconstrained by artificial conceptions, shows itself to be a semi-lattice.

A major aspect of the city's social structure which a tree can never mirror properly is illustrated by Ruth Glass's redevelopment plan for Middlesbrough, a city of 200,000 which she recommends be broken down into twenty-nine separate neighbourhoods. After picking her twenty-nine neighbourhoods by determining where the sharpest discontinuities of building type, income, and job type occur, she asks herself the question: 'If we examine some of the social systems which actually exist for the people in such a neighbourhood, do the physical units defined by these various social systems all define the same spatial neighbourhood?' Her own answer to this question is *no*.

Each of the social systems she examines is a nodal system. It is made of some sort of central node, plus the people who use this centre. Specifically she takes elementary schools, secondary schools, youth clubs, adult clubs, post offices, greengrocers, and grocers selling sugar. Each of these centres draws its users from a certain spatial area or spatial unit. This spatial unit is the physical residue of the social system as a whole, and is therefore a unit in the terms of this paper. The units corresponding to different kinds of centres for the single neighbourhood of Waterloo Road are shown in Figure 11.

The hard outline is the boundary of the so-called neighbourhood itself. The white circle stands for the youth club, and the small solid rings stand for areas where its members live. The ringed spot is the adult club, and the homes of its members form the unit marked by dashed boundaries. The white square is the post office and the dotted line marks the unit which contains its users. The secondary school is marked by the spot with a white triangle in it. Together with its pupils, it forms the system marked by the dot-dashed line.

As you can see at once, the different units do not coincide. Yet neither are they disjoint. They overlap.

We cannot get an adequate picture of what Middlesbrough is, or of what it ought to be, in terms of twenty-nine large and conveniently integral chunks called neighbourhoods. When we describe the city in terms of neighbourhoods, we implicitly assume that the smaller elements within any one of these neighbourhoods belong together so tightly that they only interact with elements in other neighbourhoods through the medium of the neighbourhood to which they themselves belong. Ruth Glass herself shows clearly that this is not the case.

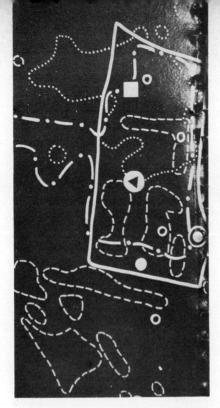

Figure 11. Middlesbrough,
Waterloo Road neighbourhood.

Below are two pictures of the Waterloo neighbourhood. For the sake of argument I have broken it into a number of small areas. Figure 12 shows how these pieces stick together in fact, and Figure 13 shows how the redevelopment plan pretends they stick together.

There is nothing in the nature of the various centres which says

Figures 12 and 13. Areas in the Waterloo Road neighbourhood.

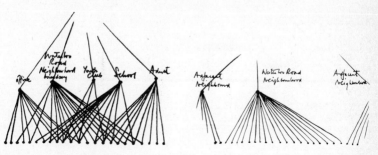

that their catchment areas should be the same. Their natures are different. Therefore the units they define are different. The natural city of Middlesbrough was faithful to the semi-lattice structure they have. Only in the artificial tree conception of the city are their natural, proper, and necessary overlaps destroyed.

Take the separation of pedestrians from moving vehicles, a tree concept proposed by Le Corbusier, Louis Kahn, and many others. At a very crude level of thought this is obviously a good idea. It is dangerous to have 60-mile-an-hour cars in contact with little children toddling. But it is not *always* a good idea. There are times when the ecology of a situation actually demands the opposite. Imagine yourself coming out of a Fifth Avenue store; you have been shopping all afternoon; your arms are full of parcels; you need a drink; your wife is limping. Thank God for taxis.

Yet the urban taxi can function only because pedestrians and vehicles are not strictly separated. The prowling taxi needs a fast stream of traffic so that it can cover a large area to be sure of finding a passenger. The pedestrian needs to be able to hail the taxi from any point in the pedestrian world, and to be able to get out to any part of the pedestrian world to which he wants to go. The system which contains the taxicabs needs to overlap both the fast vehicular traffic system and the system of pedestrian circulation. In Manhattan pedestrians and vehicles do share certain parts of the city, and the necessary overlap is guaranteed (Figure 14).

Another favourite concept of the C.I.A.M. theorists and others is the separation of recreation from everything else. This has crystallized in our real cities in the form of playgrounds. The playground, asphalted and fenced in, is nothing but a pictorial acknowledgement

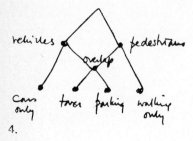

Figure 14. Pedestrians and vehicles in Manhattan.

of the fact that 'play' exists as an isolated concept in our minds. It has nothing to do with the life of play itself. Few self-respecting children will even play in a playground.

Play itself, the play that children practise, goes on somewhere different every day. One day it may be indoors, another day in a friendly gas station, another day down by the river, another day in a derelict building, another day on a construction site which has been abandoned for the weekend. Each of these play activities, and the objects it requires, forms a system. It is not true that these systems exist in isolation, cut off from the other systems in the city. The different systems overlap one another, and they overlap many other systems besides. The units, the physical places recognized as play places, must do the same.

In a natural city this is what happens. Play takes place in a thousand places – it fills the interstices of adult life. As they play, children become full of their surroundings. How can a child become filled with his surroundings in a fenced enclosure? He cannot.

The Isolated Campus

A similar kind of mistake occurs in trees like that of Goodman's Communitas, or Soleri's Mesa City, which separate the university from the rest of the city. Again, this has actually been realized in the common American form of the isolated campus.

What is the reason for drawing a line in the city so that everything within the boundary is university, and everything outside is non-university? It is conceptually clear. But does it correspond to the realities of university life? Certainly it is not the structure which occurs in non-artificial university cities.

Take Cambridge University, for instance. At certain points Trinity Street is physically almost indistinguishable from Trinity College. One pedestrian crossover in the street is literally part of the college. The buildings on the street, though they contain stores and coffee shops and banks at ground level, contain undergraduates' rooms in their upper stories. In many cases the actual fabric of the street buildings melts into the fabric of the old college buildings so that one cannot be altered without the other.

There will always be many systems of activity where university life and city life overlap: pub-crawling, coffee-drinking, the movies, walking from place to place. In some cases whole departments may be actively involved in the life of the city's inhabitants (the hospital-cum-medical school is an example). In Cambridge, a natural city where university and city have grown together gradually, the physical units overlap because they are the physical residues of city systems and university systems which overlap (Figure 15).

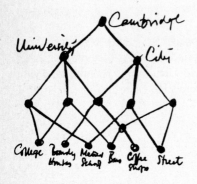

Figure 15. Cambridge University.

Let us look next at the hierarchy of urban cores, realized in Brasilia, Chandigarh, the M.A.R.S. plan for London, and, most recently, in the Manhattan Lincoln Center, where various performing arts serving the population of greater New York have been gathered together to form just one core.

Does a concert hall ask to be next to an opera house? Can the two feed on one another? Will anybody ever visit them both, gluttonously, in a single evening, or even buy tickets from one after going to a concert in the other? In Vienna, London, Paris, each of the performing arts has found its own place, because all are not mixed randomly. Each has created its own familiar section of the city. In Manhattan itself, Carnegie Hall and the Metropolitan Opera House were not built side by side. Each found its own place, and now creates its own atmosphere. The influence of each overlaps the parts of the city which have been made unique to it.

The only reason that these functions have all been brought together in the Lincoln Center is that the concept of performing art links them to one another.

But this tree, and the idea of a single hierarchy of urban cores which is its parent, do not illuminate the relations between art and city life. They are merely born of the mania every simple-minded person has for putting things with the same name into the same basket.

The total separation of work from housing, started by Tony Garnier in his industrial city, then incorporated in the 1929 Athens Charter, is now found in every artificial city and accepted everywhere where zoning is enforced. Is this a sound principle? It is easy to see how bad conditions at the beginning of the century prompted planners to try to get the dirty factories out of residential areas. But the separation misses a variety of systems which require, for their sustenance, little parts of both.

Jane Jacobs describes the growth of backyard industries in Brooklyn. A man who wants to start a small business needs space, which he is very likely to have in his own backyard. He also needs to establish connections with larger going enterprises and with their customers. This means that the system of backyard industry needs to belong both to the residential zone, and to the industrial zone – these zones need to overlap. In Brooklyn they do (Figure 16). In a city which is a tree, they can't.

Finally, let us examine the subdivision of the city into isolated

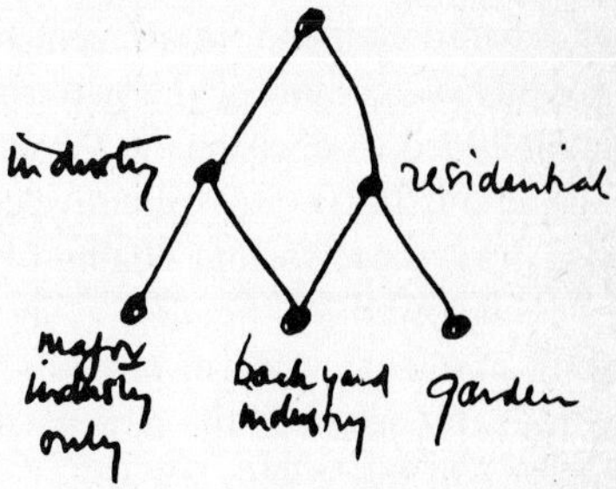

Figure 16. Backyard industries in Brooklyn.

communities. As we have seen in the Abercrombie plan for London, this is itself a tree structure. The individual community in a greater city has no reality as a functioning unit. In London, as in any great city, almost no one manages to find work which suits him near his home. People in one community work in a factory which is very likely to be in another community.

There are, therefore, many hundreds of thousands of worker–workplace systems, each consisting of a man plus the factory he works in, which cut across the boundaries defined by Abercrombie's tree. The existence of these units, and their overlapping nature, indicates that the living systems of London form a semi-lattice. Only in the planner's mind has it become a tree.

The fact that we have so far failed to give this any physical expression has a vital consequence. As things are, whenever the worker and his workplace belong to separately administered municipalities, the community which contains the workplace collects huge taxes and has relatively little on which to spend the tax revenue. The community where the worker lives, if it is mainly residential, collects only little in the way of taxes, and yet has great additional burdens on its purse in the shape of schools, hospitals, etc. Clearly, to resolve this inequity, the worker–workplace systems must be anchored in physically recognizable units of the city which can then be taxed.

It might be argued that, even though the individual communities of a great city have no functional significance in the lives of their inhabitants, they are still the most convenient administrative units, and should, therefore, be left in their present tree organization.

However, in the political complexity of a modern city, even this is suspect.

Edward Banfield, in a recent book called *Political Influence*, gives a detailed account of the patterns of influence and control that have actually led to decisions in Chicago. He shows that although the lines of administrative and executive control have a formal structure which is a tree, these formal chains of influence and authority are entirely overshadowed by the *ad hoc* lines of control which arise naturally as each new city problem presents itself. These *ad hoc* lines depend on who is interested in the matter, who has what at stake, who has what favours to trade with whom.

This second structure, which is informal, working within the framework of the first, is what really controls public action. It varies from week to week, even from hour to hour, as one problem replaces another. Nobody's sphere of influence is entirely under the control of any one superior; each person is under different influences as the problems change. Although the organization chart in the mayor's office is a tree, the actual control and exercise of authority is semi-lattice-like.

Trapped in a Tree

Now, why is it that so many designers have conceived cities as trees when the natural structure is in every case a semi-lattice? Have they done so deliberately, in the belief that a tree structure will serve the people of the city better? Or have they done it because they cannot help it, because they are trapped by a mental habit, perhaps even trapped by the way the mind works; because they cannot encompass the complexity of a semi-lattice in any convenient mental form; because the mind has an overwhelming predisposition to see trees wherever it looks and cannot escape the tree conception?

I shall try to convince you that it is for this second reason that trees are being proposed and built as cities because designers, limited as they must be by the capacity of the mind to form intuitively accessible structures, cannot achieve the complexity of the semi-lattice in a single mental act.

Let me begin with an example.

Suppose I ask you to remember the following four objects: an orange, a watermelon, a football, and a tennis ball. How will you keep them in your mind, in your mind's eyes? However you do it, you will do it by grouping them. Some of you will take the two fruits together, the orange and the watermelon, and the two sports balls together, the football and the tennis ball. Those of you who tend to think in terms of physical shape, may group them differently, taking the two small spheres together – the orange and the tennis ball and the two larger and more egg-shaped objects – the watermelon and the football. Some of you will be aware of both.

Let us make a diagram of these groupings (Figure 17).

Either grouping taken by itself is a tree structure. The two together are a semi-lattice. Now let us try and visualize these groupings in the mind's eye. I think you will find that you cannot visualize all four sets simultaneously — because they overlap. You can visualize one pair of sets and then the other, and you can alternate between the two pairs extremely fast, so fast that you may deceive yourself into thinking you can visualize them all together. But in truth, you cannot conceive all four sets at once in a single mental act. You cannot bring

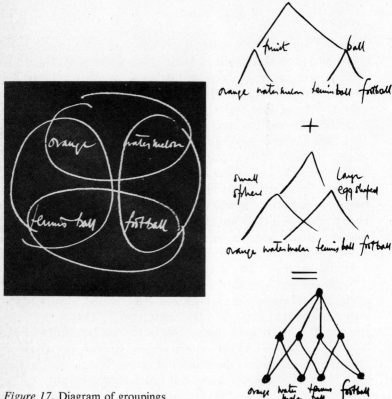

Figure 17. Diagram of groupings.

the semi-lattice structure into a visualizable form for a single mental act. In a single mental act you can only visualize a tree.

This is the problem we face as designers. While we are not, perhaps, necessarily occupied with the problem of total visualization in a single mental act, the principle is still the same. The tree is accessible mentally, and easy to deal with. The semi-lattice is hard to keep before the mind's eye, and therefore hard to deal with.

It is known today that grouping and categorization are among the most primitive psychological processes. Modern psychology treats thought as a process of fitting new situations into existing slots and pigeon-holes in the mind. Just as you cannot put a physical thing into more than one physical pigeon-hole at once, so, by analogy, the processes of thought prevent you from putting a mental construct into more than one mental category at once. Study of the origin of these processes suggests that they stem essentially from the organism's need to reduce the complexity of its environment by establishing barriers between the different events which it encounters.

It is for this reason — because the mind's first function is to reduce the ambiguity and overlap in a confusing situation, and because, to this end, it is endowed with a basic intolerance for ambiguity — that structures like the city, which do require overlapping sets within them, are nevertheless persistently conceived as trees.

The same rigidity dogs even the perception of physical patterns. In experiments by Huggins and myself at Harvard, we showed people patterns whose internal units overlapped, and found that they almost always invented a way of seeing the patterns as a tree — even when the semi-lattice view of the patterns would have helped them perform the task of experimentation which was before them.

The most startling proof that people tend to conceive even physical patterns as trees is found in some experiments of Sir Frederick Bartlett. He showed people a pattern for about a quarter of a second and then asked them to draw what they had seen. Many people, unable to grasp the full complexity of the pattern they had seen, simplified the patterns by cutting out the overlap. In Figure 18, the original is shown at the top, with two fairly typical redrawn versions below it. In the redrawn versions the circles are separated from the rest; the overlap between triangles and circles disappear.

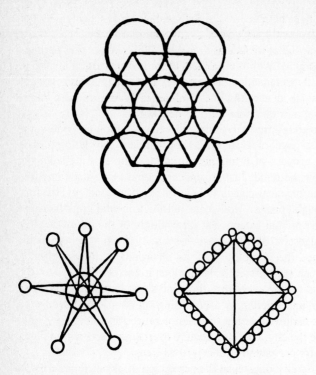

Figure 18. Bartlett experiment.

These experiments suggest strongly that people have an underlying tendency, when faced by a complex organization, to reorganize it mentally in terms of non-overlapping units. The complexity of the semi-lattice is replaced by the simpler and more easily grasped tree form.

You are no doubt wondering, by now, what a city looks like which is a semi-lattice, but not a tree. I must confess that I cannot yet show you plans or sketches. It is not enough merely to make a demonstration of overlap – the overlap must be the right overlap. This is doubly important, because it is so tempting to make plans in which overlap occurs for its own sake. This is essentially what the high density 'life-filled' city plans of recent years do. But overlap alone does not give structure. It can also give chaos. A garbage can is full of overlap. To have structure, you must have the right overlap, and this is for us almost certainly different from the old overlap which we observe in historic cities. As the relationships between functions change, so the systems which need to overlap in order to receive these relationships must also change. The recreation of old kinds of overlap will be inappropriate, and chaotic instead of structured.

The work of trying to understand just what overlap the modern city requires, and trying to put this required overlap into physical and plastic terms, is still going on. Until the work is complete, there is no point in presenting facile sketches of ill thought out structure.

Overlapping Triangles

However, I can perhaps make the physical consequences of overlap more comprehensible by means of an image. The painting illustrated (Figure 19) is a work by Simon Nicholson. The fascination of this

Figure 19. A painting by Simon Nicholson.

painting lies in the fact that although constructed of rather few simple triangular elements, these elements unite in many different ways to form the larger units of the painting – in such a way indeed, that if we make a complete inventory of the perceived units in the painting, we find that each triangle enters into four or five completely different kinds of unit, none contained in the others, yet all overlapping in that triangle.

Thus, if we number the triangles and pick out the sets of triangles which appear as strong visual units, we get the semi-lattice shown in Figure 20.

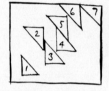

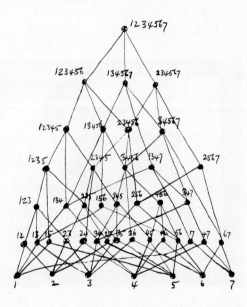

Figure 20. Semi-lattice formed by selection of triangles in Figure 19.

3 and 5 form a unit because they work together as a rectangle; 2 and 4 because they form a parallelogram; 5 and 6 because they are both dark and pointing the same way; 6 and 7 because one is the ghost of the other shifted sideways; 4 and 7 because they are symmetrical with one another; 4 and 6 because they form another rectangle; 4 and 5 because they form a sort of Z; 2 and 3 because they form a rather thinner kind of Z; 1 and 7 because they are at opposite corners; 1 and 2 because they are a rectangle; 3 and 4 because they point the same way as 5 and 6, and form a sort of off-centre reflection; 3 and 6 because they enclose 4 and 5; 1 and 5 because they enclose 2, 3, and 4. I have only listed the units of two triangles. The larger units are even more complex. The white is more complex still, and is not even included in the diagram because it is harder to be sure of its elementary pieces.

The painting is significant, not so much because it has overlap in it (many paintings have overlap in them), but rather because this painting has nothing else in it except overlap. It is only the fact of the overlap, and the resulting multiplicity of aspects which the forms present, that makes the painting fascinating. It seems almost as though the painter had made an explicit attempt, as I have done, to single out overlap as a vital generator of structure.

All the artificial cities I have described have the structure of a tree rather than the semi-lattice structure of the Nicholson painting. Yet it is the painting, and other images like it, which must be our vehicles for thought. And when we wish to be precise, the semi-lattice, being part of a large branch of modern mathematics, is a powerful way of exploring the structure of these images. It is the semi-lattice we must look for, not the tree.

When we think in terms of trees we are trading the humanity and richness of the living city for a conceptual simplicity which benefits only designers, planners, administrators, and developers. Every time a piece of a city is torn out, and a tree made to replace the semi-lattice that was there before, the city takes a further step towards dissociation.

In any organized object, extreme compartmentalization and the dissociation of internal elements are the first signs of coming destruction. In a society, dissociation is anarchy. In a person, dissociation is the mark of schizophrenia and impending suicide. An ominous example of city-wide dissociation is the separation of retired people from the rest of urban life, caused by the growth of desert cities for the old like Sun City, Arizona. This separation is only possible under the influence of tree-like thought.

It not only takes from the young the company of those who have lived long, but worse, it causes the same rift inside each individual life. As you will pass into Sun City, and into old age, your ties with your own past will be unacknowledged, lost, and therefore, broken. Your youth will no longer be alive in your old age – the two will be dissociated, your own life will be cut in two.

For the human mind, the tree is the easiest vehicle for complex thoughts. But the city is not, cannot, and must not be a tree. The city is a receptacle for life. If the receptacle severs the overlap of the strands of life within it, because it is a tree, it will be like a bowl full of razor blades on edge, ready to cut up whatever is entrusted to it. In such a receptacle life will be cut to pieces. If we make cities which are trees, they will cut our life within to pieces.

Part Five. Networks: Prospects for
Transportation and Communication

Introduction

One can foresee two alternative prospects for transportation and communication. One is that the growth of transportation will paradoxically destroy man's freedom of movement outside his dwelling, and that the growth of communications will destroy his freedom of thought within it. The alternative is that transportation may open up vastly greater accessibility for every man to everywhere, and that communications may vastly increase his accessibility to ideas. Current trends show unmistakable drifts towards the first alternative. Only a much wider recognition of the situation and an increased willingness to implement the results of careful planning can turn the tide in the direction of the second.

'The world must not bungle into the space age,' says Fritz Zwicky (Professor of Astrophysics) – as it bungled into the systems of transportation and communications networks that link the parts of a megalopolis together, and tie one megalopolis to another.

The first four parts of this book – Nature, Man, Society, and Shell – have been dominated by two extreme needs: the need for global planning to accommodate megalopolises within the natural systems, and the need for local community planning to accommodate man's desires for human identity and personal expression. The basic purpose of transportation and communication networks is to create a matrix of interconnections that can relate the individual man with a planetary society – ecumenopolis. The ekistic approach cannot tolerate considerations of short-term, cost-benefit efficiencies as the most important criteria for judging the value of a system of transportation or communication. Although it may be shown that a certain design of highway may carry the largest number of cars at the lowest cost, and that a certain communications channel, which can easily be received on cheap devices, may attract the largest audience, both may prove to be counterproductive in terms of building up an ekistic synthesis between nature, man, society, shell, and networks. In other words, both may mitigate against the development of a healthy equilibrium between man and his total environment.

Most people have by now become well aware that the intrusions of transportation may have harmful effects, especially at the two extremes of population pressure: natural parks and city centres. But very few people yet comprehend the interlocking effects of communications intrusions. The development of different means of transportation has proceeded relatively slowly from cart to train, from car to plane, but the development of communications systems is much more rapid and their effect much more subtle. Telegraph, telephone, radio, and TV are by no means the whole of the story. Automation with its numerous control devices is already with us and, as can be seen from Hasan Ozbekhan's timetable (Figure 1), we have little time to prepare for a tremendous range of new developments.[1]

This section begins by looking at some of the prospects of transportation – the major single cause of the rise of megalopolis – and ends with a brief discussion of some of the potentialities of communications.

Transportation

Transportation networks not only serve as the means of holding megalopolis together, but they are also the most powerful form-givers of systems of land use, such as systems of parks and open spaces, schools, etc.

Abstracts from two large-scale plans for adjacent areas in the United States are included to illustrate methods of formulating alternative physical plans and assessing them in terms of various criteria. In both cases maximum accessibility between the major urban components of a growing megalopolitan area provided a major criterion. The total area of each plan contained several million people with individual urban units of under half a million. Each plan considered long range time spans: the North East Illinois plan dealt with a predicted population of 9,000,000 by 1990 and the Detroit Area plan with an estimated population of 15,000,000 by 2000.

Each plan was a team study, but the two teams chose quite different methods of establishing and evaluating their criteria. The North East Illinois plan – based on Chicago – determined its alternatives by setting up a number of different patterns of the physical relations of residences, places of daily activity, and places for occasional specialized needs. These patterns were then evaluated in terms of a set of ten community 'goals', which could have quite different priorities. Members of the communities were involved in selecting the patterns that would best meet their own goal priorities ten years hence. The Detroit Area plan was based on the IDEA method, by which the alternatives were derived from a matrix in which five major location-based functions (central business districts, airports, etc.) were related to a set of criteria based on those aspects of the five ekistic elements that were considered directly relevant to the project. Decisions were then taken regarding the amount of interconnection that could be expected between the five functions and their time/cost accessibility was studied from the different residential areas on the basis of several alternative transportation networks. Although the IDEA technique does not directly incorporate public participation, it allows for backtracking and re-evaluation at any stage in the light of later information or unexpected developments, and this could include the results of a community poll, etc. Thus, the different techniques employed in the two plan proposals are not necessarily mutually exclusive, and they are presented here as examples of the kind of studies that will become more and more frequent (and more and more sophisticated) in the near future; as well as an indication that it is not difficult for the

Figure 1 (over). Function and projected applications chart. The applications map shows how the ability of computers and their software to tackle new problems (left-hand column) will lead to new areas of application (second column) with far-reaching results (third column). The flow diagram at the top left of the map illustrates how speed and cost improvements are bringing more sophistication to process. Mechanization and situation interpretation – the two lines along which process control, the basic function of computers, is developing.

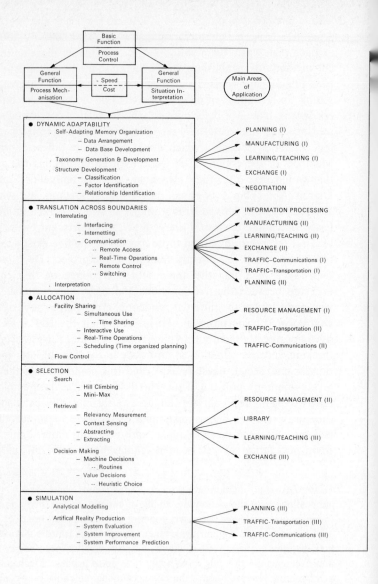

Basic
Function

Process
Control

General
Function

Process Mech-
anisation

Speed
Cost

General
Function

Situation In-
terpretation

Main Areas
of
Application

● DYNAMIC ADAPTABILITY
  . Self-Adapting Memory Organization
    − Data Arrangement
    − Data Base Development
  . Taxonomy Generation & Development
  . Structure Development
    − Classification
    − Factor Identification
    − Relationship Identification

PLANNING (I)

MANUFACTURING (I)

LEARNING/TEACHING (I)

EXCHANGE (I)

NEGOTIATION

● TRANSLATION ACROSS BOUNDARIES
  . Interrelating
    − Interfacing
    − Internetting
    − Communication
      -- Remote Access
      -- Real-Time Operations
      -- Remote Control
      -- Switching
  . Interpretation

INFORMATION PROCESSING

MANUFACTURING (II)

LEARNING/TEACHING (II)

EXCHANGE (II)

TRAFFIC−Communications (I)

TRAFFIC−Transportation (I)

PLANNING (II)

● ALLOCATION
  . Facility Sharing
    − Simultaneous Use
      -- Time Sharing
    − Interactive Use
    − Real-Time Operations
    − Scheduling (Time organized planning)
  . Flow Control

RESOURCE MANAGEMENT (I)

TRAFFIC−Transportation (II)

TRAFFIC-Communications (II)

● SELECTION
  . Search
    − Hill Climbing
    − Mini-Max
  . Retrieval
    − Relevancy Mesurement
    − Context Sensing
    − Abstracting
    − Extracting
  . Decision Making
    − Machine Decisions
      -- Routines
    − Value Decisions
      -- Heuristic Choice

RESOURCE MANAGEMENT (II)

LIBRARY

LEARNING/TEACHING (III)

EXCHANGE (III)

● SIMULATION
  . Analytical Modelling
  . Artifical Reality Production
    − System Evaluation
    − System Improvement
    − System Performance Prediction

PLANNING (III)

TRAFFIC-Transportation (III)

TRAFFIC-Communications (III)

	Main Expected Outcomes	Time-Horizon Date of Fruition of Outcomes	Probable Obstacles

PLANNING
. Long-range problem solving in all areas of application (I) — 1980–2000
. Aids for sensing and understanding environments (II)
. Feasibility testing of long-range goals (III) — 1975–80

—Problems of representation of meaning in mechanically interpretable forms

MANUFACTURING
. Replacement of sensory control of worker by more sensitive electro-mechanical devices (I) — 1966–
. Self-adaptive inventory, production and organization control (I) — 1975–80
. Multi- or general-purpose, regional (then global) interlinked tools (II) — Unlikely
. Robots - for production and services (I) — 1970–85

—Transportation costs high unit process costs declining

EXCHANGE
. General transaction facilitation and handling using new unit values (I) — 1990–2000
. Credit systems, invoice paying, purchasing, international business transactions, particularly at commercial level (II) — 1975–80
. Automated marketing through home terminals and touch-tone telephone systems (III) — 1975–80

—Cost of delivery of purchases Communication costs vs. increased leisure

NEGOTIATION
. Bargaining : automation of the search for meanings and of the determination of real issues in dispute — 1975–85
. Real issue identification and conflict identification — 1975–85

—Mechanical extraction of meaning from unstructured information

INFORMATION PROCESSING
. All areas of application — 1980–95
. Computer/information 'utility' - interlinked Data Banks
. Automation of office and institutional data handling — 1970–75
. Automated diagnostics (medical, social, mechanical, etc.) — 1980–90

—'Computer' utility unlikely as processor costs declining much faster than communication costs; also social problems of privacy

LEARNING/TEACHING
. Regional and/or global educational centres accessible through home terminals (II) — 1985–
. Substantive curriculum development (III) — 1975–80
. Generalized computer assisted instruction (I and III) — 1970–75
. Man-computer symbiosis (I, II and III) — 1985–
. Knowledge development — 1985–

—Global or large regional centres unlikely because of high communication costs vs. low processor costs

—Problems of representation

TRAFFIC-COMMUNICATIONS
. Transmission of all communications (I) — Ongoing
. High-speed message switching and handling utility (II) — 1990–
. Off-line experimentation and testing of networks (III) — 1960–75

—Installation of all-digital communication network

RESOURCE MANAGEMENT
. Complex scheduling systems (I) — 1970–80
. Optimal benefit resource application decisions (II) — 1980–2000

TRAFFIC-TRANSPORTATION
. Mass Rapid Transit (I) — 1975–85
. Air Traffic Control (II) — 1970–80
. Integrated traffic system problem solving development (III) — 1975–80

—High-speed physical object switching

LIBRARY
. Home access and retrieval (reproducing copy) — 1985–
. Text abstracting and reproduction — 1975–80
. Question answering — 1975–80
. Automatic bibliography generation — 1970–75

—Communication costs vs. printing costs

—Mechanical interpretation of questions to extract meaning

needs of the individual to be taken into account in such computerized programs, provided there is strong insistence that they should be incorporated.

Donald Janelle, working in the same geographic area as these two plans, describes how transportation innovations have changed space/time relationships within the region. His researches show that the primacy of the main centre (in this case Detroit) has been consistently reinforced with the introduction of each new transportation facility. It is quite reasonable for centrality to increase as the population grows from an ekistic community Class V (around 50,000) to Class VIII (around 2,000,000), but once growth moves beyond the metropolitan scale towards the conurbation and the megalopolis, increased centralization can only lead to disaster. The traffic overload makes a single centre intolerable. This is not a question of private car versus mass transit, it is a matter of the total overload. Yet, as Janelle indicates, the introduction of advanced systems of transportation are more than likely to produce a concentration on a single centre unless there are very strong countervailing policies. A number of proposals have repeatedly been put forward in many parts of the world – particularly England and France – for the creation of new very large centres of attraction within existing megalopolitan orbits. Such large-scale new centres have been called 'counter-magnets', 'parallel cities', and 'growth poles', and have also been proposed for developing countries. Their creation in India was strongly advocated by Catherine Bauer Wurster[2] and was elaborated in connection with the plan for the region of Calcutta by Professor Leo Jakobson and Ved Prakash.[3]

All future urban concentrations will be increasingly affected not only by mechanical transportation but by the communications media. Buckminster Fuller has often pointed out that already, everywhere in the world, man is being bombarded by a multitude of messages coming at him through the air from all directions. He has only to have the means to tune in on them. With appropriate receivers and transmitters an information centre can be established absolutely anywhere. It is not tied to a nodal population as is transportation.

Communications

Professor Jean Gottmann, who had the vision to recognize and describe the advent of megalopolis prior to 1960, notes that the traditional central city is now disappearing. The new kinds of urban centres that he sees developing have three principal components: ready accessibility to other centres of all kinds, availability of 'diverse, accurate, and up-to-date information', and an environment in which the ordinary man can find 'glamour and amenities'. These components are very different from those of former times when the emphasis has been laid on manufacturing and marketing potentials. Once we accept this new approach, we find that, as Gottmann suggests, the new 'transactional' urban centres will very likely locate in the same kind of places now found attractive by tourists and students.

Despite the obvious benefits of increased powers of communication, there is an obverse side to the coin. This appears to some extent in an extract from the discussions at Delos Four. In these discussions, it is stated that although we now receive world news in an instant of time, and we thus have increasingly close contact with world affairs, we have less contact than before with the people who live around us. The constant rush of new information means that we have little time to process it or to digest it, and – as was stated by Dr Brohi, a Pakistani philosopher – 'Our response to remote events drains off emotions energy, and there is none left for face-to-face communications.'

The transistor radio and TV have brought world news and world personalities into almost every living-room. However, for most people, news of local matters over which they can exercise direct control is of much greater importance. Yet this is being increasingly displaced. One of the major questions at Delos Four was how improved communications can be employed to enhance human contacts. This is not just a matter of increasing the quantity of these contacts, but their quality. For example, while we find that a colourful TV personality immediately becomes in great demand as a local lecturer, and that the jukebox creates a demand for local performances by the bands whose music is played, what local talent are these regional, national, or international figures displacing? What is happening to local songs, dances, art, or theatre? Is man being increasingly turned away from personal creativity in favour of passive reception, or are new forms of creative participation being opened up by the new media? Both Buckminster Fuller and Marshall McLuhan hint at possibilities of the latter: the tremendous developments that have become possible as a result of a better understanding and organization of our mental powers of learning, storage, and feedback.

NOTES

1. Hasan Ozbekhan, 'The Future of Automation', *Science Journal*, October 1967; *Ekistics* 142, p. 243.

2. Catherine Bauer Wurster, 'The Optimum Pattern of Urbanization', *International Review of Community Development*, 7 November 1961, pp. 197–213; *Ekistics* 76, pp. 85–9.

3. Leo Jakobson and Ved Prakash, 'Urbanization and Regional Planning in India', *Urban Affairs Quarterly*, Vol. II, No. 3, March 1967, pp. 36–65; *Ekistics* 148, pp. 158–65.

32. The Plan Study: Methodology

NORTHEASTERN ILLINOIS PLANNING COMMISSION

The Northeastern Illinois Area contains one of the largest and most complex urban concentrations in the world. In 1965 its six counties contained an estimated 6,689,000 persons, living principally in 250 municipalities and governed by 1,200 independent bodies. The area is expected to grow to more than 9,000,000 people by 1990.

Methodology of the Study

The Northeastern Illinois Planning Commission prepared this methodology for a comprehensive plan of development, including transportation, to the year 2015. Figure 1 is a flow chart of the comprehensive planning process utilized by the Plan Study.

Variable Factors of Urban Form and Structure

The first variable was a reflection of the distribution of various land uses in space. It was represented by a scale which ranged from extreme dispersion to extreme concentration.

The second variable was a reflection of the movement of people, goods, and messages within the urban area; it was addressed to the question: At what physical scale can (or should) a significant degree of integration take place among the various specialized activities and functions of a regional complex? This variable was represented by an axis which ranged from a metropolitan super city, 'a single system with highly differentiated and interdependent parts', to a group of small urban communities, 'each providing for most of the ordinary

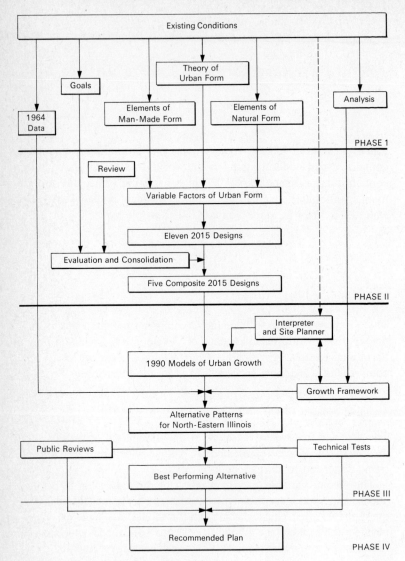

Figure 1. Flow chart of the plan study.

economic needs of an approximate cross section of the urban population'.[1]

For the sake of simplification the first variable was limited to residential land uses, and the second variable encompassed recreational and cultural trips only. A third axis was introduced to represent the distribution of daytime activities (for example, major employment centres). This latter variable reflected certain concepts of Melvin M. Webber,[2] and was represented by an axis which ranged from extreme centralization of daytime activities to extreme sub-focalization. Furthermore, this new axis dealt with the home-to-work trips. Thus, it contained elements from both of the first two axes.

Residential Concentration-Dispersion

This axis represented the degree of concentration or dispersion of residential uses. Three points were chosen on this axis to sample the complete range of feasible residential concentration-dispersion in Northeastern Illinois. Residential density and density distribution were the basic measures of the above three points. The categories of chosen residential concentration-dispersion were:

1. *Residence Concentrated:*
This category referred to a high degree of residential concentration. It was defined as such when the following requirements were met:

(a) An average net residential density of more than ten dwelling units per acre.

(b) A density distribution allocating more than 30 per cent of the dwelling units to densities of over twenty dwelling units per acre.

(c) A distribution allocating less than 15 per cent of the dwelling units to densities of under two dwelling units per acre.

(d) A minimum number of residential groupings within the entire region.

2. *Residence Clustered:*
This category referred to the medium range of residential concentration-dispersion. It was defined as such when the following requirements were met:

(a) An average net residential density of seven to ten dwelling units per acre.

(b) A density distribution allocating 15 to 30 per cent of the dwelling units to densities of over twenty dwelling units per acre.

(c) A density distribution allocating 15 to 30 per cent of the dwelling units to densities of under two dwelling units per acre.

(d) A medium number of residential groupings within the entire region.

3. *Residence Dispersed:*

This category referred to the maximum possible residential dispersion. It was defined as such when the following requirements were met:

(a) An average residential density of less then seven dwelling units per acre.

(b) A density distribution allocating less than 15 per cent of the dwelling units to densities of over twenty dwelling units per acre.

(c) A density distribution allocating more than 30 per cent to densities of under two dwelling units per acre.

(d) A maximum number of residential groupings within North-eastern Illinois.

Daytime Activity Orientation

This axis reflected the distribution of the daytime activities in the region and consequently the home-to-work trips; this axis ranged from extreme centralization of daytime activities (concentration in one area) to extreme sub-focalization (dispersion throughout the region). Three classes were identified for this variable:

1. *Intra-Grouping Orientation:*

This category represented the extreme case of sub-focalization. Grouping was defined as a continuous residential development which is capable of operating as a small community, in providing the day-to-day residential service needs. However, in this category, such groupings contained a major part of the daytime activities, i.e., jobs.

2. *Inter-Grouping Orientation:*

This category represented a situation where most daytime activities occurred in places other than one's own residential groupings or in non-residential centres. Thus, this category implied a transportation system which permitted efficient inter-group movement.

3. *Central Place Orientation:*

This category represented a situation of extreme centralization. Most of the daytime activities were located in one central location, namely the metropolitan centre.

Sub-Regional Integration-Specialization

This axis reflected the level at which a significant integration occurred among the various specialized activities and functions. The two extreme conditions identified on this axis were:

1. *Sub-Regional Integration:*

This category referred to a condition wherein each of the sub-areas of the metropolitan region contained a representative distribution of metropolitan area population, social classes, institutions, commercial and cultural establishments, recreational facilities, etc. Each of these sub-regions provided all the social and economic needs of an approximate cross-section of the metropolitan population. Therefore, the transfer of persons, goods, and messages between the various sub-regions was minimum under these conditions.

2. *Sub-Regional Specialization (Regional Integration):*

This category referred to a condition wherein the entire region acted as one economic and social unit. Thus, each of the sub-regions contained an overabundance of certain social classes, institutions, recreational facilities, etc.; consequently, it lacked others. Therefore, the sub-regions were interdependent for the total supply of social and economic needs, and required substantial movement of persons and goods between the various sub-regions.

Alternatives of Urban Form and Structure

A total of eight categories was isolated on the three variable axes of urban form and structure. These categories were defined in the preceding section. The possible combinations of these eight factors (three, three, and two) were eighteen. However, certain of these combinations were self-contradictory on the basis of the definition of terms accepted. Basically, this contradiction was due to the isolation of the variable, daytime activity orientation, as an independent variable rather than as part of the other two variables. Figure 2 shows all the possible combinations of the above categories. Each variable was numbered to facilitate easy reference to the various combinations.

Thus, the combination of sub-regional integration (100), intra-grouping orientation (10), and concentrated residence (1) is referred to as combination 111.

Self-contradictory combinations are indicated by the shaded areas of Figure 2.

The eleven remaining combinations represented eleven different, but feasible, urban alternatives. These eleven were feasible not only because they were consistent internally, but because they represented the combinations of the three variables which were shaping the urban environment in the 1960s. Each of these eleven combinations were used as the concept of an alternative design for Northeastern Illinois for the year 2015.

Evaluation of the Long-Range Designs

Goals Fulfilment Test

A goal was defined as a stated or implied end upon which a person or group of persons were prepared to take action to attain. Ten goals were identified. These goals were:

1. *Economic Health:*

Permit business and industry to operate successfully in order to provide opportunities for all the citizens and communities to improve their economic well-being.

2. *Education and Culture:*

Furnish educational and cultural opportunities which provide all citizens with access to knowledge and ideas to the point of personal fulfilment.

3. *Physical and Mental Health and Safety:*

Develop a program for the prevention of injury and physical and mental illness by eliminating the known major causes. Make treatment available to all those afflicted.

4. *Aesthetic:*

Develop an environment in which all residents may come into contact with elements of aesthetic and associational significance.

5. *Transportation:*

Provide rapid, economical, and comfortable transportation (and

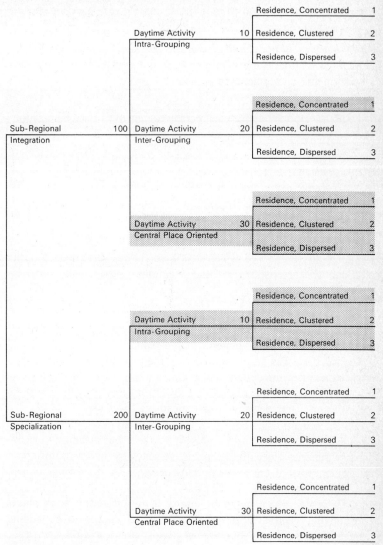

Figure 2. Alternatives of urban form.

other means of communication) to make areas and goods accessible to people as necessary for fulfilling other goals.

6. *Choice of Physical and Social Environment:*
Encourage a large variety of physical and social living conditions which will suit all segments of demand.

7. *Social Mobility:*
Provide the opportunity for each person to improve his social position.

8. *Participation in Decisions:*
Provide opportunities for all citizens to understand and participate in decisions that affect local areas. Decisions should be made at the lowest possible governmental level, consistent with reasonable efficiency. The individual's freedom of choice should be maintained, whenever public interests are not impaired.

9. *Efficient Land Use:*
Put all land to the use which it is best able to serve, based on its physical characteristics and the locational significance of those characteristics.

10. *Leisure:*
Provide a range of facilities for leisure time activities some of which are meaningful and enjoyable to each person.

Figure 3 is a bar graph representing the percentage ratings for the goals by each of the designs. An examination of the Goals Profile was made to select the designs scoring lower on every goal than a single other design. Thus design 4 could substitute for design 3.

On the basis of the above test, four designs were recommended for further consideration. Furthermore, it was felt that meaningful variations of the four alternatives could be achieved by incorporating some of the concepts of the lower ranking designs. The following composites were suggested:

1. Design 6 which might be improved by clustering work places and moving centres closer to residences, as in 2, and by adding residential variety with some higher density areas, as in 7.

2. Design 5 which could be reinforced by adding the functional specialization of work place found in 3 or 7, and by the lowering of residential densities, as recommended in 9.

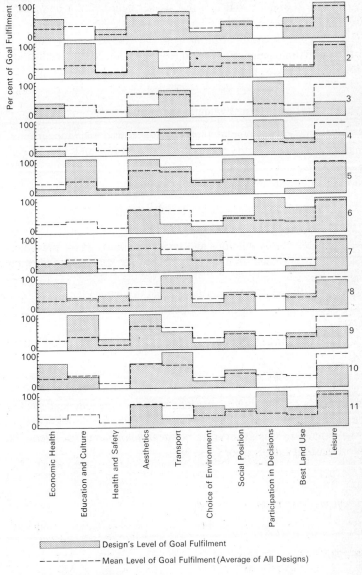

Figure 3. Goals profile.

3. Design 8 which could improve its aesthetics rating by gaining close-in open space, as in 1.

4. Design 11 which might profit from the express transportation to the Loop, recommended by 10, and from the industrial specialization of the sub-regions, as in 3.

Environmental and Form Evaluation

The following environmental factors were considered: topography, visual articulation, flood plains, drainage basins and watersheds, aquifers, soils, and mineral resources. Table 1 shows the results of the environmental evaluation.

Consolidation

On the basis of the evaluations and reviews outlined on the preceding pages, it was decided to develop for further study the following designs:

1. Designs 8 and 1, to be developed as the Finger Plan.

2. Designs 5 and 9, to be developed as the Satellite Cities–Greenbelt Plan.

3. Designs 7 and 3, to be developed as the Multi-Town Cluster Plan.

4. Designs 6 and 2, to be developed as the Dispersed Regional City Plan.

In addition to the above combinations, it was recommended that design 4 be developed as the Trends Plan. However, the basic guide for the latter plan was assumed to be the development characteristics of Northeastern Illinois prior to 1964.

TABLE ONE

Environmental Evaluation of Designs

	Designs	1	2	3	4	5	6	7	8	9	10	11
Topography Slopes	Suitable					x		x	x			
	Adaptable						x				x	
	Problem	x	x	x						x		x	x

	Designs	1	2	3	4	5	6	7	8	9	10	11
Visual Articulation	Suitable			x	x	x	x				x	
	Adaptable	x							x			
	Problem		x					x		x		x
Flood Plains	Suitable				x		x					
	Adaptable		x			x		x		x		
	Problem	x		x					x		x	x
Aquifers	Suitable	x										x
	Adaptable		x		x		x		x			
	Problem			x		x		x		x	x	
Agricultural Soils	Suitable	x				x			x	x		x
	Adaptable		x	x							x	
	Problem				x		x	x				
Industrial Soils	Suitable				x	x				x		x
	Adaptable	x					x	x	x		x	
	Problem		x	x								
Drainage Basins	Suitable					x	x	x			x	
	Adaptable	x							x			
	Problem		x	x	x					x		x
Mineral Resources	Suitable	x					x		x			x
	Adaptable		x			x		x		x		
	Problem			x	x						x	

Dispersed Regional City Design

The concept of this design resembled that of the 'Broadacre City'[3] sensitively fitted into the prairie landscape. The main features of this design were: low density residential development emphasizing detached single-family homes, utilization of the areas along major streams and rivers for recreation, and a patterning of the new urban development in broad ribbons parallel to (but not encroaching on) major streams.

Shopping facilities were dispersed throughout the region in the form of local neighbourhood shopping centres. These centres were augmented by television-telephone shopping, reducing the need for travel. A few widely spaced regional shopping centres satisfied the less frequent, but higher order, shopping needs.

Jobs were dispersed throughout the region in the form of small office clusters and individual manufacturing plant sites. Such a distribution allowed the possibility of a close proximity between homes and jobs, reducing the need for long work trips.

The Dispersed Regional City design depended on the private automobile as the prime means of transportation. Mass transit played a minor role due to the dispersed, low density pattern of development. A close-knit network of expressways and major arterial streets provided for multidirectional traffic movement throughout the region.

Finger Design (Radial Corridor)

The organizing element of this design was a network of radial commuter rail, expanded rapid transit, and expressways, originating from the urban core of the region. The resulting physical form (similar to the form of earlier cities where rail transit was the dominant mode of travel) resembled the human hand, palm, and fingers. Apartment and town-house developments occurred only at the centre or 'palm' of the design and at points along the radial corridors close to passenger rail stations. Lower density residential development filled out much of the remainder of these corridors.

The regional shopping centres were spaced at intervals along the radial transportation lines. Many places of work were clustered in a similar manner near transportation lines; however, the majority of jobs continued to be concentrated near the centre of the urbanized area.

Outside the central area the various radial corridors were separated from each other by regional parks, forest preserves, and other low density development.

The Finger Design required an integrated transportation system to achieve its design objectives. The system consisted of expressways, and rapid transit, forming a grid pattern within the centre of the region. Expressways ran closely parallel to commuter rail lines reaching towards major cities outside the region. The significant feature of this system was that the traveller had a real choice of travel means. Both private and mass transportation facilities followed the same route, thus offering truly alternative means for the same trip.

Multi-Town Cluster Design

The concept of this design was one of a major urban concentration surrounded by numerous clusters of small and specialized towns. The major features of this alternative were two-fold. The first was an attempt to offer its future citizens a wide choice of environment by allowing the individual clusters to develop specialized character; the second was to preserve the ideal of small town living in a large metropolitan area.

Most multi-town clusters were comprised of one or more adjacent municipalities each with a business district designed to serve the daily shopping and service needs within the cluster. The various clusters were bounded, served, and separated from each other by a 'regional facilities network'. The network was composed of major open spaces, large shopping centres and other major centres of activities, industrial parks, and the expressway network. This functional arrangement both preserved the primarily residential character of multi-town clusters within logical boundaries and tied together with the regional transportation system all places of regional significance. Superimposed on the regional facilities network, the radiating railroads still connected the suburbs to the principal centre of the region, the Loop.

The specialization of each town cluster necessitated an interdependence among the various sectors of the region and a mutual dependence on the Central City. To serve the above needs, a complete range of transportation facilities would be provided throughout the region. The main transportation emphasis would be on expressways. Rail transportation would be maintained at its 1964 level.

Satellite Cities–Greenbelt Design

In the Satellite Cities–Greenbelt Design the continuous expansion of the Chicago urbanized area would end during the period 1970–75. Most of the growth thereafter was to be channelled into four or five 'cities' or large clusters of communities of one to two million people, located in the outer counties of Northeastern Illinois at a distance of thirty-five to forty miles from the Chicago Loop. These cities would be separated from the Chicago urbanized area and from each other by a greenbelt consisting of agricultural land, forest preserves, estates, golf courses, cemeteries, and institutions.

Local shopping facilities were to be dispersed throughout the region, satisfying the daily shopping needs of most families. However, a major characteristic of this plan was the utilization of the large central business districts of the satellite cities as modern multi-purpose centres. Each central business district was to satisfy all the specialized and less frequent shopping needs of the families residing in the same satellite city. Jobs were to be concentrated in the central business district of each satellite city and in the older core of the region (City of Chicago).

The various satellite cities were separated from each other and from the City of Chicago by a 'greenbelt', described above. In addition to defining and separating the various satellite cities, the greenbelt would provide for convenient recreation and natural resource conservation.

Each satellite city was to reach a size and residential density capable of supporting an efficient public transportation system. The pattern of the transportation network in a satellite city would depend on the character of that city. Thus, one satellite city was to develop as a linear city; another, as a radial corridor city, etc.

Siting Decisions: Prototypes

For each alternative an area of twenty square miles, within the boundaries of Northeastern Illinois, was selected to illustrate, through its physical development, the basic concepts of the alternative design under investigation. The Data Maps presented graphically the overall growth patterns of the region. However, the scale of Data Maps was too small to illustrate some of the concepts intended to make the regional designs workable.

The prototypes were developed to serve two basic purposes. The first was to test the concepts of the various alternatives for feasibility and reasonableness. The prototypes did this by dealing with definitive scales. Furthermore, in developing these prototypes it became necessary to face certain questions of implementation – an additional test of reasonableness. The second purpose of the prototypes was to develop pictorial representations of the alternatives for use in public hearings and general meetings. The prototype helped to explain the concepts of the alternatives to the public and thus improved the quality of public response.

Finger (Radial Corridor) Prototype

The Finger Prototype depicted a five-mile stretch of a proposed development corridor. The study area was partly developed in 1965.

The development corridor focused on a commuter rail line and was bounded by two large regional parks and other low intensity developments. Located along the rail line, at about one-mile intervals, were six centres. Three of these were community centres, combining local shopping and civic activities. The other centres were: a medical centre, a regional shopping centre (developed as a centre in a park), and an industrial centre. All centres (except the industrial centre) were connected via arterial streets to the expressway. The industrial centre was located at the intersection of an expressway and the rail line, providing its workers a choice of transportation. A second industrial centre was located along an expressway and linked to the rail stop by a bus line.

Apartments and town-houses were located within walking distance of the rail stations. Medium density residential developments were located along the arterial streets leading to rail stations. Single-family homes occupied the remainder of the development corridors. Outside the corridors, only houses on more than half-acre lots were allowed.

Job opportunities within this five-mile stretch of development were provided in the industrial parks, shopping centres, and medical centres. Furthermore, the radial expressways and rail line brought the job opportunities of the Loop to within a reasonable distance.

Multi-Town Cluster Prototype

The Multi-Town Cluster Prototype depicted an area, approximately five miles by four miles, which was more than half developed in 1965.

A dominant feature of this prototype was the expressway system, developed as a grid with three-mile intervals between parallel routes.

The expressways often adjoined linear tracts of open space. Together they gave form to the regional facilities network throughout which were scattered regional centres, institutions, and industry. The regional facilities network delineated the various multi-town clusters.

Each cluster was composed of several towns, each with its own centre. Each town varied in size from 5,000 to 100,000 people. Some of the clusters had one or more community centres; however, many were served only by the neighbourhood centres. Several clusters were served jointly by a regional centre located in the regional facilities network.

Each cluster developed a special character. Some had towns designed for young marrieds or elderly couples; these towns had a high percentage of apartments. Other clusters catered more to the needs of families with children, providing them with single-family detached units on large lots.

The expressways provided the basic mode of transportation. However, commuter rail lines continued to serve the area, as many town centres were already established on these lines.

Satellite Cities Prototype

This prototype depicted for development a satellite city which expanded from a town of 100,000 in 1965 to a city of 1,000,000 in the year 2000.

The initial elements were the original city with its business and civic centres located on the river. When a commercial jetport was located to the northwest of the existing town, a large new town was built in the vicinity. By promoting and planning for rapid growth with the early provisions of all urban utilities and services, the new town played an important role in accommodating the rapid expansion of the satellite city as a whole. At this time, an existing highway between the original town and the new one was upgraded and extended on to the airport. Two expressways from the Chicago Loop linked the two towns and encouraged them to grow towards each other. Both towns, old and new, developed major business and industrial centres.

The rail line was expanded into a loop system connecting the two major business centres and provided mass transit circulation within the entire satellite city. The major centres, industrial parks, and highest residential densities were developed along the rail line.

The satellite city was surrounded, on three sides, by large areas of open space. These areas were part of the greenbelt, separating the various satellite cities from each other and from the Chicago Urbanized Area. Lakes were formed in the greenbelt to hold surplus water during times of heavy rain and supplement stream flows during dry periods. These lakes also provided recreation opportunities.

Evaluation and Testing of the Alternatives

Comparative Analyses

These analyses compared selected outputs of the alternatives, by county, to each other and to the 1964 conditions. To summarize the results of these analyses, the six counties were grouped into three sub-areas. The inner area included the City of Chicago; the intermediate area, Suburban Cook, and DuPage Counties; and the outer area, Lake, McHenry, Kane, and Will Counties. The following tables and text summarize the more significant outputs of the alternatives.

Population

The total 1990 population projected for Northeastern Illinois was approximately the same for all alternatives. However, the distribution of the population increase (1964–90) was different for each. The Dispersed Regional City, Multi-Town Cluster, and Trends alternatives distributed the additional (1964–90) population equally between the intermediate and outer areas. The Finger alternative allocated more of the additional population to the intermediate area. The Satellite Cities–Greenbelt alternative emphasized population growth in the outer area. Table 2 shows the existing and projected population by county for each alternative.

Manufacturing Employment

The 1990 distribution of manufacturing employment reflected the population distribution for that year. The Finger and Trends

TABLE TWO
Population Projections

County	1964 Inventory	Dispersed 1964–90	Finger 1964–90	Multi-Town Cluster 1964–90	Satellite 1964–90	Trends 1964–90
City of Chicago	3,488,000	80,000	161,000	67,000	5,000	47,000
Suburban Cook	1,802,000	965,000	991,000	917,000	640,000	834,000
DuPage	377,000	460,000	603,000	493,000	429,000	463,000
Kane	230,000	200,000	204,000	219,000	546,000	449,000
Lake	331,000	480,000	213,000	361,000	358,000	387,000
McHenry	84,000	130,000	53,000	128,000	189,000	195,000
Will	219,000	475,000	540,000	583,000	603,000	394,000
Total:	6,531,000	2,790,000	2,765,000	2,768,000	2,770,000	2,769,000

alternatives concentrated most of the total projected manufacturing employment growth in the intermediate areas. The Satellite Cities–Greenbelt and Multi-Town Cluster alternatives concentrated two thirds of the total projected employment growth in the outer area. All alternatives showed a decrease in the manufacturing employment of the City of Chicago in spite of the fact that all alternatives increased the manufacturing land in the City of Chicago.

Open Space

The Finger and Trends alternatives allocated 70 per cent of the projected new (1964–90) open space to the outer area. The Multi-Town Cluster and Satellite Cities–Greenbelt alternatives allocated only 55 per cent of the projected growth in open space to the outer areas. There was no significant growth (in acres) in the open space within the City of Chicago, due to the lack of vacant land.

Developed Land

Table 3 shows the additional developed land (including non-agricultural open space), by county, under each of the alternatives. The Multi-Town Cluster alternative developed the least additional land; the second lowest new land consuming alternative was Trends. The Dispersed Regional City, Finger, and Satellite Cities–Greenbelt alternatives developed the same additional total area. However, the latter two developed considerably less land than the Dispersed Regional City alternative, if land developed for regional parks was excluded.

Most of the land proposed for development was in use as agricultural land in 1964. The Multi-Town Cluster alternative converted the least area of agricultural land to urban use. However, differences among the alternatives, in regard to area of agricultural land converted to urban uses, were less significant than differences in regard to total land developed.

New Housing

The single-family detached home formed the predominant type of housing for all alternatives. The Finger, Multi-Town Cluster, and Satellite Cities–Greenbelt alternatives maintained the same percentage of population in single-family detached homes as existed in

Northeastern Illinois in 1964. The Dispersed Regional City and Trends alternatives increased the above from 51 per cent to 58 per cent and 57 per cent respectively. Furthermore, the Dispersed Regional City, Multi-Town Cluster, and Trends alternatives distributed the single-family detached houses equally between the outer and intermediate counties. The Finger alternative emphasized a higher percentage of its single-family detached units in the outer counties and the Satellite Cities–Greenbelt alternative emphasized them in the intermediate counties. All alternatives maintained 25 per cent of Chicago's housing in single-family detached units as in 1964.

The Finger and Satellite Cities–Greenbelt alternatives allocated 10 per cent of the total population to apartment living in 1990. The Dispersed Regional City and Multi-Town Cluster alternatives allocated 5 per cent of the population to apartment living. Under Trends, only 2·5 per cent of the population would live in apartments.

Evaluation

The five 1990 alternative design concepts were exposed to public scrutiny through the 1966 public hearings. Furthermore, the concepts of the alternatives composite designs were presented at a mobile exhibit, 'The Choice Train'. In addition, these plans were presented to interested groups representing various municipal, regional, and private agencies. Feedback from individuals at the public hearings and mobile exhibit was achieved through a questionnaire distributed to those in attendance. Feedback from the interested groups was in the form of statements received at N.I.P.C.'s 1966 Annual Conference.

Analyses of Questionnaires

More than 1,300 persons, residing in thirty-three communities in five counties, completed the questionnaire which was distributed during the 1966 public hearings and mobile exhibit. The questionnaire was designed to determine the preferred life style of the respondents during each stage of the adult life cycle.

The life styles of respondent communities (in 1990) for each of the alternatives was determined by the location of each community and the type of housing added in its vicinity by each alternative. The

TABLE THREE
Developed Land* (Acres)

County	1964 Inventory	Dispersed 1964–90	Finger 1964–90	Multi-Town Cluster 1964–90	Satellite 1964–90	Trends 1964–90
City of Chicago	131,200	4,300	1,100	100	2,900	2,400
Suburban Cook	242,300	181,600	144,800	111,300	122,100	117,000
DuPage	75,200	99,700	107,200	76,100	104,400	87,800
Kane	53,400	59,700	80,000	45,900	71,000	74,600
Lake	74,100	92,800	74,800	60,100	91,300	87,400
McHenry	42,300	48,600	34,700	16,800	44,700	42,600
Will	85,100	93,500	170,600	83,400	132,800	80,300
Total:	703,600	580,200	613,200	393,700	569,200	492,100

* Includes Public Open Space

TABLE FOUR

Percentage of Responses in which Alternative Provided Acceptable Life Style for Next Stage of Life Cycle

County	Number of Questionnaires	Dispersed (%)	Finger (%)	Multi-Town Cluster (%)	Satellite (%)	Trends (%)
City of Chicago	31	32	32	32	32	32
Suburban Cook	388	36	49	40	34	32
DuPage	241	43	49	44	43	43
Kane	174	39	52	52	32	52
Lake	289	35	45	41	34	39
McHenry	174	50	50	50	50	50
Will	0	0	0	0	0	0
Total:	1,266	39	49	44	38	41

acceptability of an alternative was defined as the percentage of the respondents having the same (current and future) preference for life styles as that offered close to the present place of residence by the alternative under investigation. It should be noted that a community might have the same implied life styles (in 1990) under several of the alternatives.

Table 4 shows the respondents' acceptance of the various life styles (and corresponding alternatives for their communities) for the next stage of the life cycle. The Finger alternative was most compatible, with Multi-Town Cluster alternative second.

Responses of Interested Groups

Twenty-eight agencies and groups presented statements at the Annual Conference of N.I.P.C., held on 15 December 1966. Most of these agencies had acquainted themselves with the composite designs through special presentations held during the autumn of 1966. It should be noted that by the time of the Annual Conference, the Dispersed Regional City and Trends alternatives had been eliminated by the Commission as unacceptable. This was decided on the basis of the technical tests completed at that time.

Of the twenty-eight statements presented, twenty-one concerned the development problems of the region. Eleven of these statements indicated preferences among the alternatives.

All eleven statements which indicated alternative preferences included the Finger alternative. The following list indicates the preference or preferences of each of the above eleven organizations:

Finger	Chicago and Northwestern Railway
Finger	Chicago Transit Board
Finger	Chicago Department of Development and Planning
Finger	Lake County Regional Planning Commission
Finger	Negroes for Metropolitan Planning

Finger	Welfare Council of Metropolitan Chicago
Finger and Multi-Town	American Society of Landscape Architects
Finger or Multi-Town	American Institute of Architects
Finger and Satellite	Church Federation of Greater Chicago
Finger and Satellite	Metropolitan Housing and Planning Council
Finger or Satellite	Chicago Academy of Science

The reasons generally given for supporting the Finger alternative were: (1) its strong transportation system; (2) its flexibility; and (3) its feasibility in view of the present structure of the region.

The need for an early acquisition of open space was expressed by seven statements. The importance of transportation in shaping the region and the need for further studies concerning the social implications of the various alternatives were the other two most frequently expressed ideas.

Testing

Quantitative and qualitative tests were conducted to determine the relative performance of the alternatives in terms of cost, accessibility to selected facilities, air quality, and regional resource management. An attempt was made to quantify all tests. However, the regional resource management implications under each alternative did not lend themselves to such quantification.

Approximately midway through the testing process it was apparent that the Dispersed Regional City and Trends alternatives were performing less satisfactorily than the other three, and it appeared unlikely that the former would be able to overcome their initial low scores in later testing. Therefore, the Commission decided to set aside the Dispersed Regional City and Trends alternatives from further consideration as potential plans.

When the testing process had been completed there was found to be no unanimous agreement within the results which would indicate that one alternative would perform best in all categories of function and for all sub-areas. However, the overall performance of the Finger alternative and its degree of acceptability made it stand out among the others.

The next step was to prepare a *comprehensive plan* that would accomplish the future pattern of development portrayed by the Finger alternative. It had been decided at the outset that a comprehensive regional plan would not include the detailed land use designations for a target year as typically found in municipal and county plans. While land use data had been produced for testing purposes and was essential in the process of selecting the recommended plan, it was not the plan. Rather the initial plan was to be a stated course of action in the form of recommended policy statements dealing with all major categories of development and a proposed transportation network. These policies would best accomplish a set of goals as proven by testing the predicted land use pattern against others.

The recommended policies are similar to the land use decisions of the interpreter as he interpreted the Finger composite design. While the Finger alternative offered the most promise for future land development, it was recognized that a major portion of the future population of Northeastern Illinois will be living either in the central city or in those adjacent suburban areas already well established as to their form and structure. The city of Chicago has adopted a comprehensive plan which incorporates the concept of high accessibility corridors similar to those of the Finger Alternative. The older, near-by suburban communities have largely developed according to the concepts of the Multi-Town alternative. For this inner suburban area, the staff revised the plan to incorporate Multi-Town concepts, thus suiting the plan to existing realities.

The initial comprehensive plan will later be expanded with plans for public open space, water supply, sanitary and storm sewers, and solid waste disposal. These plans will only deal with elements of regional significance such as major forest preserves and trunk sewers. The several parts of the initial plan will also be due for re-evaluation and revision as new information becomes available. The methods and techniques recommended for utilizing the plan have been set down in a separate document to be published by the Commission.

The comprehensive plan is thus not an orthodox physical plan, but constitutes in fact the policies referred to above which are published as the Comprehensive General Plan for the Development of the Northeastern Illinois Counties Area. Sometimes called a 'policies plan', this document may be revised from time to time as comprehensive studies for public open space, water supply, sanitary and storm sewers, and solid waste disposal are completed and any other information becomes available.

NOTES

1. Catherine Bauer Wurster, 'Form and Structure of Future Urban Complex', in *Cities and Space*, ed. Lowdon Wingo, Jr, Baltimore, Johns Hopkins Press, 1963.

2. Melvin M. Webber, 'The Urban Place and the Non-place Urban Realm', in *Explorations into Urban Structure*, ed. Melvin Webber, Philadelphia, University of Pennsylvania Press, 1963.

3. Frank Lloyd Wright, *The Living City*, New York, Horizon Press, 1958.

33. The IDEA Method for Regional Planning

DOXIADIS ASSOCIATES

The purpose of the 'Developing Urban Detroit Area Research', which is the full title of the project, is to provide guidelines for those concerned with taking decisions that affect the future of the Detroit area – planning authorities, industrialists, civic groups, etc. The study has been conducted on three levels of scale: the position of Detroit in the urbanizing Middle West – the Great Lakes Megalopolis; the immediate zone of influence of Detroit – the Urban Detroit Area; and a more detailed study of the administrative City of Detroit.

The IDEA method was evolved for this area – the Urban Detroit Area (Figure 1). The purpose was to find out how the presently overloaded centres of Detroit's main functions could be relieved and expanded so as to operate efficiently with a projected population of some 15,000,000 people living there in the year 2000.

The method consists in setting up a theoretical matrix which can contain all reasonable alternatives, and then proceed systematically to eliminate those that are less satisfactory (if necessary adding in other dimensions en route to help refine the process) until one arrives at a single solution.

In the early stages of elimination only one decision can be made; whether an alternative, or a group of alternatives, should be accepted or rejected. Later, as the total numbers of alternatives become less astronomic, numerical values are assigned, measuring the quality (or value) of each alternative, and this provides a means for rejecting those that fall below a certain level (Figure 2).

The word IDEA was coined to describe the two actions that must take place at each successive stage of this process: ID = *isolation* of the *dimensions* to be studied; then EA = *elimination* of *unnecessary alternatives*.

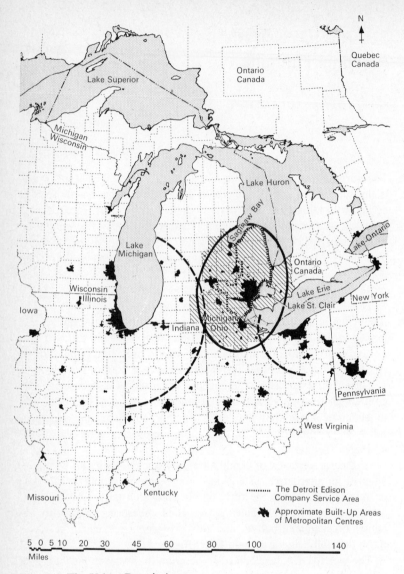

Figure 1. The Urban Detroit Area.

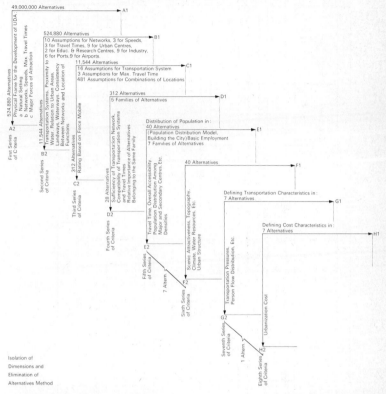

Figure 2. The IDEA methodology.

One axis of the Detroit matrix consisted of a set of location-based functions, the other of a set of ekistic criteria (Figure 3). The ekistic criteria were based on those aspects of the five ekistic elements that were directly relevant to this project, and they were introduced in the order in which they could be evaluated.

The set of location-based functions remained the same throughout the Detroit study, except that the names shifted from those of five abstract functions – central business districts, education and research centres, industrial centres, ports, and airports – to the code numbers of actual physical locations.

Parameters of People		Parameters of Functions																													
		Urban Centres					Major Educational and Research Centres					Industrial Poles					Ports					Airports					Other Functions				
		1	2	3	4	5	1	2	3	4	5	1	2	3	4	5	1	2	3	4	5	1	2	3	4	5	1	2	3	4	5
Population	1																														
	2																														
	3																														
	4																														
	5																														
Densities	1																														
	2																														
	3																														
	4																														
	5																														
Transportation Networks	1																														
	2																														
	3																														
	4																														
	5																														
Speeds of Transportation	1																														
	2																														
	3																														
	4																														
	5																														
Maximum Travel Time	1																														
	2																														
	3																														
	4																														
	5																														

Figure 3. Theoretic matrix alternatives.

The set of criteria along the vertical axis were related to specific Detroit problems – population size, population density, types of transportation, speed of travel, travel time from home to destination. The method enabled these to be considered simultaneously although introduced, grouped, and regrouped at different stages.

Initially each item on the matrix was arbitrarily given five alternative values, making a grand total of 49,000,000 possible alternative solutions.

Before going further, it must be noted that this study is only concerned with the needs and movements of the population *additional* to their needs and movements that can be contained within a well organized urban unit of around a quarter of a million people. Such cities, or urban agglomerations, would be contained within most of the 10×10 kilometre squares of this project. Thus, the Urban Detroit Area study is concerned only with the higher order groupings of the functions listed, such as now occur in the downtown area of Detroit itself where the present congestion is already alarming and the journey to work intolerably long.

Step A

Having *identified* the first range of *dimensions* to be studied, the task was to *eliminate* the unnecessary *alternatives*. Thus, the population alternatives were reduced from five to one – a population of 15,000,000 in the year 2000. The grounds were that if the solution worked for this population at that time, it would not much matter if, in fact, the 15,000,000 population was reached slightly before or slightly after that date. Next, the consideration of density was eliminated from this stage, but reintroduced later. On the other hand, it was decided necessary to increase the alternative types of transportation to be studied from five to ten permutations on three networks (a metropolitan network, 10 kilometres apart; a regional network, 30 kilometres apart; and a national network, 150 kilometres apart) and two systems (radial and gridiron). The five alternative assumptions on speed were then reduced to three: movement at 100–170 k.p.h. along the metropolitan network of freeways and mass transit routes; movement at 170–400 k.p.h. on the regional network, and at 400–700 k.p.h. on the national network. Both latter speeds were assumed to be related to new means of transportation. The final group of maximum travel-time alternatives were also reduced to three: a fast one of twenty minutes from the centroid of the 10×10 kilometre unit square to the point of destination (central business district, industrial centre, etc.); an average period of thirty minutes (generally considered quite acceptable); and a slow one of forty-five minutes. At a later stage it was decided to concentrate only on the thirty-minute journey.

Along the other axis of the matrix, the possible locations of central business districts, industrial centres, and airports was increased from five to nine; but the possible locations for ports were reduced to four and the educational research centres to two.

These changes cut the number of possible alternative solutions to 525,000 – still over half a million.

Step B

This stage concentrated on rating the nodality of the nine alternative locations in terms of their suitability as central business districts, as industrial centres, and as airports. The criteria chosen were: their accessibility to the national network, their proximity to Detroit, their proximity to the lakeshore (central business districts), and their proximity to a seaport (industrial areas). This study reduced the nine possible locations as follows:

Central Business Districts	4 alternative sites
Industrial Centres	4 alternative sites
Airports	3 alternative sites
Ports	4 alternative sites
Education and Research Centres	2 alternative sites

Step C

The goal of this stage was to discover the most advantageous grouping of these five functions by evaluating the amount of interconnection existing between their five poles of attraction. This evaluation was partly based on assumptions concerning the relative basic pull of each (rated from 100 for the central business district to 10 for the airport) and partly on the importance given to their close physical proximity (rated from 1 to 5). The combination of these factors gave a composite figure that was called an illustration of the 'force mobile', and the results of this study produced thirteen possible groupings of the five functional centres (Figure 4).

Figure 4. Step C2: the force mobile.

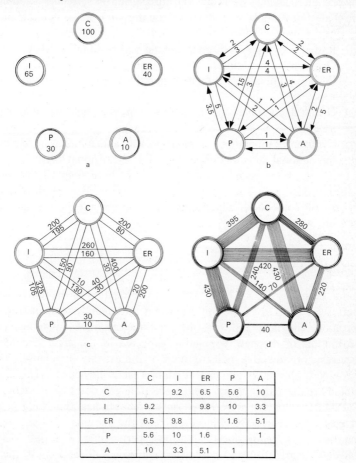

	C	I	ER	P	A
C		9.2	6.5	5.6	10
I	9.2		9.8	10	3.3
ER	6.5	9.8		1.6	5.1
P	5.6	10	1.6		1
A	10	3.3	5.1	1	

Steps B and C had drastically reduced the feasible alternative solutions to 312.

Step D

At this stage, the transportation systems were reconsidered in the light of the development up to now. Five were eliminated as redundant or unworkable, leaving two radial and three gridiron systems (including one that almost duplicated its radial counterpart). These five remaining systems were:

1. Radial combination of metropolitan and regional networks.
2. Gridiron combination of metropolitan and regional networks.
3. Radial combination of metropolitan, regional, and national networks.
4. Gridiron combination of metropolitan, regional, and national networks.
5. Gridiron combination of metropolitan and national networks, with the national networks implemented at the regional level.

These decisions reduced the number of alternatives to twenty-eight, but this figure was immediately increased to forty by the introduction of some new dimensions, required for the next stage of analysis.

Steps E and F

Major decisions having been taken on the location of the functional centres for the Urban Detroit Area and the main systems of transportation, the next task was to examine the most advantageous distribution of the new population expected in the area, and any necessary or advisable redistribution of the existing population. To accomplish this task, two new variables were introduced. The first related to the employment pull of the different poles of attraction. The figures allocated were based on current studies, that were projected to the year 2000 (Figure 5). Next the question of population densities was reintroduced. Various permissible densities were assigned to areas of land based on their scenic attractiveness, their

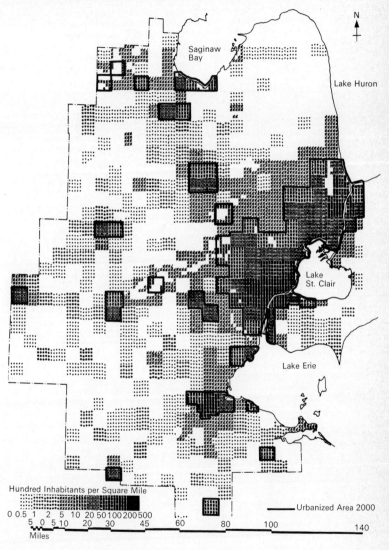

Figure 5. Example of groupings of the force mobile model.

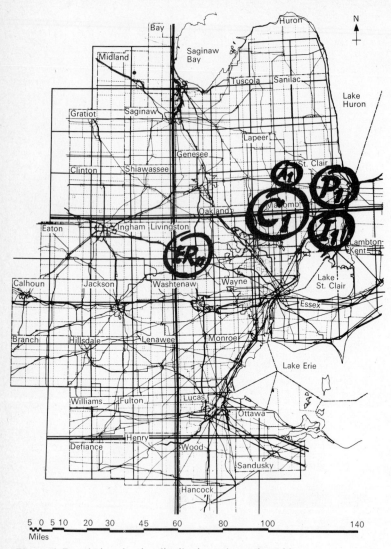

Figure 6. Population density distribution: alternative 120.

topography, their soil-bearing capacity, their microclimate, etc. (Figures 6 and 7).

The upshot was a group of seven alternative solutions. Four of these had Detroit as the only major centre (all major functions being grouped there). Two of these four assumed high levels of dispersal of employment to existing secondary centres within the Detroit area, both having a radial transportation network (Nos. 104 and 136). The other two assumed all major employment to remain concentrated in Detroit itself, one with a radial, the other with a gridiron transportation network (Nos. 106, and 114). The remaining three alternatives postulated a second major centre within the Urban Detroit Area, one at Port Huron (No. 120), one at Flint (No. 132), and the other at Toledo (No. 126). All these had gridiron systems of transportation.

Steps G and H

In choosing between the final seven alternatives, the question of costs had to be considered. This was arrived at by first establishing the frequency of the journeys that would be made to each of the poles of attraction from everywhere within the Area and then using this as a basis for modifying the theoretic transportation systems to meet the anticipated loads (downgrading little-used routes, etc.).

The frequency of the journeys was estimated on the basis of two surveys, made in 1953 and 1965/6. These provided data that could be extrapolated to the year 2000 in the following proportions: the journey to work was anticipated to account for 20 per cent of all trips made (instead of 26 per cent as in 1953); journeys to the central business district for 26 per cent; to education and recreation centres for 34 per cent; and non-home-based journeys accounted for the remaining 20 per cent (Figures 8 and 9).

In the two schemes illustrated here (No. 106, which has Detroit as the main centre with 51 per cent employment there, and No. 120, which has Port Huron as a second major centre), the costs of the transportation networks were low in No. 106 (22·4 billion dollars) and high in No. 120 (26·5 billion dollars). But this was far more than offset by the costs of urbanization, which were high in No. 106 (301·8 billion dollars) and low in No. 120 (240·6 billion dollars). These costs

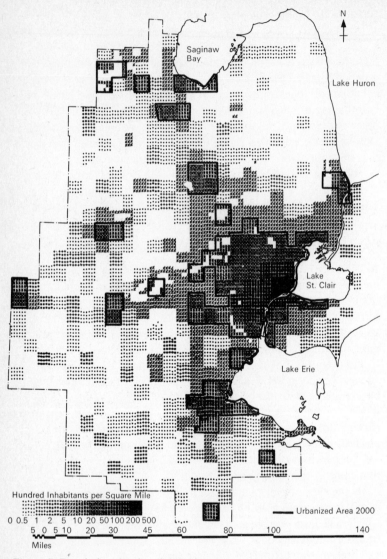

Hundred Inhabitants per Square Mile

0 0.5 1 2 5 10 20 50 100 200 500 ··· — Urbanized Area 2000

5 0 5 10   20   30   45   60   80   100   140

Miles

Figure 7. Population density distribution: alternative 106.

Figure 8 (opposite). Transportation characteristics: alternative 106.

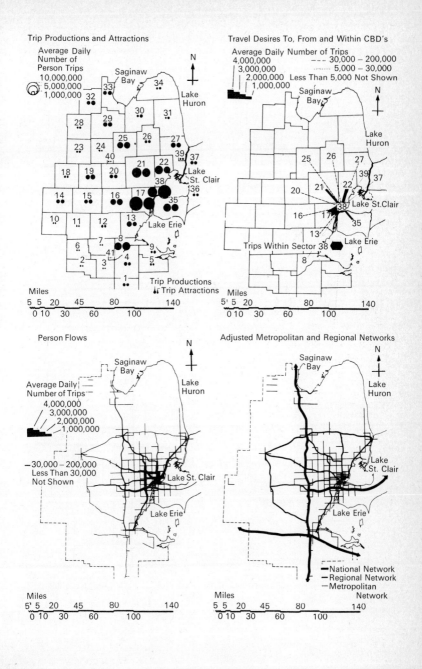

Trip Productions and Attractions

Average Daily Number of Person Trips
- 10,000,000
- 5,000,000
- 1,000,000

Saginaw Bay

N

Lake Huron

Lake St. Clair

Lake Erie

Trip Productions
Trip Attractions

Miles
5 5 20   45   80   140
0 10 30   60   100

Travel Desires To, From and Within CBD's

Average Daily Number of Trips
- 4,000,000
- 3,000,000
- 2,000,000
- 1,000,000

--- 30,000 – 200,000
...... 5,000 – 30,000
Less Than 5,000 Not Shown

Saginaw Bay

N

Lake Huron

Lake St. Clair

Trips Within Sector 38

Lake Erie

Miles
5' 5 20   80   140
0 10 30   60   100

Person Flows

N

Saginaw Bay

Lake Huron

Average Daily Number of Trips
- 4,000,000
- 3,000,000
- 2,000,000
- 1,000,000

— 30,000 – 200,000
Less Than 30,000 Not Shown

Lake St. Clair

Lake Erie

Miles
5' 5 20   45   80   140
0 10 30   60   100

Adjusted Metropolitan and Regional Networks

N

Saginaw Bay

Lake Huron

Lake St. Clair

Lake Erie

— National Network
— Regional Network
— Metropolitan Network

Miles
5 5 20   45   80   140
0 10 30   60   100

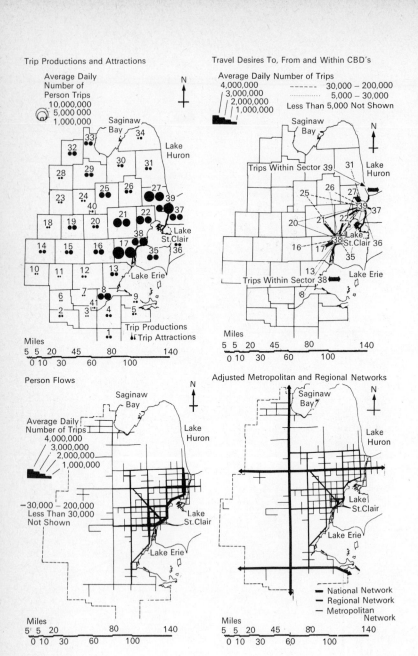

Trip Productions and Attractions

Average Daily
Number of
Person Trips
10,000,000
5,000,000
1,000,000

Saginaw Bay

Lake Huron

33 34
32
30 31
28
29
23 24 25 26 27 39
40 37
18 19 20 21 22 38
Lake St.Clair
14 15 16 17 35 36
10 11 12 13 Lake Erie
7 8
6 41 9
2 3 4 5
1

Miles
5 5 20   45   80   140
0 10 30   60   100

Trip Productions
Trip Attractions

Travel Desires To, From and Within CBD's

Average Daily Number of Trips
4,000,000   ------ 30,000 – 200,000
3,000,000   .... 5,000 – 30,000
2,000,000   Less Than 5,000 Not Shown
1,000,000

Saginaw Bay

Lake Huron

Trips Within Sector 39   31
25 26 27 39 37
20 21 22 36
16 17 38 Lake St.Clair 36
35
Trips Within Sector 38   13   Lake Erie
8

Miles
5 5 20   45   80   140
0 10 30   60   100

Person Flows

Saginaw Bay

Lake Huron

Average Daily
Number of Trips
4,000,000
3,000,000
2,000,000
1,000,000

– 30,000 – 200,000
Less Than 30,000
Not Shown

Lake St.Clair

Lake Erie

Miles
5 5 20   80   140
0 10 30   60   100

Adjusted Metropolitan and Regional Networks

Saginaw Bay

Lake Huron

Lake St.Clair

Lake Erie

— National Network
— Regional Network
— Metropolitan Network

Miles
5 5 20   45   80   140
0 10 30   60   100

were based on the replacement of 70 per cent of existing dwellings by the year 2000, and a relationship between dwelling types and costs and densities of development. Costs of community structures were found from various studies to amount to approximately 30 per cent of the costs of residential structures. The costs of roads within each 10×10 kilometre unit was related to the density of development, and the costs of utility services – after a number of detailed studies had been made – was finally established at 50 per cent of the cost of the roads within each unit. After serious consideration, land costs were eliminated from the study.

Feedback or Re-run

After Stage H had shown that alternative No. 120, with a second major centre established at Port Huron, best fulfilled all the criteria, it was decided to organize a re-evaluation of all the forty alternatives with which Step E had started, setting up a standardized system of rating all criteria to facilitate the comparison of the results.

This means that a formula was worked out for each item that had been tested, giving the average for each a value of 0, and then measuring how much better or worse each of the alternative solutions were than this average. All the items listed under the heads of Nature, Man and Society, Shells and Networks were re-evaluated according to this formula, and the final results showed the following ratings for the seven final contestants:

	Highest Score	*Lowest Score*	*No.106*	*No.120*
Nature:	+0·66 (No. 126)	−0·93 (No. 132)	−0·47	+0·41
Man and Society:	+0·57 (No. 106)	−0·88 (No. 104)	+0·57	+0·51
Shells and Networks:	+0·50 (No. 120)	−0·50 (No. 114)	−0·46	+0·50
Overall Rating:	+0·49 (No. 120)	−0·25 (No. 104)	−0·05	+0·49

This corroborative verdict seemed to confirm the earlier conclusion that No. 120 – a second major centre at Port Huron – would provide the most satisfactory solution to the problem of how to handle the

Figure 9. Transportation characteristics: alternative 120.

distribution of the major functions of the Urban Detroit Area so as best to serve the economic and human interests and needs of the population anticipated in the year 2000.

This also shows one of the main advantages of the IDEA method – that it is not difficult to re-evaluate or re-examine the situation, which may be changed by the need to upgrade or downgrade certain considerations in the light of later knowledge or unexpected developments. However, if the original matrix truly represents a universe in terms of the problem to be studied, all new developments would find a place somewhere within it – though one might have to go further back than Step E in the re-evaluation.

34. Spatial Reorganization:
A Model and a Concept

DONALD G. JANELLE

In this study, the concept of spatial reorganization identifies a process by which places adapt both the locational structure and the characteristics of their social, economic, and political activities to changes in time–space connectivity (the time required to travel between desired origins and destinations).

A model has been designed to depict a normative process of areal development. Later this model (the basic model) will be expanded so as to present a more comprehensive view. Although these models are intended to be applicable to urban-exchange economies typical of the United States and Western Europe, the writer believes that they may have some predictive value in forecasting the areal development of areas which have only recently begun progressing through the industrial-commercial revolution. Before describing the models, a concept which is central to the overall process of reorganization needs to be considered – this is the notion of *locational utility*.

Locational Utility

In contrast to place utility, locational utility is defined in a context which, in part, overlooks the individualistic and subjective connotation of value. It is a measure of the utility of specific places or areas, which in this case is defined by the aggregate time-expenditure (cost or effort) in transport required for that place or area to satisfy its operational needs. Operational need refers to those natural and human resource requirements which permit the place or area to fulfil its functional roles in the larger spatial system of places and areas. The alternative possibilities of a place, either to decrease, maintain, or increase its existing competitive status within the bounds of either its present spatial system of socio-economic activities or in an expanded sphere of influence, are here considered to be functions of its locational utility. The locational utility or value of places and areas increases as travel-time expenditure per unit of operational success (profit or some other form of amenity benefit) decreases. Whereas a first degree linear function is used to express this relationship, it is likely that a second, third, or higher degree function would be more appropriate.

Once the surface of utility has been described, one can then focus attention on a more significant problem – the dynamics of surface change. For example, the depletion or the discovery of a resource which is an operational need for the success of a given economic activity would alter the utility surface for that activity, and could necessitate the selection of a new production site.

In that locational utility is defined as a function of time-expenditure, it is evident that innovations which speed transportation will also lead to changes in the utility surface. Such changes pose many questions of practical relevance. For example, are these innovations and certain distributive forces leading towards greater equilibrium in the utility surface and thus possibly towards a more homogeneous distribution of man's socio-economic activities? Or, do transport improvements and certain agglomerative forces lead to increasing spatial variance in locational utility and, thus towards greater place-concentration of human enterprise?

These questions, along with the process of spatial reorganization, will be clarified as the concepts integrated into the model in Figure 1 are defined. These concepts include: demand for accessibility; transport innovations; time–space convergence; spatial adaptations – centralization and specialization; and spatial interaction.

Demand for Accessibility

Accessibility is a measure of the ease (time, cost, or effort) in which transfer occurs between the places and areas of a system. The demand for accessibility, then, is really a quest to decrease the transport effort expended per unit of operational success or, very simply, to augment locational utility. A useful and more objective measure of accessi-

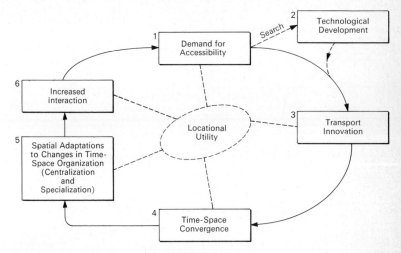

Figure 1. A process of spatial reorganization.

bility (not used in this study) is provided by the graph theoretic approaches employed by Garrison, Kansky, and others.[1]

Transport Innovations

In this study, transport innovations are any technologies or methods which serve to increase accessibility between places or which permit an increase in the quantity of goods or the number of passengers that can be moved between these places per unit of time.

Time–Space Convergence

Time–space convergence is a result of transport innovations that cause travel-time between places to decrease and distance to decline in significance.[2] An example of this phenomenon is illustrated in Figure 2 for travel between Detroit and Lansing, Michigan. As a consequence of such convergence, man has found that it is possible and practical to adapt the spatial organization of his activities to their evolving time–space framework (step 5 of the model).

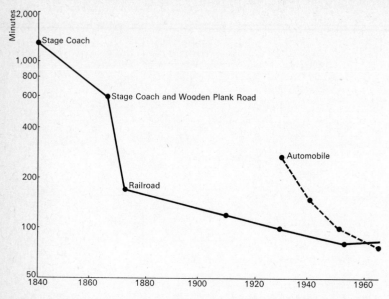

Figure 2. Time–space convergence: Lansing and Detroit, 1840–1965.

Spatial Adaptations to Changes in Time–Space Organization

In the basic model under consideration, the spatial adaptations of man's activities to their changing time–space framework will lead to the centralization and specialization of secondary and tertiary economic activities in specific places and, as is frequently the case, to the specialization of primary economic activities in the resource-oriented hinterlands of these places.

The greater the centralization and specialization of man's activities, the greater is the need for efficient transport and increased locational utility (steps 1–4 of the basic model). As man speeds up his means of movement, it becomes possible for him to travel further in a given time, to increase his access to a larger surrounding area and, possibly, to more and better resources. This idea is in line with Ullman's concept of transferability.[3] Likewise, secondary and tertiary functions can serve more people; and the perishable agricultural products and other primary products can be profitably marketed over a larger area. In essence these changes are manifestations of an increasing degree of locational utility (greater operational success can be derived per unit of time-expenditure from a given place) that permits the increasing centralization and specialization of human endeavours.

Unlike centralization and specialization, suburbanization (a form of spatial decentralization) represents an alternative response to time–space convergence which is not treated in this basic model. Improvements in individual mobility have made it possible for some families and for some firms to trade off central accessibility for the amenities associated with suburban life and industrial parks. These adaptations are considered in the expanded model of spatial reorganization (Figure 3).

Increased Interaction

Step 6 of the basic model indicates that an increase in interaction results between places and areas that experience increasing centralization and specialization.

Figure 3. An expanded model of the process of spatial reorganization.

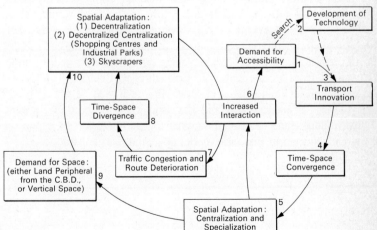

The increasing intercourse that results from the concentration of human activities at particular places is likely to lead to an over-extension of man's transport facilities and result in their deterioration from over-use and in the development of traffic congestion. It is, therefore, likely that the operational success of these places can only be continued through increased costs. Consequently, the increasing interaction that results from centralization and specialization leads to further demands for increased accessibility, greater degrees of locational utility, and transport innovations (see basic model). Thus, the spatial reorganization of human activities is perpetuated in what, theoretically, is a never-ending and accelerating cycle. This notion of a multiplier effect or positive feedback implies that the state of a system (that is, the degree of convergence between interacting settlements, their demands for accessibility, and so forth) at a given time is determined completely from within the system and by the previous state of the system.[4] The positive feedback system, as indicated by the completed circuit in the basic model, is self-perpetuating.

Support for the notion that a transport improvement, in itself, encourages increased interaction is also available. Studies by Coverdale and Coplitts show that improvements in highway facilities result in traffic volumes greater than the number accounted for by the diverted traffic.[5] That is, many new facilities (that is, bridges and freeways) will attract considerably more traffic than would be expected had the previous facilities continued to operate alone. This increase is frequently termed 'induced traffic'. The volumes of induced traffic encouraged by bridges replacing ferries have ranged, in many instances, from 65 per cent to 75 per cent of that before the improvement. For the Philadelphia–Camden Bridge it was 78 per cent, and for the San Francisco–Oakland Bay Bridge it was about 64 per cent. This finding lends additional support for the inclusion of a positive feedback system in the basic model of spatial reorganization.

An Evaluation of the Basic Model

Changes in the time-spatial and spatial organization of human endeavours present places and areas with possibilities for greater scale economies and with problems of developing more efficient means of transport. It is man's awareness or perception of these possibilities and problems that enables him to take advantage of the changes in the time–space structure of his activities. In reality, however, the process that has been described is not so simple – not all men will perceive the changes described in the model nor will they see the implications of these changes in the same way. Furthermore, some of the assumptions of the model lack complete accord with reality.

Varying Conceptions of Utility and Time

Whereas the basic model is based on an objective measure of locational utility (time-expenditure), utility is inherently individualistic; that is, it is perceived according to one's values, goals, and technical and institutional means of living. At the level of places and areas it is likely that the criteria for utility are based on factors other than just the expenditure of time.

It is also apparent that man's perceived value of a given unit of time has increased as the tempo of his activities has increased. A component to represent this change is not included in the model. Yet, by sole reason of the tremendously greater commodity, passenger, and information flows today as compared with past periods, man is motivated to seek greater utility for his expenditure of time. Imagine the magnitude of storage that would be necessary if New York City had to store food for its population to meet their needs over the winter months. With faster transport, the city can rely on more distant sources. Food can be moved to the city when it is needed, thus reducing its storage costs and increasing its operational success.

There is the additional likelihood that a person's perception of the utility of time will differ for various travel purposes. For example, an individual may be willing to spend an hour in travel to receive the medicinal services of an eye specialist; but, he may only grudgingly give up ten minutes to purchase a loaf of bread. No model of the process of spatial reorganization could account for all of the multitudinous goals and criteria of all persons, places, and areas, and the changing values of time for each. Therefore, in the development of the model, a standard pattern of human place-behaviour has been assumed.

A Basic Assumption: Rationality in Human Place-Behaviour

The principal assumption upon which the spatial process model is based is that man is rational. This concept of a rational man or the economic man has been well developed elsewhere and only the implications relevant to this discussion are presented.[6] These include the following:

1. Man has perfect knowledge. Thus, in an aggregate sense, places and areas show complete awareness of all factors operative in the areal reformation of their activities; they are aware of all their operational needs and of all the possibilities for fulfilling these needs.

2. Man has no uncertainty – he has perfect predictability. Thus, the rational place foresees the time–space convergence that will result from any transport innovation; it foresees the degree of increased interaction that will be derived from greater centralization and specialization of its activities.

3. Man is interested solely in maximizing the utility of time at a given place.

Limitations and Omissions of the Model

There may be lags or delays in the process resulting from man's inefficient behaviour – his slowness in adapting the spatial organization of human activity to its changing time–space framework, or his slowness in introducing more efficient forms of transportation. It is also possible that improvements in transfer technology will lag behind the need for such development. It will be noted from Figure 1 that the development of technology, although intimately related, is considered exogenous to the system depicting the process of spatial change. Such development may take place independently of any need present within the system – innovations developed for an entirely different purpose may be applicable to transportation.

An Expanded Model of Spatial Reorganization

If the restraints of rationality, as defined above, are relaxed, and, if another factor, the demand for land, is introduced, then the mechanism of the basic model breaks down. In reality, places and areas do not always seek to maximize their degree of locational utility and, in many cases, they find it impossible to do so. Thus, if there is no demand for increased accessibility in response to increases in interaction or if there is no technology available for meeting demands for greater accessibility, then it is likely that either traffic congestion, route deterioration, or both will occur. This, in turn, would lead to time–space divergence (places getting further apart in time–space). This is indicated by steps 7 and 8 of the expanded model depicted in Figure 3.

The demand for land or space (step 9) is a form of decentralization which is a direct consequence of the centralization and specialization associated with time–space convergence. Factories, warehouses, and so forth, which seek to augment scale economies, find land scarce and expensive in the central areas of cities and, thus, move to the peripheries of the built-up areas where it is available and comparatively cheap. Jobs created by this expansion may increase the population attraction power of places and lead to further developments for land. Additional factors accounting for a demand for land peripheral to the built-up areas include the population holding power of the urban area itself and the amenity goal to gain more elbow room – to get out of the noisy, crowded city. This demand to leave the central city results as interaction accelerates beyond a tolerable threshold. It seems likely that this demand for land coupled with time–space divergence will lead to a completely different form of areal adaptation than was the case with convergence.

492 Networks: Prospects for Transportation and Communication

Spatial Adaptation: Decentralized Centralization and the Expansion of the City

Because the land available for expansion is generally peripheral to that portion of the city area which is already developed, the new and relocated establishments (residents, retail and service firms, and so forth) find themselves at a time disadvantage in attaining goods and services that are only offered in the central core of the city. To obviate this problem these families and firms can either demand greater transport access (steps 1–3), or they can encourage the location of new establishments in the city's peripheral area to serve and to employ them (step 10). Frequently, the demand for new commercial, industrial, and cultural establishments is met prior to any substantial improvements in transport access. The pattern of such development is typified by shopping centres carrying on many retail and service functions and by the nucleation of secondary activities in planned industrial parks.

With the continuance of this process, it is easily seen how sub-nucleated secondary and tertiary activities can eventually become a part of the very core of the urban area – the increasing concentration of activities within the urban core and within the subnucleated secondary and tertiary centres leads to further demands for land (step 9). It is possible that they will engulf each other in their expansion and become fused into one highly integrated unit – a megalopolis.[7]

In the absence of planning, it is evident that decentralization is merely an intermediate or lag-stage in the general process (described by the basic model) leading towards an expanded area of centralization and specialization. This model highlights only the basic components of spatial reorganization and clearly expresses the cyclical tendency towards the increasing centralization and specialization of human activity.

The Process of Spatial Reorganization and the
Concept of Relative Advantage

The concept of relative advantage states that the process of spatial reorganization in the form of centralization and specialization will accelerate most rapidly at those places which stand to benefit most from increasing accessibility. In other words, transport innovations are most likely between those places which will benefit most from a lessening in the expenditure of time (cost or effort) to attain needed and desirable goods and services. Relative advantage is defined in terms of the benefits of operational success (inclusive of all economic, political, and cultural benefits) that can be derived from a particular place with a given expenditure of time.

Since locational decentralization, as defined in the expanded model, is simply an intermediate or lag-stage in the overall trend towards centralization, it is possible to confine the evaluation of the relative advantage concept to the basic model of spatial reorganization. The question is, where will this process be likely to accelerate most rapidly? Or, where is man most likely to introduce a transport improvement? In seeking answers to these questions, the concepts of relative advantage and spatial reorganization will be applied to a selected set of cities in the northern midwest of the U.S.

Relative Advantage for Transport Improvement in
Southern Michigan

In Figure 4a a closed system of seven major Michigan cities and eleven highway links has been selected to evaluate the concept of relative advantage. The immediate objective is to predict highway status for 1925 on the basis of information for 1900 and, similarly, to project the status of highways in 1965 from information known in 1940. For the initial years of each period, 1900 and 1940, the principal highway trunk lines were nearly homogeneous in quality – mostly unimproved clay and sand roads in 1900 and mostly two-lane paved roads in 1940. Thus, the calculation of travel-times between cities for

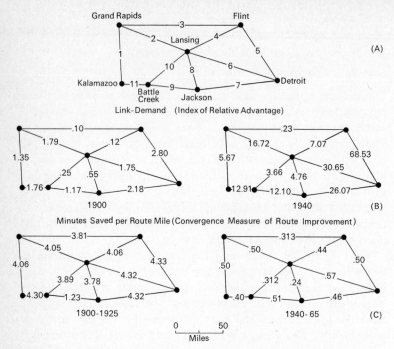

Figure 4. Relative advantage for highway improvement and time–space convergence for major Michigan roads 1900–1925 and 1940–65.

these two years assumes standard speeds of ten miles per hour for 1900 and forty miles per hour for 1940. For the years 1925 and 1965, travel-times are based on the following criteria:

1925 unimproved roads   (10 miles per hour)
      gravel roads   (25 miles per hour)
      brick roads   (35 miles per hour)
      paved two-lane roads   (40 miles per hour)

1965 (Where possible, actual travel-time data from the Michigan State Highway Department are used.[8])

     Otherwise:

      paved two-lane roads   (45 miles per hour)
      divided highways   (55 miles per hour)

limited access roads   (60 miles per hour)

Through application of the above criteria in calculating travel-times, a convergence measure of actual route improvement – minutes saved per route mile – is derived for the two periods in question. This convergence measure will be used to evaluate the success of the predictive variable – relative advantage. The hypothesis under investigation is as follows: the degree of innovation will increase as relative advantage increases. The surrogate used to represent relative advantage is an index of link-demand derived from the simply gravity model

$$\frac{p_i p_j}{d_{ij}^{2}}$$

where $p_i p_j$ is the product of the populations of the two places joined by the link, and d_{ij}^{2} is the square of the route mileage between them.[9]

The above procedure is complicated somewhat when a system has several places demanding travel over the same link. For example, the demand for travel over link 9 in Figure 4b is not only a function of travel-demand between Battle Creek and Jackson (see Figure 4a), but it is also a function of the demands for travel between Detroit and Battle Creek, Detroit and Kalamazoo, and Kalamazoo and Jackson. Thus, as illustrated in Figure 5, the link-demand for a high-

Figure 5. Link-demands calculation: Battle Creek to Jackson (1900).

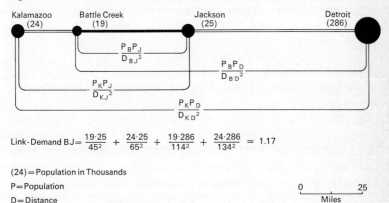

Link-Demand $BJ = \dfrac{19 \cdot 25}{45^2} + \dfrac{24 \cdot 25}{65^2} + \dfrac{19 \cdot 286}{114^2} + \dfrac{24 \cdot 286}{134^2} = 1.17$

(24) = Population in Thousands

P = Population

D = Distance

way improvement between Battle Creek and Jackson represents the sum of the gravity model indices for each pair of places whose inter-connection requires use of link 9. The demand values for the other ten links were determined in similar fashion and are shown in Figure 4b for the years 1900 and 1940. Shown in Figure 4c are the convergence values of actual route improvement for the periods 1900–1925 and 1940–65.

Spearman's rank correlation technique was used to measure the statistical association of the rankings of the demand and improvement variables. This technique yielded R values (significant at the 95 per cent level) of $0 \cdot 74$ for the 1900–1925 period and $0 \cdot 69$ for the 1940–65 period. The results, though not conclusive, are encouraging. It is evident that the inclusion of places outside the chosen system of seven cities such as Chicago, Toledo, Saginaw, and others might have greatly altered both the rankings of the link-demand and the results. Furthermore, the gravity model used here may be a comparatively crude measure of the relative advantage for transport improvement.

Although a comparison of the rankings of the link-demands for 1900 and for 1940 show a high degree of stability ($R = 0 \cdot 87$ at the 99 per cent level of significance), a similar comparison of the convergence rankings for the two periods reveals some signs of significant change in the time–space connectivity of Michigan's transport network. For example, link 2 from Grand Rapids to Lansing moved from eighth in the convergence ranking for 1900–1925 to fourth during the 1940–65 period. On the whole, however, the changes for 1940–65 were consistent with those of the 1900–1925 period of route improvement ($R = 0 \cdot 67$ at the 95 per cent level of significance).

In general, this evaluation suggests that highway development in Michigan has varied with the changes in relative advantage. And, owing to the pronounced stability in the rankings of the link-demands, it is evident that transport innovations helped to confirm and to augment the existing advantages in time–space connectivity for dominant places. For example, during both periods, Detroit ranked first among the seven cities in the average number of minutes saved per route mile along each of its radiating links. In essence, Detroit has been favoured by a greater increase in locational utility than any of the other six places in the system. Thus, in accordance with the norm of spatial reorganization as outlined in the basic model (Figure 1), Detroit should also be favoured by the greatest increase among the seven cities in the centralization and specialization of human activity.

NOTES

1. W. L. Garrison, 'Connectivity of the Interstate Highway System', *Papers and Proceedings of the Regional Science Association*, Vol. 6, 1960, pp. 121–37; K. J. Kansky, *Structure of Transportation Networks*, Chicago, Department of Geography Research Paper No. 84, University of Chicago Press, 1963.

2. For a more thorough discussion of time–space convergence, see D. G. Janelle, 'Central Place Development in a Time–Space Framework', *The Professional Geographer*, Vol. 20, 1968, pp. 5–10.

3. E. L. Ullman, 'The Role of Transportation and the Bases of Interaction', in W. L. Thomas, Jr (ed.), *Man's Role in Changing the Face of the Earth*, Chicago, University of Chicago Press, 1956, pp. 862–80.

4. An excellent discussion on both positive and negative feedback systems is provided by M. Maruyama, 'The Second Cybernetics: Deviation-Amplifying Mutual Causal Processes', *American Scientist*, Vol. 51, 1963, pp. 164–79; also, see L. von Bertalanffy, 'General System Theory', *General Systems*, Vol. 1, 1956, pp. 1–10.

5. Coverdale and Colpitts, Consultant Engineers, *Report on Traffic and Revenues, Proposed Mackinac Straits Bridge*, New York, Coverdale and Colpitts, 22 January 1952, p. 18.

6. R. M. Cyert and J. G. March, *A Behavioral Theory of the Firm*, Englewood Cliffs, N.J., Prentice-Hall, 1963; J. H. Henderson and R. E. Quandt, *Micro-Economic Theory, A Mathematical Approach*, New York, McGraw-Hill, 1958; H. A. Simon, 'Some Strategic Considerations in the Construction of Social Science Models', in P. F. Lazarsfeld (ed.), *Mathematical Thinking in the Social Sciences*, Glencoe, The Free Press, 1954, pp. 388–415.

7. J. Gottmann, 'Megalopolis, Or the Urbanization of the Northeastern Seaboard', *Economic Geography*, Vol. 33, 1957, pp. 189–200.

8. Michigan State Highway Department, *Highways Connecting Pertinent Cities with O'Hare Field (Chicago) or Metropolitan Airport*

(Detroit), Lansing, Michigan, Michigan State Highway Department, 1963.

9. For a good review and appraisal of the gravity model, see G. Olson, *Distance and Human Interaction*, Philadelphia, Regional Science Research Institute, 1965.

35. Urban Centrality and the Interweaving of Quaternary Activities

JEAN GOTTMANN

The dispersal of urban functions across the land has led some authors to question the centrality function of the modern city. Prefacing a new edition of Max Weber's classical essay on *The City*, Professor Don Martindale, of the University of Minnesota, implied that the solidly organized community and central place Weber was talking about was disappearing.[1] What used to make the tight organization of the urban community was becoming diffused across the country, and the nation was replacing the city as the framework of economic or social evolution and of the organization of space. This way of thinking seems to have been largely propagated by a school of sociologists from the American Middle West. Settlement has been very fluid in the central and western parts of the United States for more than a century. Still in these very regions, the student of landscapes can hardly deny that large cities have been growing larger, that some small cities have been lagging and decaying while others developed fast, and that in many centres new skylines sprang up and proliferated, fostered by the anxious and eager endeavours of local communities vying with one another.

So much investment and energy, poured into the old cores of cities and into a few spots selected to serve as new cores in larger metropolitan systems, indicates some need for grouping together the activities which correspond to the centrality function, traditionally located in central districts. But both the theoreticians of urban analysis, who seemed overwhelmed by the suburban sprawl and interpreted modern urbanization solely as a process of diffusion of the city, and the politicians of most countries where urbanization developed fast, worried about the increasing concentration of population and employment in and around a small number of the larger urban centres in their respective countries. In the United Kingdom, it was the flow towards Greater London and the surrounding counties in the South-east; in France, it was the growth of the Paris Region; in the Netherlands the growth of the 'Randstadt Holland' and more particularly of Amsterdam; in Switzerland, Zurich and, to a lesser extent, the Lemanic belt from Geneva to Montreux. In Canada, the region extending from Montreal to Windsor, Ontario (which still drains population and employment to a degree that alarms other parts of Quebec and Ontario) is looked upon with suspicion by the rest of the country. In the United States, the trends were more diversified as the national territory and economy were so much vaster and undergoing faster change; on the whole, concentration continued to develop in a small number of areas which were acquiring in the process more central functions, while larger areas within the country were being thinned out.

During the last twenty years about 400,000,000 people were added to the population of metropolitan areas of 100,000 and more. Probably two to three hundred million more will be added to these agglomerations during the 1970s. Obviously many more buildings, taking up more land around old cores or between older cities, have to be added to the standing mass. The master plan for the Region of Paris, published in 1965, indicated the need for building, during the following ten years, as many new housing units as were counted by the 1962 census in the City of Paris proper. Some people saw in this an indication that something equal to the old City of Paris had to be built anew and outside it. Certainly most of the new residential units have to be built outside the municipal limits of Paris, adding to the suburban sprawl. But the City of Paris is much more than a grouping of residences and of services of the kind that cater to the daily needs of residents. The differences between the residential function and the sum total of the Parisian community is made up, in part, of the conglomeration of industrial plants inherited from the period of manufacturing concentration and, in part, of those special functions and services which give the city its national and international centrality. This encompasses government, finance and business management, higher education and research, mass media, and entertainment of all kinds. Specialized trades and large-scale merchandise marts are also an important element of the system.

Some components of this system could be decentralized and sent away. The Citroën Automotive Works are to be moved to the outer periphery, north of the city. The central produce market of Les Halles has been moved to the southern suburb of Rungis near Orly airfield. Many smaller industrial establishments and some large government offices have been 'decentralized' to more distant locations. For some thirty years legislation has fostered decentralization of industry and restricted the growth of other kinds of land use in the Paris region, including offices. Nevertheless, total employment in the region kept on growing at a faster rate than the national average until very recently. The same trends of concentration were observed and similar legislation enforced in Greater London with rather similar results. In the late 1960s it seemed that the flow of people and employment concentrating in the London and Paris conurbations was slackening and that other urban regions in the two countries were growing as fast or faster. Whether this slowdown in concentration was the result of legislative and economic incentives, or a reaction against the over-congested environment of the great metropolises, or whether deeper economic and social forces had determined this shift in trends, has not yet been elucidated.

It remains clear that while the intense concentration of centrality functions in great international hubs, such as London and Paris, is somewhat decreasing in relative terms, more concentration is developing around a few other cities in England and France. We are still far from being able to acknowledge objectively a decrease in the centrality of large cities, at least of some of them. In fact, trends similar to those in American cities may be observed in the leading cities of Western Europe: in the central cores land speculation remains very lively. Land values have been rising and more construction is taking place: office buildings, civic centres, arenas, theatres, museums, and hotels. Redevelopment leads, however, to an urban core of a more specialized kind. The core is losing some of the manufactures, crafts, residences, and shops that it used to have. But it is developing in other ways typical of the centrality of a great crossroads system. The economic activities which keep agglutinating in the urban centres or in their vicinity belong to a somewhat different gamut than before.

The Interwoven Quaternary Activities

Fundamental linkages exist between a good many of the economic activities now expanding in the centres of those cities which are still vigorously growing. Common characteristics of these economic activities are their concern with and operation through abstract transactions, which direct the processes of production and distribution by more or less remote control. These transactional activities were traditionally carried on in urban locations and were the product of administration (including the administration of justice), politics, business management, the gathering and interpretation of information (and therefore of the mass media) but also of scientific research, higher education, the performing arts, and the specialized commercial trades aiming at special categories of customers.

All these activities are at some stage interdependent. This we know by logical deduction as well as by empirical observation of the way in which each of these activities operates. We have not tried, however, to analyse systematically the linkages between all these economic activities. In the past the total number of personnel involved in transactional work was very small. The managerial and professional occupations represented a negligible fraction of the labour force, even in the most advanced countries. The total amount of information available to this specialized and scarce personnel was rather limited and processed at a few major nodes of traffic. The concentration of wealth, power, and knowledge would therefore group the few competent people at selected spots well served in terms of information flow. Large seaports and major seats of political power used to be preferred locations for such concentrations.

The characteristics of transactional work have changed, especially in quantitative terms, during the twentieth century. Rapid progress in the technology of transport and communications on the one hand, and in the geographical expansion of the economically developed world on the other, have been the main factors inflating the quantity of decisions to be made, the variety of factors at play in the decision-making, the volume and intensity of the flow of information in all fields. To handle this work, the personnel needed to manipulate the data, make the decisions, and perform transactions had to expand. The managerial and professional occupations represent now a substantial proportion of the labour force in advanced countries: about 13 per cent in England and Wales (1966), 15 per cent in France (1968), 10 per cent in Switzerland (1960), 12 per cent in the Netherlands (1960), 17·5 per cent in Sweden (1965), 21 per cent in Canada (1968), 21·8 per cent in the United States (1967). These figures are not quite comparable, as the definitions of occupational categories vary from country to country; but the general picture is clear: the 'high status' occupations requiring personnel with special training and qualifications form the most rapidly expanding sector of the labour force.

In the early 1950s, the educated public opinion was stunned to learn from a report prepared by UNESCO that of all the scientific and technological personnel that ever lived, about 97 per cent were alive. This percentage may have been established on the basis of debatable estimates about past centuries; still there was little doubt that it was close enough to the truth. By 1966 the total number of the people employed as faculty by the higher education establishments in the United States rose to 657,000, about 1 per cent of total non-agricultural civilian employment, and surpassed the number of all employees in the mining establishments in the country, which remains the largest mining producer in the world. Higher education establishments cannot be found in every village. They are often grouped in or near large urban agglomerations, and such gatherings will attract to their proximity other activities such as research laboratories and institutes, libraries, museums, specialized trades, etc., all requiring rather specially trained personnel. There is a sort of cycle and snowballing effect in the interweaving of transactional activities.

The function of urban centrality is returning closer to what it used to be before the Industrial Revolution started; it is again dominated by transactions and by executive, legislative, judicial, and commercial functions. However, two new categories of academic work and research, have to be added to the constellation of activities generating urban centrality. And at the same time a new revolution brings about a novel organization of the labour market for a highly qualified and specialized personnel, which in turn needs the assistance of large numbers of specialized clerical staff. This labour problem becomes one of the major factors of concentration for new jobs, adding to the situation inherited from the past in which the networks of information were centralized in hubs of power and accessibility.

The old classification of occupations and economic activities in three sectors – the primary, producing raw materials; the secondary, processing them into finished goods; the tertiary, consisting of the services – is no longer adequate. We must recognize a *quaternary* sector of economic activities corresponding to the transactional work which now employs a large and growing part of the labour force. Studying the concentration of white collar workers in Megalopolis, I suggested in 1961 this new *quaternary sector* for labour statistics. It is being gradually adopted as a useful distinction to assess modern trends. In the occupational structure, the quaternary sector is usually meant to include only the managerial, professional, and higher level technical personnel. In fact, it ought to be extended to a part of the more numerous category of occupations designated as 'clerical'. Perhaps, as time goes on, the upper strata of the clerical occupations will be increasingly taken over by personnel with higher technical skills and academic degrees qualifying in the professional category. At present, however, many clerical workers participate in the data gathering and interpreting process, which integrates them with the quaternary rather than the tertiary sector of services. The tertiary sector would remain essentially concerned with the transportation and manipulation of goods, with domestic services, and with the less qualified operations of distribution and sales.

The quaternary sector permeates not only the services but also some of the secondary sector. Publishing, for instance, is considered a manufacturing industry and therefore belongs to the secondary sector of economic activity. A large part, however, perhaps the majority of employment in publishing firms, consists of managerial and editorial staff belonging rather in the quaternary sector. This also is the case of the research personnel of large manufacturing concerns. Research, even in a technical laboratory, is part of the process of data gathering and analysis and this is largely a transactional activity.

To understand the modern *community at work* in the central city, we must observe the interdependence of the quaternary activities.

They have a trend to group themselves together. The large cities have a well-known internal geography of adjoining districts which are highly specialized: the financial district, the press and mass media district, the law courts district, the corporation headquarters area, are all subdivisions of what is usually designated as a central business district. In recent years the unity of this C.B.D. has been broken up in many cities into two or more groupings. But these different groups remain very much interwoven in their daily work. The interweaving of the quaternary activities has determined the rise of the skylines, the expansion of office buildings, and the very intensive traffic between the various components of the quaternary community within the metropolis on the one hand and between several central cities on the other. This is why decentralization of the upper level of the services has been more difficult to achieve than the dispersal of manufactures or of rank and file offices. This is also why the cities with a large quaternary sector are so bustling and struggling against congestion.

Every time I have affirmed the results of my findings, particularly in America and in France, but also in other countries, including Japan, as to the obvious concentration of contemporary quaternary activities in a few central cities, the question has been thrown at me: 'Isn't dispersal going to occur soon owing to progress in the technology of communications?' It is noteworthy, and the Cowan team recognizes it in their book,[2] that no signs are as yet present that transactional quaternary work can be dispersed if this means restricting or avoiding direct personal contacts. In fact, such contacts are proliferating on a scale and at a frequency hardly imaginable a quarter of a century ago. Scientific and technological work is increasingly pursued as teamwork; decision-making multiplies consultations, conferences, and committees.

Indeed, the transactional activity of a larger centre is no longer measured only by the payroll or the floor space of the offices gathered in and around the place. One ought to take into the tableau the movement of participants in the transactions who come into the centre from the outside. The movement in and out of Central London, of people who do not live or have their employment in the G.L.C. area, is enormous and, expanding. It is very difficult to measure it quantitatively and, even more, qualitatively, that is, in terms of its role in the total volume of transactions that are actually negotiated or considered in London. The equipment that services these participants in the work of London offices, though outsiders in terms of statistical count, occupies a large part of the central city. It includes the hotels of the West End, restaurants, theatres and other establishments of the performing arts, specialized shops, luxury department stores, hospitals, museums, libraries, etc.

The analysis of quaternary activities is indeed poorly served by studies which limit themselves to one category of land use, though the work on office location and growth pursued by so many geographers, architects, and planners brings a worthy contribution in terms of improving the precision of our knowledge about land use patterns in the various cities covered. In this respect the work on London is probably the most advanced,[3] although some good analysis has been conducted on central Paris (for the 'Schéma Directeur' prepared by the District of the Paris Region in 1965, and by the team of the Atlas of Paris under the direction of Jean Bastié and J. Beaujeu-Garnier).[4]

In Search of the Centre's Coherence

The most notable cases of successful decentralization for rather large offices have been achieved with respect to governmental agencies, or at least some of their bureaux. This is true in several countries of Europe as well as in the United States. It may be related to the fact that the trends in the distribution of offices are now caught between two forces: on one hand, powerful socio-economic factors work for more concentration within the area easily accessible for frequent personal contact; on the other, political pressures work for dispersal over the whole territory of a nation. One of the basic socio-economic forces is the competitive nature of our society and perhaps of the human species altogether. Competition does not have the same importance for governmental agencies as it does for establishments that do not enjoy the monopolistic privileges of government. It is easier to send offices away from strategic centres that do not compete for survival with others in the same field. A competing enterprise wants to be where it can get information, personnel, and clients as good as its competitors do. Competition is an extremely potent reason for being on the spot, 'where the action is', to both employers and employees. The former compete for the success of their enterprises, the latter for more opportunity and success in their careers. Competition as a phenomenon is extremely difficult to reduce to model form, and even to analyse. It is certain, however, that location is an important factor in the competitive position of any activity that is part of the social and economic processes of society. Inversely, the competition among firms and people must be a factor in geographical distribution, and in the trends of concentration or dispersal. Competition between cities and within the city strengthens in fact the coherence of the urban system.

The analysis of linkages is still based on land use although it has been usually recognized, but more intuitively than systematically, that location in certain vicinities has the advantage of proximity to other establishments with which the functioning of the first establishment considered is deeply involved. This involvement may be partly a matter of the routine work of the establishment, partly a matter of personnel recruitment, partly a matter of prestige or status. This was rather well brought out as a general theory by W. T. W. Morgan.[5] But it would be wrong to disregard the local environment of a certain city which may be particularly advantageous to office work if it is endowed with facilities for entertaining, lodging, servicing transient visitors; especially if it can also offer expert opinion on matters external to the usual routine and add to this constellation the excitement of artistic, literary, and scientific events. All these circumstances can hardly be equally duplicated in an ever-increasing number of places.

The competitive value of a given location depends therefore on more than just the categories of offices with related interests. In the transactions of a large centre today there are links between establishments and activities that contribute to the quality of the community at work. The modern method of analysis has been isolating particular cases and categories, instead of addressing itself to the general organization of a local man-made and fluid environment, the inner wiring of which should be better understood. The centrality of a city has a certain coherence, which the map of land use insufficiently demonstrates.

Caught in the conflict between forces fostering concentration and the policies of dispersal, the quarternary activities have been fighting an onslaught of chaos.

There is little doubt that the main international hubs of transactional activity, such as New York, Washington, London, Paris, Amsterdam, Tokyo, Moscow, are growing so big and so complex that they appear hardly manageable. Very little is known about the way they work. In the constantly self-refining and subdividing division of labour that now affects the masses of white-collar workers, some stages of work require presence in large hubs and others could be performed elsewhere. What can be decentralized and to where is a question which has been little studied in terms of general principles. The practice has chiefly been to forbid new building for certain uses in certain zones. This restrictive zoning or prohibitive legislation was first applied to manufactures and warehouses, then to offices. While pressure was exerted to push some employment out, incentives were provided either by the central government or by local government, and sometimes by both, to bring the moving activities to areas or places of lagging growth, or even economic decline.

It may be time to investigate the situation in cities of intermediate size (that is, with populations of between 100,000 and 1,500,000) and see how these communities work in terms of urban centrality. Such cities may be able to receive easily new industrial plants and warehouses, but it may be much more difficult for them to accommodate quaternary activities.

Many urban centres grew up owing to the presence of manufactures and did not develop substantial interwoven local networks of transactional nature. Whether such an environment would provide more than exile for quaternary establishments is a question that has seldom been examined. A few cases are known in which some large corporation headquarters tried to move out of a large transactional centre to a smaller one, and most of such experiments are known to have failed. The converging moves have on the contrary been frequent and generally successful. It would seem indispensable to study the linkages of quaternary activities in those cities of intermediate size where some networks have developed, either because of a large volume of industrial activity, often linked to a seaport or hub of trans-

port function, or because a network has formed around a large institution of potent transactional role, such as a great university (Oxford),
a governmental function (Edinburgh), and sometimes a religious
(Geneva) or recreational function (Nice or Miami). Some research
was conducted in this respect on French provincial cities (especially
by Jean Labasse and Michel Rochefort) to prepare the choice of the
eight 'métropoles d'équilibre'.[6]

Such an inquiry should not be restricted to the analysis of the
specialized function or agency which may dominate the local situation, but it should focus on the linkages bringing about a network of
interdependent activities around the original nucleus.

Classifying the Factors of Interweaving

From our quite inadequate knowledge of the interweaving of quaternary activities in the hubs of the greater cities, one may derive a tenta-
tive classification of the linkages, not in terms of land use and physical
proximity, but as categories of factors affecting functional needs of
the clustering activities. Nine categories of such factors seem to be
present in the large and best organized transactional centres.

1. *Accessibility* is the first prerequisite for the development of centrality. Transactional centres usually develop at major crossroads of
well-travelled itineraries. In some cases an isolated seat of power may
have determined the location of transactions, but these took on substantial volume and acquired a certain permanence only when adequate accessibility was provided to the isolated site. Means of access
have, of course, varied through the ages. In the Roman Empire, all
roads led to Rome. In nineteenth-century France, the networks of
highways and railways were obviously woven around Paris as the
dominant centre. In modern Britain, the major rail lines and motorways all radiate from London. The airport has now supplied a third
means of accessibility, especially important in large countries (such as
the United States, Canada, the U.S.S.R., and Brazil), or for insular
positions.

There are three major competing means of transport today, besides seafaring: the motor car, the train, and the aeroplane. The motor car has been a factor of dispersal of economic activities and has greatly congested access to central spots for large numbers of people who want to gather there, particularly at peak time. The problem of parking has been and will remain the nightmare of active urban central districts. American cities have, in most cases, generously provided for parking in the heart of the cities, increasing the cost of land in such areas and lowering the density of profitable use. The maintenance of central coherence in large transactional centres requires rapid public transit, that is, some kind of rail transit. The railway station is still an important factor of centrality in European cities. A frequent rail shuttle serving cities which want to preserve or develop a transactional network between them has proved to be essential in areas of great density of urban centres. A remarkable system of such rail connections is offered by the Trans-Europe Express trains between major European cities. The T.E.E. trains have become part of the communications and transactional network of Western Europe, and many transactions are prepared on board during the trip. The new Tokaido line between Tokyo and Osaka is another illustration of the same trend, as is the success of the Metro-Liner between New York and Washington. On the local scale one notices the number of cities building or expanding underground metropolitan rail systems (such as Stockholm, Milan, Paris, Toronto, Montreal, etc.). In the United States, however, the rail is badly lagging behind. Although most of the mail in American cities is still handled through the central post office located near the railroad station, today most of the mail travels by air, and considerable lorry movement around the old post offices adds to the congestion of city streets.

The airport is rapidly becoming a factor of centrality. When located far from the central district, it attracts various establishments, starting with large inns and hotels equipped for conferences and specialized shopping, so that the surroundings of O'Hare Airport, for instance, begin to look like a new loosely designed central district in the suburbs of Chicago. As air traffic expands, airports are bound to attract more services and transactional activity to new locations. This may be noticed in the southern suburbs of Amsterdam, and around the London Heathrow Airport. Twenty cities, located in ten countries, generated in 1967–8 about 80 per cent of all the air traffic carried by airlines in the non-Communist world.

2. *Information flows* are the second prerequisite of successful centrality. This has always been the case and the coffee house is often mentioned as an ancestor of modern offices. Information is the basic raw material of decision-making and transactions. One never has too good information for the decisions one is responsible for. The phrase of Thomas Jefferson that 'knowledge is power' is certainly as true as ever. Information today does not flow only through the offices, publications, and broadcasts of the mass media, but it requires an ever-extending and subdividing network of communications. Every quaternary activity heavily depends on the availability of diverse, accurate, and up-to-date information.

Information flows criss-cross at a variety of meeting points, outside formal offices: around luncheon or dinner tables, at cocktail parties, in clubs, in the lobbies of conferences, on selected golf courses, and on T.E.E. trains. Whether direct personal contact is essential for the exchange and interpretation of information is now being greatly debated. Electronic equipment to date has not succeeded in disrupting the rapidly growing need for more and more face-to-face meetings for all kinds of purposes from simple managerial decisions to conferences of national or international experts.

The study of the possibility of transacting quaternary business by wire or over the waves does not appear at present to give as satisfactory results as does physical presence. Communication over an electronic network may be satisfactory between individuals who know one another intimately and trust one another fully. Between individuals who do not have such a close relationship, communication over networks usually leads to more personal contacts. The reasons for this need of physical presence, a major factor of urban centrality, seem to be imbedded in human psychology and in the highly competitive character of a dynamic society.

3. *Transactional performance* is a complex set of factors rather difficult to separate one from another, and to evaluate in quantitative fashion. It is closely related to the imperatives of competition. Various conditions can improve transactional performance in a given locale. In addition to providing an environment with excellent physical

accessibility and the volume and quality of information, the highest efficiency of work involves the participants being kept in the best possible
mood, fitness, with all the desirable equipment available. Personnel,
services, and physical environment must all be considered. The co-
incidence of so many different conditions will obviously be difficult
to achieve outside the few centres which have been endowed with at
least some of the needed assets by the past, and where the investment
necessary to provide for the desired environment can be afforded.
Hence the competition between cities to put together and maintain
a transactional centre.

4. The *labour market* is a fundamental condition for good performance. It has to be considered at different levels of personnel.
Personnel of managerial and professional status is difficult to recruit
and to keep outside those areas where it has traditionally gathered or
to which it is now attracted by some kind of special glamour and
amenities.

To perform their regular duties this upper strata needs the assistance of a larger number and a great variety of workers at a lower
salary level but quite indispensable to the good performance of the
establishment. Thus, a well organized transactional centre must offer
easy recruiting in a great variety of diverse occupations: from secre-
taries to sales clerks and restaurant waiters; from accountants and
physicians to computer programmers and librarians. Modern technology and automation have accelerated the subdivision of labour in
the white-collar occupations, and this process has been still further
refined by the rapid expansion in the volume of information transactions. The volume of the labour market needed at the various levels of
the quaternary activities will be expanding for some time; the demand
is still rising faster than the supply. In a competitive situation the
larger centres can offer greater choice to the employer and more
opportunity to the employee.

5. Transactional work employs rather well-paid and choosy personnel. Transactions are better performed in an environment providing *amenities and entertainment*. A centre of quaternary activities is
normally a large consumer of entertainment, and in competitive situations this may be an important part of the transaction. Moreover, the
quality and availability of such services are part of the amenities

which make the place more desirable for the workers that are the most in demand. A great variety of amenities and of entertainment services enters into the constellation of activities making up urban centrality. It does not always have to be at the doorstep of the customer, but must be within easy reach by a short trip. There are good reasons why Covent Garden and Soho are in a central location in central London, why the Paris theatre district clusters around the Opéra, interspersing with financial offices, and why Broadway and Times Square are in the heart of Manhattan. Entertainment is not limited, of course, to the performing arts and to catering; it involves museums, art galleries, monuments, and a variety of events. Amenities include physical as well as cultural local features.

6. *Expert consultation* and specialized services of a professional kind, including medical services, are another constellation of factors favouring and improving the transactional environment. The need for such services illustrates well the importance of the labour market, especially at its upper level; a large volume of transactions may be expected to attract what could be called a 'market of talent' in the professional field. And this links, of course, with the world of entertainment as well as with white-collar employment in general.

7. The *market of money and credit* involving the presence of a diversified financial community is another obvious category of linkages for any kind of transactional activity. The money market lives by information and generates more of it.

8. *Specialized shopping facilities* are another part of the amenities of the place for visitors from the outside as well as for the recruitment of labour at various levels. Office managers often report difficulties in finding good secretarial and clerical help in areas distant from good shopping facilities. There is a well understood time budgeting involved, for visitors as well as for local people, in having the greatest possible variety of trading services at hand near the offices.

9. Last but not least, the *educational facilities* are a factor in transactional work. When the Port of New York Authority began to offer floor space in the skyscrapers of its projected World Trade Centre, institutions such as the Berlitz School of Languages were among the first interested to rent space in a large agglomeration of offices specializing in international trade. The linkage is obvious. Another

linkage has to do with the labour market: white-collar workers prefer a location with good educational establishments, either for the education of their children, or to promote their own competence through improved training. Moreover, a university campus usually adds to the liveliness of a city, to the quality of expert advice locally available, and to the customers of the performing arts and other amenities.

We have thus enumerated the nine major categories of interlocked factors through which one may analyse the functional linkages between the various economic activities of a large transactional community, and also the linkages that make for the clustering of each category of activities.

New and Ancient Components of Centrality

The needs and functions of centrality in the modern city are largely reminiscent of very ancient components of the central urban district. Most of the factors enumerated in our nine categories were present in the Athens of Plato's and Aristotle's times. Novel elements are found in the greater variety of the means of transportation and particularly in the disruptive influence that the motor car and the airport exert on inherited locations. Also, the greater variety of expert consultants, of specialized shopping, the much greater role of higher education and of the amenities for the majority of the labour force are new considerations and components of centrality.

The need for security in a large agglomeration, including the security of the transactional activities, is an essential aspect of 'urbanity' and it has been too often disregarded until the present wave of criminality began sweeping the streets. What is particularly new and would have been fiercely resented by the political philosophers of classical Greece is the much greater role assumed in the activities of the city by visitors from the outside, usually coming from other cities to perform transactions. The function of receiving these transients, without whose presence a great deal of the transactional activity would lapse or migrate to some other place, causes a certain imbalance in the organization and the coherence of a community. The movement of the outsiders is not included in the usual counts, but it is essential to the routine of the modern central urban district.

It is significant that offices and quaternary activities are beginning to be carefully studied in the more developed countries, but the process of urban evolution will not be understood and attended to by limiting investigations to land use and employment. The central city today is a more complex, interwoven body than that. A city undergoes in its evolution erosion in some parts, fluidity, transfers, and sedimentation in others. It must be looked upon as a process with some physical features; but its dynamism is animated by abstract transactions, by an interwoven network of linkages binding together in that place a variety of transactional activities. Too often we avoid the analysis of these interwoven activities, which are the crux of the matter, in the vague hope that new machinery, a wonderful technology, will sometimes tomorrow undo the knots and simplify our work. In the meanwhile, if the city expresses our society, it also contains it, and the mismanagement and misunderstanding of the urban process gravely add to the ills of society.

NOTES

1. Max Weber, *The City*, trans. D. Martindale and G. Neuwirth, New York, 1966.

2. Peter Cowan et al., *The Office: A Facet of Urban Growth*, London, 1969.

3. P. W. Daniels, 'Office Decentralization from London: Policy and Practice', *Regional Studies*, Vol. 3, 1969, pp. 171–8.

4. Association universitaire de recherches géographiques et cartographiques, *Atlas de Paris et de la région parisienne*, Paris, 1967.

5. W. T. W. Morgan, 'A Functional Approach to the Study of Office Distribution', *Tijdschrift voor Economische en Sociale Geographie*, Vol. 52, 1961, pp. 207–10.

6. Délégation générale au district de la région de Paris, *Schéma directeur d'aménagement et urbanisme de la région de Paris*, 1965.

36. Need for More Balance in the Flow of Communications

DELOS FOUR*

Extract from the Report of Delos Four

Communications serve the citizens' possibilities of choice and variety:

1. As with transport, a fuller network of communications can re- lieve the load on centres of over-high density by permitting activities to be more widely diffused.

2. But diffusion alone does not solve the more fundamental problems created by the massive force of communications bombarding modern man. The fact of wider knowledge is one of his great liberations and enables him to exercise citizenship at different levels in his planetary society. Yet in the last analysis each citizen has only so much span of attention and this scarcity demands priorities. Some are already apparent. He needs a balance between the flood of information streaming in through increasingly efficient channels from all round the world and the local coverage of situations for which he may have immediate responsibility. He needs protection against new technological forms of intrusion on his privacy. He needs keener education in the distinction between fact and guess and a deeper understanding of the value and depth of different types of information.

3. Above all, his need for direct personal contacts should be enhanced and not diminished by the modern network of communication.

* Participants in the Fourth Delos Symposion included: A. K. Brohi, R. Buckminster Fuller, Hedley Donovan, C. A. Doxiadis, Garrett Eckbo, Roger Grégoire, Bertrand de Jouvenal, Reginald S. Lourie, Marshal McLuhan, Richard L. Meier, Marie C. McGuire, Kenzo Tange, Arnold Toynbee, C. H. Waddington, Fritz Zwicky.

Discussion

The success of man staying on earth will be related to the effectiveness of his means of intercommunication.

Cities were designed when representative government was based on communication by word of mouth and mail received by horse transportation. Then there was a 1:1 correspondence of communication and transportation. We have speeded up the rate of information distribution but have not speeded up means of reacting to it.

Systems of communications brought about great changes. The postal system was still transportation, but the telegraphic wire enabled a head of state (Lincoln) for the first time to have direct contact with a battle front. With radio the world became interconnected.

Children learn early that non-verbal communication is often more important than verbal communication: that they must disguise what they say to be properly understood.

A study showed that $4\frac{1}{2}$–5 feet is a neutral distance for non-verbal communication, and 20–30 inches for verbal communication. A distance of $5\frac{1}{2}$–8 feet discourages discussion. Physical distance controls the content of communication. How can one immediately set the tone of a communication along the hot line between Washington and Moscow?

Much of our communication is a one-way system. There is no means of setting up a dialogue. In former times man received all information about his family, most about his neighbourhood, less about his city, and very little from the outside world. Now we receive world news in an instant, but have lost contact with those who live close to us. Man must be a processor of information, not just a receiver or a transmitter. The overflow of information from outside means that we have little time to process it. We need to strengthen man's ability to process and pass on information to his family and small group, but this means there must be opportunities for dialogue.

Something has happened to modern man that makes things that are distant acquire a greater importance than things that are at hand.

Even within the family circle children prefer to read or watch television than to converse together. The solution does not lie in reviving ancient models but in transforming the psychic life of modern man. Emotional energy is required to cope with the new scale of communications, but there is no increase in the emotional reserves of man. Our response to remote events drains off emotional energy and there is none left for face-to-face communications.

The interest in distant events is not so much due to change in people as to economic influence. Top-level world news is easier and cheaper to obtain than well presented local news.

Individual communication has been replaced by group communication to influence people in education, law, policy, politics. In doing so, a dimension has been lost.

Communication demands are growing twice as fast as the already high transportation demands. They are also cheaper to meet. We need sanitary engineers of the electronic environment to deal with interference in reception of communications (pollution).

Communications stress has the effect of sending animals into a state of shock, and their sensitivity is passed on to the next generation, which can then tolerate even less stress.

It is possible to plan the forms of communication, but what about their content? Since indiscriminate communication of all facts is impossible, economic resources dictate a sort of censorship. How much control of the content do you need to produce an orderly form?

A possible system of measurement is to count, with the help of a computer, the number of social transactions that people willingly undertake within a city. It is assumed that each transaction results in an improvement of personal welfare, but some are more important than others, so there must be a method of weighing them. Perhaps this can be done by giving ratings for time and culture related to the transaction.

Unless a means of assessing the quality of the service is decided upon and included, you will computerize a lot of nonsense.

It can be implicitly assumed that transportation generates more transportation, and communication more communication. Coverage of something on television leads to demand for print coverage of the same things, etc. Although we are sometimes overwhelmed, we are receiving and handling far more information today than would have been thought possible fifty years ago. Education continues to fit people to do just that.

As greater funds of information are made available to the individual, screening becomes more important. We need a new breed that can deal with a greater degree of stimulation without reacting.

We need a communication system closely linked to our powers of tolerance. We need to learn enough about privacy to devise effective filters.

We suffer from strangulation of communications through the written word. Little information about a lot of subjects makes one want to know what went into the waste-basket. Governments have to find a technique for communication so that talent at the local level can make use of its services.

What is the size of a communication system that an individual can cope with? There is at present a misuse of high-powered means of communication for reasons of snobbery. Old fashioned written letters gave one time to consider the answers to them.

Papers

Kenzo Tange

The second Industrial Revolution, which has begun only recently, is a revolution created by information theory and communications techniques, a revolution in which man is learning to extend the functions of his nervous system.

If we were to consider society, together with its physical manifestations, as an organic body, the change brought about by the first Industrial Revolution would be classed as metabolic functions, and the fruits of the second Industrial Revolution would be classed as control functions. In the physical structure of contemporary society, the metabolic functions are becoming ever more active, and a more complete and intricate system of control functions is now developing which can raise the whole to a higher and better organized organic level.

Society contains several different dimensional levels including the individual, the family, the legal person, the city, the nation. A gradual functional differentiation is taking place among these compositional elements, and this differentiation has given rise to much of the diversity that characterizes contemporary society. Nevertheless, the differentiated elements are linked within their own dimensional level or with other levels by mutual communication, which maintains the life of the organisms as a whole. Norbert Wiener, the creator of cybernetics, has described communications as the 'cement of society'.

According to Wiener, the connections that tie society together are of two types: energetic couplings and informational couplings. Energy couplings are like the alignment of atoms in a mineral and perhaps like the links between cells in a plant. Analogically speaking, the ancient society based on fixed classes or ranks was a society held together by energetic couplings.

An informational coupling, on the other hand, is the sort of connection that links together the cells of an animal. It involves a nervous system along which information is sent and returned in order to control action. In other words, it is a link that requires the possibility of mutual exchange or feedback. A society in which the informational couplings are strong is apt to be a highly democratic society.

It is with human speech that the informational couplings in human society begin. The important point here is that although language and the communication it permits are as old as mankind, some of the most important techniques for transmitting, exchanging, and storing and treating information have taken place in the twentieth century, and particularly in the past decade or two. We are, in effect, undergoing a great revolution in the science and technology of communications, and as a result, the whole organization of contemporary society is being transformed.

Through the various present-day media of communication – mass media such as publishing, radio, and television, as well as the more personal media represented by the telephone, the telegraph, and teletype – mankind receives an untold mass of information each day. Indeed, it is sometimes complained that human beings are being stifled by a communications overload. Still, man devises communications techniques to cope with the vast quantity pouring in: our electronic computers and man-made brains absorb millions of bits of information, remember them, arrange them, compile them, sift them, and otherwise dispose of them in such a way as to help us to make decisions and take actions.

The suggestion has been made that these new means of communication will obviate the necessity for face-to-face contact among people. I, however, agree with the many scholars who think that the effect will be just the opposite, and that these various marvels of indirect communication will create an even greater need and urge for direct communication. The contemporary age is the age of organization: in other words, it is the age of the conference. Important decisions are no longer very often made by individuals. They are made by groups sitting in conference, or by even more complicated organizations. And the conference is basically a meeting of men in direct communication with one another.

Roger Grégoire

Communications technologists, as well as experts in communication theory, tend to ignore the qualitative aspects of the 'information' to be transmitted, that is, the real aim of communications.

From this point of view, 'information' can be distributed *grosso modo* into four groups:

1. Signals (or orders), the results of which should be preconceived and predecided reactions (for example, you press the button and the elevator operator moves his machine to meet you).

2. Educational information, leading to personal reaction by the recipient, who may modify his previous attitudes (for example, political and scientific information).

3. Propaganda, using, apparently, the educational approach, but aiming at imposing reactions from outside (for example, advertising).

4. Exchanges, which may have no justification other than pleasure of the dialogue, but which lead to joint attitudes or action (for example, all kinds of love exchanges).

The progress of mankind assumes the continued dehumanization of communications of type 1, containing nothing but 'Signals' (for example, the electronic brain of the elevator will respond to my button rather than an elevator operator). Urban development goes happily in this direction.

Both types 2 and 3 – 'Educational' information and 'Propaganda' – are being more and more efficiently extended by 'mass media', which work far beyond urban settlements. For these communications there is nothing nowadays to gain (or lose) by living in big cities.

The key point is that of type 4. 'Exchanges' assume *some* physical relations. Close distance is not indispensable. A voice (even on a record) may suffice, or the personal style of a letter.

R. Buckminster Fuller

I often play a mental game, which I started a great many years ago. I patterned it after the physical discipline, with which all humans are familiar, of lifting progressively heavier weights on successive days, thus gradually becoming more physically powerful. When I started playing my mental game, my scheme was to ask myself a little larger and more difficult question each day. I also gave myself a basic playing rule, that I must always answer the questions from my own direct experience. I have been playing that game for a long time. Finally I came to the question: What do you mean by the word 'universe'? And I said to myself, if you can't answer that question, you must give up the use of the word universe, because you are being deceitful to yourself and others by suggesting that it has a meaning. Following my own rules, I gave myself the answer: 'Universe is the aggregate of all humans' consciously apprehended and communicated (to self or others) experiences.' Because I had answered in terms of experience, my definition has withstood all subsequent testing by myself and others. I haven't been able to find any thinkable aspect of universe that has been overlooked. We have experiences of dreaming, falsification, multiplication of the numbers of words in the dictionary, and so on. I don't find any experiences that are not included in the definition. So, for the time being, I go along with that definition. It has been fruitful.

Playing the same kind of game and starting with universe as defined, I found that the universe definition included metaphysics because metaphysics deals with thoughts which are weightless. The physicist defining the physical universe (Einstein's famous definition) had deliberately excluded metaphysics because they are imponderable. So, I found it interesting that I had a definition that also included the metaphysical universe – of mathematics, thoughts, and dreams as realistic experiences. And because all of my experiences had beginnings and endings, they were finite. I said, therefore, that the aggregate of finites must also be finite. Therefore, the universe, including both physics and mathematics, is finite.

In playing that kind of game I now had the advantage of being able to start not only with total finiteness but logically – as men, lacking a definition of the whole universe, had not been able to start logically before. This gave me many advantages, for the whole system was finite. I thus came logically to some mathematical discoveries regarding the thought process. I would like to give you a simple way of looking at things, which I found appropriate once one starts with a definition of the finite whole.

I also found this process of working with finite logic from the whole to the particular to be a very effective kind of strategy in trying, for instance, to think our way through to understanding what our human function in the universe might be. I found that, when I was confronted with a vast question and an enormous amount of material and experience, one of the first things I always tried to do was to make a basic division of the universe and therefore to subdivide the relevant part into progressively smaller halves, always, successively, selecting the half most clearly containing – and therefore relevant to – the problem until I reached an understandable and very local level in universe. In developing the solution to complex problems in modern information theory, which governs the designs of computers, this same principle of progressive subdivision and selection of the relevant half is used and each progressive subdivision is called a 'bit' and the number of subdivisions totally required are known as 'so many bits'.

I found it is quite possible to subdivide the universe instantly by developing the concept of a 'system'. A system is a local phenomenon in the universe that is geometrically definable because it returns or closes upon itself in all directions. Systems may be symmetrical or asymmetrical. I found that systems are the first subdivision of universe for they subdivide the universe into all the universe that is inside and all the universe that is outside the system. This divided the universe into the macrocosm and the microcosm. Then came the extraordinarily surprising and sudden discovery that this system concept led to an important understanding of − what we do when we think.

I am quite certain that thoughts are not bright ideas mysteriously inserted into a vacuum chamber in the head. I'm quite confident that what we do when we think is to behave as follows:

We dismiss the irrelevancies. I find that our brain is filled with constant reports and notices in which we're being told about various events around us. All of us have experiences of saying to one another, 'What's that friend's name? You know, the man we both know. We were with him for three years.' And neither of us can remember his name right away. But we all experience suddenly recalling the name possibly five minutes later, possibly the next morning.

The main point is that there is a definite lag in the search to memory storage and its feedback and that there is a great variety in the rates of lag between some recalls and others that we have stored deeply. Because we do get such feedbacks; we are always receiving a great deal of feedback from questions we had even forgotten that we had ever asked. On my way here today I looked at a tree and I said, 'What kind of a tree is that?' And I asked many other questions as I went along. I am asking myself questions all the time; and because the lags are very different for the different kinds of memories, I find that when I am lying down in my bed and trying to go to sleep, I get report after report coming back telling me about things that I had asked questions about and forgotten that I had asked them. At all times we are the almost chaotic focus of brain-dispatched messengers trying to come into our conscious thought pattern to give us the answer to questions we or others in our presence have asked. Therefore, I have discovered that what I do when thinking is to say: 'Keep those messengers outside for a moment. That's very interesting. I am glad they're there but please keep them outside because all I want to think about right now is this glass of water.'

I discover, then, that thinking is *a momentary dismissal of irrelevancies*. That decision immediately gives you one of those enormous opportunities further to divide the residual definition into two. This is possible because irrelevancies fall into two main classes: all the events that are irrelevant because they are too big to have any possible kind of bearing on the particular focus of our thought, and all the irrelevancies that are too small possibly to build up any significant relationships to alter the focal subject of our thinking. You find that what you have been trying to think about has a definitive experience and frequency magnitude. Thus we find that all the irrelevancies that are too small are dismissed inwardly into the microcosm because they can't catch up to the magnitude zone of the wave length and magnitude that we are working on; and the irrelevancies, that are irrelevant because they are too big to have any effect on our considered focal system of consideration, are dismissed outside the system, that is, into the macrocosm.

Fritz Zwicky

Man has blundered and bungled into city building, communication, and means of transportation, just as he blundered into the scientific, industrial, and atomic age, arriving at a build-up which, by most people, technically and humanly, is judged to be only partly physically effective and humanly satisfactory. Here we are concerned first with the elimination, as far as possible, of the errors already committed, as well as the errors likely to be made: in particular, it is of the greatest importance to mobilize all technical knowledge and human good will to avoid bungling into the *space age*, including *inner space* (the interiors of the earth and of the planets), and *outer space* (interplanetary and interstellar space) as well as the surface of the bodies of the solar system which are destined to harbour human activities. Secondly, we must engage in *long-range planning* concerning all new projects for inner and outer space.

The projects just delineated therefore fall into the following two categories:

1. *A Holding Action* which will prevent any precipitous further large-scale bungling and which will at least do away with some of the worst aspects now bothering the human society; and

2. *Long-Range Planning and Actual Realization* of material and spiritual activities optimally suited to generally agreed upon needs of the human community and the world we live in.

For the pragmatist, to proceed with his holding actions and his future optimal constructions and activities, a complete inventory and mastery of all available so-called *pegs of knowledge* must be available. These pegs are of two kinds: that is, some of them are actually available for our use while others are reasonable projections of what new materials, phenomena, devices, and methods will be available to us in the not too distant future.

1. *Types of Holding Actions*

Alleviation or elimination of nuisances and dangerous circumstances such as:

(a) *Smog* in Los Angeles and other cities, much of which could be eliminated within a short time by legislative and technical means (propellant flow batteries or power cells, giving exhaust of N_2, CO_2, and liquid water instead of noxious nitrogen oxides, CO, and partly burned hydrocarbons).

(b) *Easing snarled-up air traffic* through switchover to hydroplanes – erroneously abandoned around 1930 but now technically highly feasible and desirable – or to large submarines powered by hydrojet engines using hydrofuels or nuclear power and making 300 knots; or running most electric traffic in underground tubes drilled with the aid of terrajet engines – highly desirable, because of liberation of excessively valuable ground, and economically very feasible in Switzerland.

2. *Long-Range Planning and Actual Realization*

This refers to surface installations, to inner space (that is, the interior of the earth and, most important, to establish ourselves underground on the moon) and to outer interplanetary space, especially the reconstruction and relocation of the cosmic bodies of the solar system.

This long-range planning makes sense only after a comprehensive review of human valuations, and after some basic mutual consent among a sufficient number of men of good will has been reached about which values should be accorded priority.

In order to be ready for all emergencies, both as the holding actions and the long-range projects are concerned, it is necessary to clearly visualize *all essential pegs of knowledge* and make all men aware of the nature of these pegs of knowledge.

Marshall McLuhan

Electronic technology has extended the brain itself to embrace the globe; previous technologies had only extended the bodily servants of the brain. The result now is a speed-up of information that reduces the planet to the scale of a village – with this difference, that the volume of information movement is on a planetary rather than village scale. A global consciousness thus becomes the new human scale.

We are inhibited in understanding and exploiting this because of our lingering devotion to the older technologies of the pre-electronic age – a fragmentary, specialist, compartmentalized, and individual age.

The electronic extension of our brain involves each of us totally in the family of man, an involvement which constitutes a new kind of continuous learning, as involuntary as seeing when one's eyes are open. This global extension of the human brain is an enormous upgrading of man. We must not fail to exploit it. The most important task of the planner is to prepare the environment for the exploitation of this new tremendous opportunity.

What does this imply in terms of human settlement when *learning a living* supplants earning a living? Production itself is left to automated machines and the work-force withdraws from the factory to the seminars for programmers of computers – seminars that can be dispersed, decentralized, without need for large agglomerations of population.

Since the central purpose of human settlement in the electronic age becomes learning, human settlement must be a projection, a multidimensional model of our new global consciousness.

*Part Six. Synthesis: The Example of
the Tokaido Megalopolis*

Introduction

In the introductory section to this book, it was briefly explained that the editors decided to present a number of studies of the Tokaido megalopolis of Japan as an indirect example of the synthesis of man and megalopolis. The phenomenon of megalopolis is far too new for any real synthesis to have emerged, and one can only point to some positive or negative tendencies that are already apparent.

The Tokaido megalopolis – centring on Tokyo – illustrates well two different approaches to an ekistic synthesis. First, all of the ekistic elements interrelate within its bounds and the major megalopolitan problems emphasized in the sections on Nature, Man, Society, Shell, and Networks are depicted in a single frame. Second, the Tokaido megalopolis presents a unique image of man (human identity) and megalopolis, illustrating the synergistic interrelations of one ekistic element and one settlement scale.

Ekistic Elements

Nature

The Tokaido megalopolis stretches well over 300 miles from north of Tokyo to south of Osaka in Japan. It already contains around 70,000,000 people and is the largest of the three undisputed major megalopolises existing today.

If we return to the four natural zones considered in the section on Nature, we find that rapid expansion of Japan's urban industrial landscape is threatening its agricultural-productive areas and its protective areas, while wild speculation is taking place in its transition zones. The relative proportions of land occupied by these four zones are rapidly changing and the balancing effects, considered so important in the section on Nature, appear to be in jeopardy.

Catharine Nagashima notes the existence of a rapid growth of pollutants and deterioration in environmental quality. Urban sprawl is spreading out into the limited and very carefully planned flat lands which produce about 80 per cent of Japan's total food requirements from a smaller acreage of arable land per head than almost any other country: for example, Japan feeds the equivalent of a quarter of the population of India from one tenth of the area of India. It is clear that the delicate balance of Japan's economy is greatly endangered. Richard Meier suggests that the growing megalopolis will need completely different food sources and cites a variety of developments which might possibly be adopted.

Fortunately, the Japanese archipelago is blessed with both a variegated coastline and spectacular mountain ranges which provide sufficient areas for protection of the natural environment as well as for the leisure pursuits of megalopolitan man.

Man

In the earlier section, the needs of man were discussed in terms of achieving different kinds of balance. One of these is very apparent in the descriptions of man's life in the Tokaido megalopolis: the balance between man's private life and his collective life.

The sudden entrance of Japan into the megalopolitan era occurred with an abrupt change of personal life styles. This was achieved by the rapid and widespread adoption of new patterns of life acquired via the mass media. Richard Meier and Ikumi Hoshino examine the effect of this transition as it was manifested after a decade. They attributed the acceptance of 'alien images' primarily to the influences of foreign cinemas, television, and magazines, secondarily to extensive foreign travel, and thirdly to 'a huge volume of public face-to-face interaction' in the crowded entertainment areas of the cities.

Society

The dimensions and attributes of the small community within the megalopolis represented the main focus of Section 3, Society. In Tokyo, Meier and Hoshino noted that from 1951 to 1966, 'we see a precinct opening up into a ward and beyond; a ward that opened to involvement in an enlarged metropolis, if not nascent megalopolis, and a metropolis which began to deal on a businesslike basis with any place in the world'.

Maintenance of neighbourhood identity is seen to be extremely crucial in this pattern and a positive case study is presented of the 'rag-pickers villa' – a street group of fifty families. From this study, Koji Taira draws certain conclusions 'for minimizing the social costs of dynamic urban industrialism'. These include a vigorous housing and planning policy 'to regenerate and strengthen the personality, outlook and will to live of the hard-core poor'. It is this last point that is behind the attitude of many of the articles throughout this book, especially in the sections on Man, Society, and Shell, which, in their different ways, point out that there are possibilities for permitting greater rather than less freedom of personal expression in the conditions of increasing population density that face us all.

Shell

The provision of communal spaces and allowance for the individual to form his habitat were the two priorities noted in Shell.

Kenzo Tange, the foremost architect-planner of Japan, approaches these priorities in terms of providing the frame in which small-scale variety may be manifest. He comes out boldly for a linear development between Osaka and Tokyo: 'a long belt with forces of flow moving back and forth along its length'. He likens this to the trunk of a great urban tree 'with the various architectural works as its leaves'. This is in keeping with the policy expressed in Tange's 1960 plan to replace the enclosed civic centre of Tokyo by an open-ended civic axis.

Networks

Kenzo Tange points out that the most permanent physical elements of a city are its infrastructure and not its architecture, and it is generally recognized that it is the transportation systems that have enabled megalopolis to evolve from a number of interconnected metropolises. The Tokaido megalopolis is no exception, and the rapidity of its development is attributed to the existence of long-established ties between Tokyo and Osaka (cities which are 300 miles apart) as evidenced by the ancient Tokaido post road and a banking system that dates back to feudal times. The fast Tokaido rail line is thus a continuation and intensification of an historic axis.

The need for rapid interconnections, not only for the elite 'men-on-the-move', but for the ordinary urban commuter, is taken up by R. Kakumoto. He puts the limit of commuting travel time at thirty minutes, and suggests that the future development of the megalopolitan region should include new towns of 300,000 people (large enough to meet all normal requirements and thus reduce needs to visiting the major centres except for very special purposes) from which high-speed commuting trains would whisk some 60,000 persons daily to and from the office buildings of the C.B.D. This may be compared with the urban units of similar size suggested as the components of the Detroit and Chicago sections of the U.S. Midwest megalopolis that are discussed in the section on Networks.

Synthesis: Man in the Tokaido Megalopolis

How can this collection of data and comment be said to arrive at any sort of synthesis? We have already stated many times that the whole phenomenon of megalopolis is so new that we are still immersed in its birth pangs. The only two distinguishing features that seem to come out fairly from this set of articles are: that at the large scale, megalopolis needs a really strong physical and social framework, particularly in the areas of physical communications systems and social institutions; and at the same time, at the small scale, human behaviour should be given the utmost freedom. This finding cuts across much current practice: we tend to develop explicit plans – physical and administrative – at the small scale (buildings, dwelling groups, neighbourhoods) and to be much more vague in proposals and implementation at the larger scales, except for a few clear-cut operations (high-speed railways, legal systems, etc.). The occasions when large-scale planning becomes put into practice are usually accompanied by an authoritative form of government that finds it impossible to countenance large measures of individual freedom at the small scale.

It is Tokyo's achievement of personal identity in man's relation to the megalopolis – both positively and negatively – that makes the Tokaido megalopolis such a 'marvellous engine for development', in the words of Richard Meier.

The conditions Meier lists as essential to Tokyo's successful development have relevance for all growing megalopolises. But he notes that each positive factor has a reverse side and that these – in some people's views – show a trend towards a mass society that is spiritually shallow, though materially prosperous. The positive and negative aspects of these factors can be summarized as follows:

Positive	*Negative*
1. Ready response to novelty	Ready response to superficial imitation
2. Widespread diffusion of new ideas	Over-estimation of novelty
3. Education system that encourages achievement	Over-emphasis on results at the expense of critical appraisal
4. Easy transference from job to job	An absence of commitment
5. Close contact between government and industry	Encouragement of conspiracies
6. Business contacts across social barriers	Emphasis on opportunism

Opportunities for man's personal involvement in shaping his environment can occur in all the pedestrian islands that form the human-scale meshes of the technological network of megalopolis. In Tokyo these include the apparent confusion of the downtown urban jungles as well as the residential districts with their maze of narrow lanes. J. M. Richards not only finds the contrast between the Japanese urban 'jungle' and its meticulously planned countryside visually stimulating, but he suggests that (under the pressure of the huge population of a megalopolis) a great freedom of self-expression is the only way of creating cities 'where a full life can be lived' as well as of preserving the countryside from being overrun: 'The dynamic quality of Japanese cities is created by layer on layer, receding in perspective, of moving objects and incidents, inextricably interwoven, each justifying its presence in the jungle by the way it involves people.'

This aspect of Japanese life is related to the absence of the linear thinking that has been such a strong component of western development ever since the 'Gutenberg Era'. The differing effects upon the urban scene are well described by Professor Shigeru Itoh:

Westerners have a strong tendency to put all kinds of social or physical phenomena in order: to classify them and to locate them within a general system. This tendency naturally encourages Western traffic engineers to separate pedestrians from carriage traffic and to give them different physical facilities, such as sidewalks and pedestrian malls. One can draw a simile from the fact that Western people use various kinds of table implements, knives and forks of different kinds, to eat different kinds of foods. In other words, the Western approach is to find a special treatment and solution for each phenomenon. The Japanese view of life is different. To take the same example, the Japanese and other Oriental people use only one pair of chopsticks for any number of different kinds of dishes. They have never had the idea of using a different type of chopstick for particular dishes. They tend to admit one solution for a number of heterogeneous phenomena. This way of thinking is obviously related to Buddhism.

It was not until the Meiji Restoration and the entry of Western thought and commerce in the mid nineteenth century that roads with sidewalks were first built. However, up to now, it is common to find all the narrower urban streets with no sidewalks. In 1917, the famous American botanist Edward Morse wrote, 'There are no sidewalks (in Tokyo) except in the Ginza quarter. People are used to walk completely in the centre of those narrow streets.' Mr Morse said 'there are no sidewalks' but in fact it was the other way round: there were no carriageways. All the road systems of Japan were basically pedestrian ways, whereas Western countries had stage coaches bowling along a main arterial road system. The basic national transportation structure of Japan was by sea and by rail, not by road.[1]

Almost until the advent of the automobile, all traffic in Japanese cities was on foot – hand carts, rickshaws, and plain pedestrian scale (the human scale) – and few streets were wider than three metres (about ten feet). These narrow winding streets were the centres of social life (see the article by Kurokawa on p. 394), but they were totally unsuited to the invasion of the automobile. Popular and professional opinion is divided as to how far they should be preserved or whether they should be completely redeveloped. To establish some guidelines, Jaqueline Tyrwhitt carried out a short research project with the aid of two graduate students at the University of Tokyo. The study seemed to show that, even with 100 per cent car-ownership, pedestrian islands measuring some 400 metres square and penetrated only by these narrow lanes would inconvenience no one. Furthermore, they would provide many opportunities for the kind of casual freedom that J. M. Richards rightly demands as the price for being deprived of the possibilities of untrammelled roaming around a free countryside.

Thus, in Tokyo, the child, the mother, and the old are accommodated in a safe and friendly environment, the young adult finds a challenge in the exploration of the urban jungle, and the 'men on the move' are whisked with ease to their appointments throughout the megalopolis.

The example of the Tokaido megalopolis is a heartening indication that – at least in the setting of a proud and ancient culture – human dignity and human diversity still find free expression amid the flood of technocratic innovations.

At the opening of this book, we stated that 'the question that must be faced is how these myriad cities can continue to develop at an accelerating rate without destroying all that we believe makes life worth living'. We then suggested that the answer lay in devising – and using – suitable methodologies for, first, 'understanding population characteristics, planning for future growth, and the creation programs for present action'. We then proceeded to show how the ekistic approach can provide just a methodology. And we have concluded with the example of the Tokaido megalopolis which suggests that, despite its many very apparent problems and dangers, a way may be found for mankind to reach new thresholds of individual dignity as we plunge into the twenty-first century.

NOTES

1. Shigero Itoh, 'Pedestrian Separation from Automobile Traffic', *Ekistics* 129, August 1966, p. 123.

37. Megalopolis in Japan

C. NAGASHIMA

Introduction

Contemporary megalopolis, as 'the cradle of a new order in the organization of inhabited space', was first recognized by Jean Gottmann as occurring along the eastern seaboard of the United States in the form of a huge string of central cities, suburbs, and satellite towns. It is gigantic in scale; supreme in human organization; a city of ideas in the sense that one of its special characteristics is its very dense concentration of highly educated and skilled people with an ever-increasing need to exchange information.

The phenomenon that cities expand and coalesce with surrounding towns, eventually ·forming large clusters of urban and suburban sprawl, variously described as metropolitan regions and as conurbations, had previously been recognized. Megalopolis differs from these not only in size, including several such metropolitan clusters, but also in density of activities and movements. It is not easy to decide when, precisely, two or more conurbations become one megalopolis, but, in addition to an increase in the size and density of the population of intervening areas, signs of the merger include an increasing interdependence of the component settlements and, above all, an increasing mobility.

Although megalopolis is essentially an urban concept, it does not preclude a certain amount of rural activity within its boundaries. As megalopolis intensifies, there is a tendency for urban–rural distinctions to become less definite, and for agricultural land to give way to suburbs. But, nevertheless, in the U.S. east coast example, Gottmann found that agricultural output and wooded areas were actually increasing. It is wrong, therefore, to imagine megalopolis as a continuously built-up area. Agricultural land, woodland, and parkland can be incorporated within megalopolis.

Megalopolis contains large areas of dense population, but the crowding of people coincides with affluence rather than with poverty. It is a crowding of a rich variety of people and activities; of diversity and competition; of strength and wealth. The new urban civilization sprouting all over the earth is accompanied by scientific and technological progress. Diseases are being conquered; human life prolonged; labour saved and leisure increased; new means of transport innovated; more convenient household appliances devised. Gottmann found the U.S. east coast megalopolis to contain the richest, best educated, best housed, best serviced group of people of similar size in the world.

But megalopolis is ugly. It is an unplanned spawning monster. Its air is polluted, and so are its rivers; it is a noisy place; its streets are congested with traffic. The gains in health are offset by air pollution and road hazards; gains in leisure by the long journeys to work; gains in home comforts by the lack of beauty in the environment outside the home. Man has not yet adjusted to the new megalopolitan environment, to the mobility, the need to acquire new knowledge, and the constant social change. Traditional family life and moral and aesthetic standards have been disrupted. Gottmann observed that the impact of megalopolis has created a new concern in man for his mental health, and that this has become a general social problem that never existed before on any significant scale.

It would seem, then, that megalopolis is in danger of choking itself with its own machinery, offsetting efficiency with inefficiency. Megalopolis is the contemporary heir to the traditional fruits of the city. The city has given birth to the world's major civilizations. The city has been the centre of wealth, authority, responsibility, initiative, and culture. It has been a place where persons of diverse skills and talents gathered, met each other, and exchanged ideas and knowledge. It has, very often, been itself a work of art. Unless megalopolis can restore beauty and harmony to man's environment, and provide for his need for human contacts in an increasingly anonymous electronic world, megalopolis might poison its own inheritance.

Megalopolis in Japan

Japan's population is almost 100,000,000 – the seventh largest in the world, exceeded only by Communist China, India, U.S.S.R., U.S.A., Pakistan, and Indonesia. It is also the fifth densest country, after the Netherlands, Taiwan, Belgium, and the Republic of Korea. When one considers that less than 20 per cent of Japan's land surface can be classified as habitable area, these facts seem quite remarkable.

Figure 1 shows population densities and densely inhabited districts. A densely inhabited district is defined as one with a density not less than 4,000 per square kilometre, and at least 5,000 inhabitants. It is possible to identify at least three large clusters of population which form solid blocks of densely inhabited districts. The largest occupies the Kanto plain, and contains Tokyo and Yokohama; the second is in the region of Osaka, Kobe, and Kyoto; the third around Nagoya. A chain of densely inhabited districts stretches from Tokyo to the north of Kyushu, contained within a belt where the density seldom drops below two or three hundred per square kilometre. The density of the Japanese Pacific coast, particularly the stretch between Tokyo and Osaka, matches that of the east coast megalopolis of the U.S.

As can be seen by comparing Figure 1 and Figure 2, there is a remarkable similarity between the distribution of population and that of relief. The high concentrations of population coincide with areas below 100 metres; almost wherever there are plains and valleys there are people.

Historic Background

From feudal times, post towns were located at regular intervals along the country's overland routes to provide resting places for travellers, invariably pedestrians. The most famous of these were the fifty-three resting places along the Tokaido route, which became important during the seventeenth century as the link between the cultural and

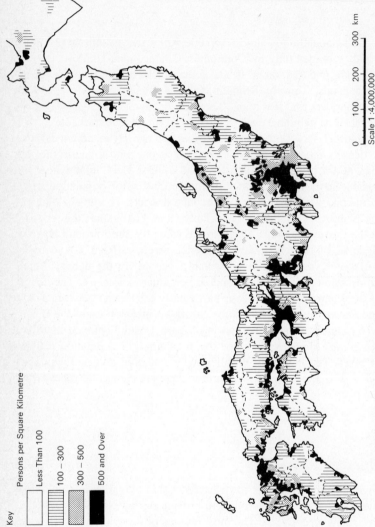

Key

Persons per Square Kilometre

Less Than 100

100 – 300

300 – 500

500 and Over

Scale 1 : 4,000,000

0   100   200   300 km

Figure 1. Population density by city and country, 1960.

Key

☐ Over 100 Metre Contour

Scale 1:4,000,000

0   100   200   300 km

Figure 2. Land over 100 metres from sea level.

economic capitals of Kyoto and Osaka and the political power centre of Tokyo (Yedo). This route was mainly frequented by organized groups of feudal lords commuting to and from Tokyo, but also by merchants travelling to Osaka and scholars visiting Kyoto. It became, in a sense, the axis of the nation. Thus, the skeleton of modern megalopolis existed even in feudal times.

The Meiji Restoration of 1868 marked the collapse of the feudal system and the establishment of a centralized authoritarian government, anxious to develop the country into a modern capitalistic state. The Meiji government gave strong support to the Industrial Revolution and promoted the expansion of military forces. Thus, the pattern of the old feudal cities was radically changed.

It should be pointed out that conditions in the feudal period paved the way for the progress of the Industrial Revolution. Even before the Meiji Restoration there were (pre-steam-engine) systems of mass production of manufactured goods, especially of textiles and ceramics (notably in the Kinki region, around Osaka); a banking system, and money transactions between Tokyo and Osaka; and 60 per cent of the population were able to read. These factors combined to assist the rapid take-off of the Japanese economy during the last two or three decades of the nineteenth century.

The new framework for the strategic development of the country came to be the railway network. The main theme of the transformation of settlements was industrialization, though regional administration and military functions were promoted in selected centres. The general tendency was for settlements situated along the railway lines to thrive, and for those isolated from railways to decline.

Tokyo

Tokyo, previously the seat of the feudal government, became the political and cultural capital of the nation with the transfer of the Imperial Court from Kyoto. Tokyo was also the strategic focus of the national railway system and the centre of the developing industrial region. By 1900, its population had reached 1·3 million.

Osaka

Osaka suffered a temporary decline of its commercial function, but with the development of shipbuilding, textiles, and machinery after 1886, it prospered as an industrial centre, and had a population of 0·9 million in 1900.

Kyoto

Kyoto, no longer the capital, concentrated on promoting medium industrial enterprises, but was hampered by lack of a convenient waterway, and by 1900 its population was still only 0·3 million.

Nagoya

Nagoya had been a comparatively large feudal centre, and with the growth initially of textile industries and subsequently of ceramics, precision machinery, and vehicles, it rapidly became an industrial city. Its population in 1900 was 0·3 million.

Emergence of Tokaido Megalopolis

The three major conurbations, Tokyo (including Yokohama), Nagoya, Osaka (including Kobe and Kyoto), and their environs are growing about three times as fast as the nation as a whole. Figure 3 shows population changes in Japan between 1960 and 1965, by prefecture, and of those prefectures gaining 10 per cent or more during the five-year period, the four in the Tokyo area averaged 18 per cent; the two in the Osaka area 16 per cent; the one containing Nagoya, 14 per cent. The national average was 5 per cent.

Population growth was most rapid in the areas surrounding the central cities: not in Tokyo-to (12 per cent), but in the neighbouring prefectures of Chiba (17 per cent), Saitama (24 per cent), and Kanagawa (29 per cent). The population of the seven fast-gaining prefectures, which could perhaps be called the core of megalopolis, adds

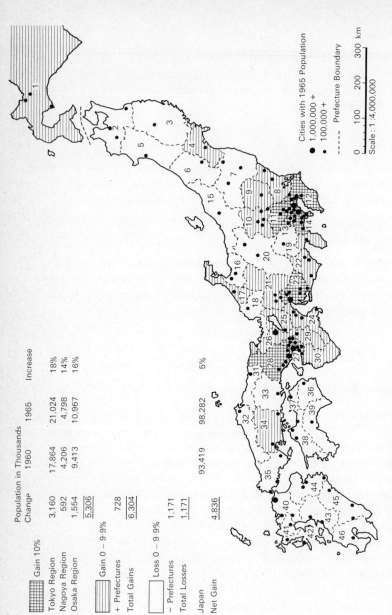

	Population in Thousands			
	Change	1960	1965	Increase
▦ Gain 10%				
Tokyo Region	3,160	17,864	21,024	18%
Nagoya Region	592	4,206	4,798	14%
Osaka Region	1,554	9,413	10,967	16%
	5,306			
▥ Gain 0 – 9.9%				
+ Prefectures	728			
Total Gains	6,304			
☐ Loss 0 – 9.9%				
– Prefectures	1,171			
Total Losses	1,171			
Japan		93,419	98,282	5%
Net Gain	4,836			

Cities with 1965 Population
● 1,000,000 +
• 100,000 +
- - - - Prefecture Boundary

Scale : 1 : 4,000,000

0   100   200   300 km

Figure 3. Population changes in Japan, 1960–65.

up to some 37,000,000 people. A crude estimate of the total mega-lopolitan population can be seen in Table 1.

TABLE ONE

	1965 Population in Thousands	
Fringe Prefectures		*5,184*
Ibaraki	2,056	
Tochigi	1,522	
Gunma	1,606	
Tokyo core		*21,124*
Saitama	3,015	
Chiba	2,702	
Tokyo	10,877	
Kanagawa	4,430	
Intermediate		*2,912*
Shizuoka	2,912	
Nagoya core		*4,799*
Aichi	4,799	
Intermediate		*5,296*
Mie	1,514	
Shiga	853	
Kyoto	2,103	
Nara	826	
Osaka core		*10,967*
Osaka	6,657	
Hyogo	4,310	
Megalopolis		*50,282*

Figure 4 summarizes the state of Japan's population distribution. A more rural society would have a population distribution curve located further to the right of the graph; theoretical ecumenopolis would appear as a horizontal line with practically 100 per cent living in one place of indefinite or infinite size. The figure shows the sequence of population curves for Japan between 1920 and 1965. The upward

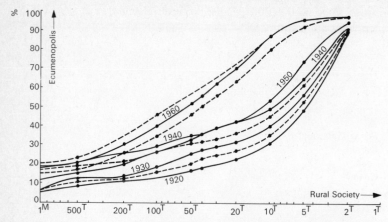

Figure 4. Trends in population distribution by size of place, 1920–65.

tendency, away from rural society and towards, eventually, ecumeno-polis, appears to be remarkably rapid. In 1920, places of 100,000+ contained 12 per cent of Japan's population and those of 400,000+, 8 per cent. By 1965 these ratios had risen to 46 per cent and 23 per cent respectively.

Intensity of Movement of People

The modern successor to the old Tokaido post road is not the almost completed expressway, nor the Tokaido railway of the Industrial Revolution, nor the domestic air-route between Tokyo and Osaka. The new axis of Japan is the New Tokaido trunk railway line. The combined one-way daily carrying capacity of these various routes and projects connecting Tokyo and Osaka has been estimated by Kenzo Tange to be about 300,000 persons. The New Tokaido trunk line alone can account for 100,000 of these.

Opened on 1 October 1965, the New Tokaido line express trains stop only at Nagoya and Kyoto, and cover the 500-kilometre distance in 3 hours 10 minutes (maximum speed 250 kilometres per hour).

This makes it possible to travel anywhere within the Tokyo–Osaka megalopolis area within half a day.

In the first year of its operation, this railway carried over 62,000,000 passengers, and its trains travelled over 31,000,000 kilometres. A study made by Japan Railways showed that the carrying capacity of the old Tokaido railway reached saturation point in 1962, with 26,000,000,000 passenger kilometres a year. By 1966, with the New Tokaido line, there was an increase to 35,000,000,000 passenger kilometres, and the forecast for 1976 is 51,000,000,000.

Tokaido Megalopolis

Figure 5 shows a first approximation of the megalopolis and its extensions.

1. Tokyo–Aichi Region·

The two main cores are still Tokyo and Osaka. Aichi (Nagoya) is the next most important centre, but is perhaps becoming more an extension of the Tokyo area than a separate centre. The filling-in process between Tokyo and Nagoya is quite evident by the importance not only of Kanagawa but of the other intermediate prefecture, Shizuoka.

2. Osaka Region

Osaka, on the other hand, is definitely a centre in its own right, flanked by Kyoto and Hyogo.

Megalopolis Fringe

The Tokyo region and the Osaka region form the poles of what has been called 'Tokaido megalopolis'. Between and around these regions is a sort of buffer zone which is in some ways semi-megalopolitan.

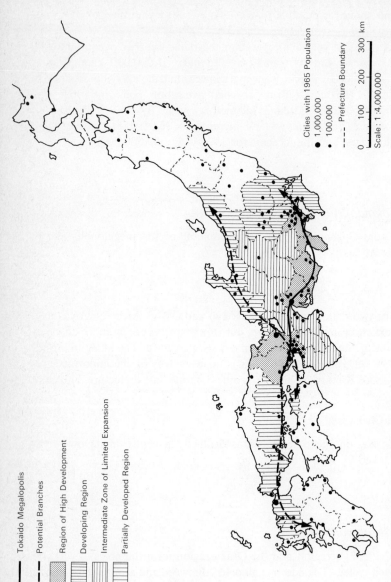

Tokaido Megalopolis
Potential Branches
Region of High Development
Developing Region
Intermediate Zone of Limited Expansion
Partially Developed Region

Cities with 1965 Population
● 1,000,000
• 100,000
- - - Prefecture Boundary

Scale : 1 : 4,000,000

0   100   200   300 km

Figure 5. Japan megalopolis.

1. Kanto Fringe

To the north of Tokyo is the Kanto fringe area, consisting of Gunma, Tochigi, Ibaraki, Saitama, and Chiba. All are rather well off for habitable land, and the three former seem to have room for population expansion. Saitama and Chiba are already becoming quite heavily populated and land values are high. The whole of this Kanto fringe area is an important transportation centre although otherwise economically undeveloped.

2. Intermediate Zone

The prefectures of Yamanashi, Nagano, Gifu, Mie, Shiga, Nara, and Wakayama are an intermediate zone within Tokaido megalopolis. They are potentially important for transport although their population prospects are perhaps not as important as the Kanto fringe prefectures.

Megalopolis Branch Lines

The Kanto fringe, the Tokyo–Aichi region, the intermediate mountainous zone, and the Osaka region together form Tokaido megalopolis. Four other regions show characteristics which could make them part of a potential Japan Megalopolis.

1. Sanyo Region

Okayama, Hiroshima, and Yamaguchi prefectures are in some ways part of megalopolis. Okayama is a significant education and publishing centre and Hiroshima is the focus of the region. The future development of this region as part of megalopolis is handicapped by lack of habitable land.

2. Kyushu Region

The Kyushu region perhaps has more potential than the Sanyo region. It is relatively well off for land, though only in Fukuoka, the regional centre, are megalopolitan conditions at all evident.

3. Shikoku Region

Shikoku does not yet seem to be involved in megalopolis.

4. Hokuriku Region

The region includes the prefectures of Fukui, Ishikawa, Toyama, and Niigata with the focus in Kanazawa in Ishikawa. As a whole, the region is important for transport.

Specific Problems of Japan's Megalopolis

1. The environment of megalopolis is noisy and ugly. Its settlements are expanding haphazardly, spoiling the landscape and obliterating man's contacts with nature. Japan's industries, too much concerned with economic motives, paid little respect until recently to environmental conditions. As a result, not only is the air of megalopolis polluted with automobile exhaust and factory fumes, but the rivers are filled with industrial waste products. The people are suffering from a lack of outdoor recreation amenities. Japan as a whole provided 2·3 square metres per inhabitant of urban parks and other open spaces in 1966, but Tokyo provided only 0·66 square metres in 1964.

2. Compared with Western Europe and North America, Japan is underdeveloped in terms of services such as sewerage. In 1966, the average number of households in Japan having a main sewerage system was only 20 per cent. Places with a million inhabitants or more had 44 per cent (Osaka 52 per cent and Tokyo 31 per cent). The Government plan for 1971 foresees an increase in these per-

centages to 72 per cent (cities 1,000,000+); 70 per cent (Osaka); and 56 per cent (Tokyo) respectively, but Tokaido megalopolis cannot hope for a complete sewerage network for several decades.

3. Tokaido megalopolis is probably the most densely populated area of a similar size in the world. But although Tokyo has much higher population densities than London, Paris, or New York, the average number of storeys per building in Tokyo's 23-ward area was only 1·9 in 1966.

TABLE TWO

Central Cities	Date	Area in Sq. Km.	Population in Thousands	Density per Hectare
Tokyo, 23-ward area	1960	569	8,310	146
	1965	569	8,901	153
London, former L.C.C.	1961	303	3,200	106
Paris, Dépt de la Seine	1962	479	5,688	125
New York City	1960	819	7,782	95

The high densities of the Tokaido megalopolis are achieved only at the cost of extremely crowded living conditions. In 1965 the Tokyo Metropolitan Government estimated that 550,000 families in the Tokyo area were short of homes, and 44 per cent of the citizens had housing problems. At the time of the 1960 census, 18 per cent of Tokyo's households had less than two tatami (= less than 3·3 square metres) per person: barely enough room to lie down in comfort. The people of the Tokaido megalopolis are among the worst housed in Japan in terms of floor area. Indeed, their living environment might be intolerable were it not for the specifically Japanese way of living and sleeping in the same space, dispensing with beds and stacking up the sleeping mats in a cupboard during the day.

4. The advent of the automobile is having a profoundly disturbing effect on Japanese cities. Vehicles are increasing at a rate of 20 per cent per annum in Japan's major cities, yet the road network is still basically a relic of the pedestrian age. There was no transitional horse–carriage period in Japan, and the expansion of the road network is failing even more drastically to keep up with the demands

of traffic than in other parts of the world. In 1966 there were 13,895 deaths from traffic accidents in Japan, the highest rate per vehicle of any country in the world. Tokyo, in spite of spectacular new urban motorways, still has only 12 per cent of its land in roads.

5. The commuter problem is becoming increasingly serious in Japan. Land prices in the six major cities in 1966 were ten times higher than in 1956, and in Japan as a whole, they were seven times higher (according to a survey by the Japan Real Estate Institute). Land development costs are also extremely high. The housing shortage in the urban centres combined with high land development cost compels people to seek homes further and further away from their work places, and to spend many hours commuting. In the Tokyo area, 1·2 million people spend an average of over two hours daily travelling to and from work. Of Tokyo's commuters, 80 per cent use the rapid transit systems (national railways, private suburban railways, and subways), and 20 per cent of all rapid transit passenger traffic is concentrated into one hour: the morning rush hour.

38. Notes on the Creation of an Efficient Megalopolis: Tokyo

RICHARD L. MEIER

Foundations for a New Urbanism

The meaning of megalopolis can never be made precise and scientific, because each major constellation of urban centres will possess a noticeably different sequence of interpenetration and reorganization.

Nevertheless, it is already possible to identify some new phenomena which are clearly megalopolitan. For example, the need for transportation between neighbouring metropolitan areas creates a demand for very frequent airline flights, for expressway construction, and a high-speed railroad. To this is added a microwave relay system with a large amount of channel capacity for telephone, television, teletype, and data transmission, and a high voltage electric power grid. Systems of distribution of goods and services are thereupon reorganized to fit the megalopolitan region, so warehousing, marketing, and advertising tend to develop service areas that correspond to the geographer's ideas concerning the physical boundaries of the megalopolis. River basins are reconstructed for joint water sources, and high amenity recreational areas are monopolized by people from the megalopolitan region. Megalopolis formation, we now see, implies an adaptation of urban services to fit the needs of the 'man-on-the-move', a tiny minority in the population at the moment, but a much more numerous category after affluence has begun to permeate the centres and interstices of the overall region.

Possible Japanese Contributions

Japan's dynamic nominee for megalopolis formation, the Tokyo–Nagoya–Osaka corridor, possesses some characteristics that could make it easily the most imitated urban development. The Tokyo Metropolitan Area is predominantly a postwar phenomenon. The original metropolis of 4–5 million residents was largely destroyed and was reconstituted with up-to-date physical facilities. When establishing its effective limits, kilometre by kilometre, this area could be shown to encompass 23,000,000 persons in 1969, or about 50 per cent more than New York City, calculated on the same basis. Thus, Tokyo has been created by the most mature forces of the Industrial Revolution, upon which has been superimposed the new communications and information revolutions. The Industrial Revolution is no longer a net producer of new jobs in Tokyo. Its institutions have begun what is expected to be a long period of slow decline, while the communications trades make steadily increasing demands upon the labour force, and the information-based activities virtually explode. Tokyo's advancement into the post-industrial era is certainly behind that of New York, Washington, Los Angeles, and San Francisco, but it has probably moved ahead more rapidly than any Western European metropolis. The statistics available are of quite good quality – generally superior to those available in the United States – because Tokyo's household registration, operated in Oriental fashion by the police, is kept up-to-date, month by month.

In Tokyo the Japanese have constructed the most marvellous 'engine for development' that the world has ever seen. It imports people, ideas, and information, uses them to transform ordinary commodities into products and services saleable throughout the world, and retains a surplus. The 'value added' in the city has been growing 15–20 per cent per year on the average for at least a decade and a half. Performance in Osaka and Nagoya has been highly creditable, according to international comparisons, but it so pales in comparison to Tokyo that many express the opinion that Tokyo has appropriated to itself growth that might have been generated in these other cities. These arguments are dubious because there is little evidence that extra investment in the other centres would have triggered large increases in production.

Our ignorance about the sources of performance in such engines for development is still profound, but the essential sub-assemblies can be distinguished, and even a few of the component parts can be described. The Economic Planning Agency insists that the propulsive power in the economy as a whole is the rate of saving (34 per cent for Japan as against 27 per cent for West Germany and 18 per cent for the United States).

The nub of the performance question, however, hinges upon the distribution of investment effort among new projects in both the socialized and the private sectors. Ordinarily one would expect that the extra 'savings power' would be employed in second- and third-rate projects with low rates of return, but this has not been the case. The mix has remained astonishingly good. Why? Standard economic analysis says that a large body of knowledge existed in the world which could be transported in plant-size packages to Japan and be put into production one to three years after the decision had been made. Thus, Japan spurted because it was 'catching up'. But this argument still does not get at the heart of the matter, because a dozen other countries were geographically and culturally closer to the sources of this knowhow than Japan and therefore were in a better position to take advantage of the opportunities it presented.

Equally deficient is the assertion that, having accepted a non-militaristic non-coercive role in international affairs, the absence of a military bias in its investment program yielded these excellent results, because half the world has accepted the American nuclear shield but still none of these countries has continued to grow at anywhere close to a comparable rate.

A number of other reasons put forward by economists can be demolished with the same kind of logic. We shall propose a non-economic explanation – the cities of Japan, particularly Tokyo, made the difference between rapid growth and ordinary growth. The cities nurture institutions, public, private, cooperative, and hybrid, and Japanese cities expedited their interaction. It reduces the problem to a matter of providing conditions for the creation of organization. If there was anything that Tokyo excelled at, it was this.

Some of the conditions required for ready synthesis of organization can already be specified:

1. A continuous sensitivity to novelty and innovation in customs, styles, technology, and national policies elsewhere in the world must be maintained. Natural curiosity must be reinforced by the highest-grade reporting and analysis, as well as the technical equipment needed for communication. These institutions were virtually

compelled to pick up and move to Tokyo, because it was far more willing to assign priorities to the needed facilities.

2. These novel ideas must be generally diffused through multiple channels. They should be presented as popular culture (as well as to the specialist elites) so that the resonances with local markets and political values can be sensed.

3. An educational system must be created that produces people knowledgeable about their own culture and encourages achievement so that almost everyone is looking for short cuts and improvements. Meanwhile a relatively competent fraction must work hard for diplomas and higher degrees – they are primarily 'trainees for organizational roles'.

4. Channels of recruitment must be opened up that move graduates into *expanding* organizations (where the opportunities for private or social profits are great).

5. A pragmatic association must be fostered between the firms and government (with standards of conduct jealously guarded by auditors and reporters for the national press) so that the initiative for specific regional or technological developments can be passed back and forth, paying great attention to learning from mistakes in gauging what could actually be implemented.

6. Face-to-face contacts, many of them across barriers in rank, must be encouraged so that relatively dependable information can move up the status hierarchy as readily as the orders move down. The remarkably liberal expense and entertainment accounts in Tokyo build bridges between organizations, that enable the unusual, often complicated, deals to be consummated while the opportunity still exists. Even the extraordinary stress on job security and promotion on the basis of seniority, with all their deadening effects upon individual achievement, are made to serve a useful purpose by causing the young men to invest their time developing contacts with their peers and counterparts and greatly reducing the proportion of 'yes men'.

7. Both the physical and social apparatus must be designed so that organizations can have short response times, and can grasp opportunities ahead of the competition, even though this may require a con-

siderable amount of slack and apparent idleness on the part of some white-collar and production workers.

Compiled in this fashion such conditions sound reasonable but obvious. However, it can be pointed out that a disproportionately large share of the best educated people decry these same conditions because, counting item by item, point 1 results in 'faddism' and superficial imitation of foreign concepts; point 2 fosters a preference for foreign artists over the indigenous schools; point 3 opens up higher education to the masses and emphasizes strictly manipulative use of the culture rather than its critical appreciation; point 4 indicates a preference for graduates lacking a personal commitment to career beyond becoming 'organization men'; point 5 encourages conspiracy between civil servants and profiteers; point 6 asks that people become quite calculating regarding their social contacts; and point 7 puts a positive value upon idleness and opportunism.

In short, the urban society that makes this engine work so well is shallow, bourgeois, uncommitted, ideologically unformed, and shifty. It appears both rudderless and anchorless. Therefore, many of the people who profess to know what is best for society will do their utmost to reform it. Perhaps the policies of one such group will win out − if so, the engine for development may be expected to set up noisy gear-grinding conflicts and will lose momentum.

There is little doubt that the major contribution the Japanese can make to megalopolitan concepts lies in the experience they are accumulating from the construction and the tuning of the developmental engine that provides the motive power in the progress towards megalopolis. They may not be able to communicate what they have learned in a set of explicit instructions, but perhaps they may be able to produce specific recommendations when called in to assist other countries.

Planning for a Megalopolis

The urban geographer and the physical planner are cousins: one speaks about the city of the present and the forces which brought it into being, while the other intends to direct these forces so as to create a more desirable city in the future. Both conceptualize the city as a sequence of maps which, when laid one upon the other, reveal much of the regularity and order it possesses. Yet the institutions that constitute the present engine for development in Tokyo, whose dynamism forces planning on a larger scale than that conducted at the metropolitan level, refuse to be contained so neatly.

One method, based on some ideas of Professor M. M. Webber[1] but modified to suit Japan, would search out those jobs and other social roles in urban society whose scope covers an area greater than a city or even a metropolis. For example, a mayor would not count, but a member of parliament would. A local television broadcaster would not be included, but one on the national network would. Similarly an applied scientist solving a production problem in a factory would not be in the select circle, unless he published his findings in a journal read nationally or internationally. A yachtsman on the open ocean should be counted, but one that stays behind the breakwater remains parochial. In Japan we expect to find that less than 1 per cent of all social roles have larger than metropolitan responsibilities. Once a representative sample has been identified, their home addresses can be plotted on a map along with their most common working addresses. The world-serving professions in science, international relations, and trade are superimposed upon the nation-serving professions in the civil service, politics, mass media, defence forces, and the like. Those who serve large regions within the nation are small in number but will be mingled surprisingly closely with the others. Together they constitute the 'men-on-the-move', because they must continually re-establish personal contacts and check on performance. The number of these people, during a period of economic growth, increases much more rapidly than the size of the city. The future megalopolis is needed to handle the vastly expanded collection of such people, since the population with more limited responsibilities can be served reasonably well with today's ordinary urban and suburban facilities, if somewhat improved.

Once the physical planner has these points on a map he will ask further questions. What kinds of transportation and communication networks are needed to link up the men-on-the-move? What intersections in the network are likely to become bottlenecks due to congestion? How much land is needed? What about water, sewers, and power? Is it possible to rationalize the networks by revamping the settlement pattern?

As technological opportunities are analysed to find answers for such questions, it will be discovered that the key modern institutions depend upon urban services for their quick response times. The energy supply systems (electric power and petroleum products) require automatic controls that operate within fractions of seconds or seconds, therefore making heavy use of telecommunications systems. Telephone and teleprinting permit interactions between points in around one minute, while elevators and office building designs promote face-to-face meetings within the organization in about a ten-minute reaction time. The plant-to-office and home-to-office movements approach a hundred-minute travel time limit.

The spatial implications of the hundred-minute limit are most intriguing – since it seems to define the extent of the 'fleshy' portion of the megalopolitan 'body'. Curiously, the boundaries need not be contiguous. As airport centre developments evolve in Tokyo, Osaka, and Nagoya, the hundred-minute zone will contain 'islands' of megalopolis as much as 500 kilometres away. They, too, will contain important concentrations of nation-servers and world-servers. True, Tokyo's periphery must be reconstructed to meet the demands of this future, but the demands of megalopolis could strike virtually anywhere in the Japanese islands as new organizational demands crop up. For example, a cluster of resorts that offer skiing, mountaineering, and boating, according to season, could well become a major conference centre if it maintained excellent airline connections. Speculating in another direction, it seems likely that a major geophysical research centre of world-wide interest could also achieve megalopolitan character. Each of these must be within a thousand or so minutes of all other such centres, associated with the other megalopolises of the world.

It is worth standing back at this stage of the analysis to note the kinds of arguments which have been adduced. The megalopolis in Japan was defined first according to special strata in a hierarchy of social roles which it must facilitate, and only then was it located in space. Following that, the concept of reorganizational reaction time, so important when grasping economic opportunities elsewhere in the world, was added. It had further spatial implications. This procedure is a fruitful way of combining the expertise of the physical planner with that of the urban systems planner.

Now, after the analysis, comes the synthesis. What projects can be proposed to expedite the activities of men-on-the-move? As noted before, some of these will involve communications technology, particularly the new communications satellites and the time-shared computer systems. Others would integrate the design of office blocks with the terminals of high-speed transport lines. Even more expensive could be the successor to the New Tokaido line – a tube transport channel that connects at most half a dozen key centres with an average speed of 400–500 kilometres per hour, or a V.T.O.L. network that whisks people from sub-centre to sub-centre at 300 kilometres per hour. International links are already scheduled to be shortened by means of supersonic airline installations.

Implementation of Plans

Just as the Tokyo Metropolitan Government has been designed to look after the larger interests of the Tokyo metropolis, and to find the compromises that resolve conflicts between special groups in that urban region, some agency must come into being to promote and administer the projects for the megalopolis. What kind of an organization might it be? Since we cannot foresee at this time what conflicts will arise between megalopolitans themselves, we are not in a position to recommend a suitable form of constitution. The administrative needs are more predictable because in virtually all instances they involve simultaneous control over points separated by hundreds of kilometres. Thus, quite large organizations would have to be brought into being over a very short period of time (one to three years).

Perhaps only a public corporation, with wide latitude to enter into associations with foreign firms or private sector organizations, could have these capacities. The projects it administers should, to the greatest extent practicable, be self-financing, because there is no reason to subsidize the wealth-producing sector, even at the start. Large loans might be extended at going interest rates, and even grants for indirect services performed for governments, but annual returns to labour and capital must compare favourably with alternatives available inside the country and among competitors elsewhere in the world. Any 'megalopolis' that could not compete in this fashion would be a monumental fraud, a trigger for inflation and political instability.

Developing Its Human Resources

The future megalopolitan will be quite a different kind of person from the typical metropolitan resident. I have tried to isolate this sub-population which would be predominantly 'men-on-the-move', working for and served by institutions operating in two or more metropolises. How do such men come into existence?

In Japan there may be a hundred thousand or more people who already approximate the behaviour of megalopolitans (Table 1), albeit a bit clumsily because quite a few of the facilities that would enable them to use their time efficiently are not yet in operation. The majority of these live and work (most of the time) in Tokyo. Because the Tokaido megalopolis is denser, and the primate centre is away from the load centre, it should generate more inter-city traffic than its parallel in America. Fares and toll charges are roughly proportionate to income, so they do not influence the comparison strongly.

Miscellaneous reports on trends in the labour force suggest that the demand for these men-on-the-move is growing far more rapidly than the prospective supply. Thus, many more of them are needed in the future. Planning for the megalopolis must include projects for the production of nation-serving and world-serving skills.

The variety of specialization is unprecedented. An efficient megalopolis must draw upon a greater range of advanced technicians and artists than any metropolis. Several strategies for obtaining this broad distribution of specialized services appear to be open. One would expedite the circulation of the rarest specialists by giving them priority in high-speed transport. Another technique would employ the most modern communications media so that their wisdom could be effectively transmitted. Ultimately, however, the stretching of scarce skills

TABLE ONE

Men-on-the-Move: Japanese Megalopolis versus American Megalopolis

	Corridor Length	Daily Trips		Daily Telephone Calls		Population in Region	Television Channels	Radio Channels
Tokaido (Tokyo–Nagoya–Osaka)	500 km.	New Tokaido line	80,000	Trunk lines	140,000	30,000,000	8	8
		Old Tokaido line	41,000	Microwave relay	119,000			
		Airlines	6,000					
		Total	127,000					
U.S.A. East Coast (Boston–New York–Washington)	740 km.	Rail	27,000	Not reported		30,000,000	5*	33
		Auto and bus	51,000					
		Airlines	7,000					
		Total	85,000					

Source: Koji Kobayashi, 'The "Knowledge Industry" and Economic Growth', in *Ekonomisuto*, 25 October 1966, p. 64.

* Basis for counting not evident. Perhaps what is meant is the maximum number of independent programs.

reaches the point of diminishing returns, so the graduate and professional schools must expand and produce a larger supply of nominees for these roles. On-the-job training superimposed upon a university education will suffice for most of the remainder. Therefore, the key to the development of the human resources for the megalopolis lies in the universities, requiring curriculum reforms and expansions.

The priorities which establish what skills, and how much of each are needed, are to a large extent set by the competition to be anticipated from the megalopolises elsewhere. On the Atlantic seaboard the military and political power of Washington is counterpoised by the influences of the executive offices of New York and the negotiating tables of the United Nations, thus forming a rapidly expanding megalopolitan structure upon an otherwise static and ageing constellation of metropolises. The dynamism of Los Angeles, now America's second city, with its extraordinary capabilities for communication and organization-building, do not threaten the Eastern leadership, but it is an urban force to be reckoned with all over the world in the 1970s when satellite communications systems become routine. London's expediting of world trade far outdistances the nearest competitor, but its position is vulnerable because it has been slow to innovate. Moscow's formulas for 'socialist competition' seem to become more effective as the central controls are relaxed, so it is likely to expand its role as coordinator of the non-capitalist world. The direction that Shanghai's future will take is very much in doubt.

These are the principal actors with which the Tokaido megalopolitans must share the stage. What will be the roles they learn? How will they mobilize the resources to play them well?

Somehow the Tokaido complex must evolve a few specialities in advance of the world. So far it has made rapid progress with a policy of 'balance' between sectors so as to reduce the costs of social change, but a program of this sort cannot produce leadership. Specialized knowledge is the elevation from which the leadership ladder is climbed, and the knowledge is accumulated by institutional complexes such as corporations, agencies, libraries, and professions. Therefore, some features of the 'knowledge industries' must disregard what is known elsewhere in the world on that subject and the newest knowledge must be put to work in as many places as possible. In

Japan leadership has been assumed in a few quite narrow fields (for example, cameras, transistor circuitry, power production equipment, some phases of microbiology and marine biology, fisheries) but many more are needed.

Promoting the Knowledge-Based Complex

Graduate schools in Japan have doubled in size over a six-year span. This is not a particularly rapid growth for the 1960–66 period, since it is being matched in most other developed countries. In fact, it only keeps pace with the growth in demand for undergraduate education, a fact that will lead to many complications in the immediate future.

The megalopolis will need perhaps a full dozen intellectual centres, a third of them being primarily scientific and technological. Each must be well-connected with the rest of the megalopolis. Residential areas with amenities should be readily accessible. Hotels for conventions and conferences are essential. The planning must be undertaken both at the national level and the institutional level. Once started it cannot be dropped, because constantly changing emphases in an ever-expanding body of knowledge will require planned adjustments in the university communities.

An interesting feature of such communities, which arises quite naturally from their world-serving purposes, is that they establish the deepest and strongest ties in the urban region with other cultures. An important fraction of the residents will originate from western countries and from the developing areas of the world, while many of the Japanese employed in the institutional complex will have spent some years of their life overseas. The flow of temporary visitors will steadily expand. Therefore, the communities must have the freedom to make a broad spectrum of cultural adjustments.

Financial Planning

An important step can be taken in the reform of tax laws in most countries. As yet investments in education are usually not recognized as tax-free investments by the law, so that double taxation results. The income used to finance the education of the children in the family is taxed before it is invested. The argument used is that education is a service and therefore a form of consumption just as much as recreation. The incorrectness of this assumption has caused an overemphasis upon 'hardware' in the investment program of a nation and this bias will become increasingly serious as the superstructure of the megalopolis comes into being.

The present effects of this imperfection in tax policy is that donors are enabled to give money for university buildings tax-free but must pay taxes for gifts applied to scholarships or endowed chairs. An equalization, including the financing of children's education, is likely to bring an immediate burst of investment, and a rapid improvement of education.

Food Supplies, Agriculture, and Urban Space-Making

The future relations between town and country have no parallel in history, so they must be discussed as the merged outcome of several strong trends which can already be identified.

Some time ago I was discussing the problems of urban expansion in the United States with specialists in the distribution of market produce. It appears that the severest difficulty encountered is spoilage. In New York and London about 50 per cent of the vegetables and fruits are spoiled before they reached the consumer. Cities of a few million persons reported losses of 30–40 per cent, while those of a few hundred thousand experienced noticeably less, if their market operated independently of the dominant metropolis. Spoilage rates offer the most important explanation for the high prices paid by the consumers of fresh fruits and vegetables in the very large cities. Transportation costs, although often believed by townsmen and farmers alike to be culprit, are of secondary importance.

Curiously, it was found that refrigeration of fresh fruits and vegetables did not have much influence on the fraction lost, since it extended the 'season', and a low risk of spoilage over a longer time was comparable to a high risk over a shorter period. In addition, the extra steps in the distribution process required by refrigerator storage took their own toll. Therefore – my informant speculated – when cities get truly large (say 50,000,000), their residents will be at the end of such a very long distribution chain that the predominant share of the fruits and vegetables will perish along the way, and only a teasing trickle will get through to all but the most affluent consumers. The moulds and bacteria responsible for most of the spoilage will get the lion's share of the produce shipments. This states very well the predicament for feeding the megalopolis.

What are the trends in Tokyo today? First, residents are spending an increasingly smaller share of their incomes on food. Family expenditure declined from about 48 per cent in 1954 to about 38 per cent in 1964 and, as income continues to rise, this proportion is expected to drift to about 35 per cent. The difference is being spent on travel, recreation, and (somewhat differently from the rest of the world) on clothing. Second, we see reductions in the consumption of rice and other staples of traditional diet and rapid increases in other farm produce. Receipts of perishables in Tokyo during the 1960s have been growing at a rapid rate (Table 2). Third, an even more remarkable boom in meat, milk, and egg production has been under way, though it fails as yet to make up for the recent decline in the supply of fish.

TABLE TWO

Supply of Foodstuffs, 1956–65*

	1956	1960	1965
Tokyo Central			
Wholesale Market			
Vegetables	187,781 tons	234,166 tons	282,290 tons
Fruit	141,664 ,,	186,510 ,,	242,474 ,,
Japan as a whole			
Eggs	6,639 million	9,560 million	18,606 million
Milk	1,154 tons (000)	1,887 tons (000)	3,228 tons (000)
Cattle	139,116 tons	142,450 tons	207,541 tons
Swine	107,772 ,,	147,318 ,,	364,923 ,,
Marine Fish	4,668,376 ,,	6,102,768 ,,	4,050,000 ,, (est.)

* *Source:* Monthly Statistics of Japan, July 1966

In the rural areas to the north and west, that serve primarily as vegetable and fruit suppliers to Tokyo; a drastic reorganization is in the offing. The pressures began to build up during the 1950s when large numbers of youths migrated to Tokyo, and advanced a further step in the 1960s when non-farm income could be obtained in rapidly increasing amounts. Thus, the farms are being worked by an older population containing far more women than men. The size of the operating unit must expand several-fold for an income to be earned that is compatible with a job in the megalopolis. Takeju Ogura cites data to suggest that only about 10 per cent of the agricultural households could match probable urban incomes in 1964, but these produce fully a third of the agricultural output.[2]

Increasing mechanization will free much more farm labour and probably at least half the present farm workers will become available for other kinds of employment. The exact fraction will depend upon the bargain that can be struck with the urbanites, most of whom will live in the Tokaido megalopolis, for any change in land policy is inextricably bound up with urban growth.

Breathing Space for the Megalopolitans

Now let us return to the needs of a highly integrated urban region of some 50–80 million population. By some time in the 1980s or earlier, a redoubling of national income can be expected. The household expenditure level would then exceed anything to be found in European capitals today. What will they buy with this extra income? What indirect effects upon food supplies can be detected?

Most young city dwellers in Japan dream of having a car of their own. Even if it is of modest size this automobile will require as much space for parking and manoeuvring as the present housing for two people. Thus a 'European' ratio of one car for every six urbanites would require that at least a quarter of the urban spaces be given over to the automobile. In the neighbourhood of Tokyo (and Osaka) extra space can be only provided at the expense of agriculture, because the reclaimable surfaces offshore have been allocated primarily to industry.

The same population will pay perhaps three times as much rent as today. For that money they will get better protection from the environment, including electrical heating in the winter, some air conditioning, and more sound-proofing. However, more than anything else they will seek more living space. Some of this extra space will certainly be obtained by building upward, but most will come from moving outward. Already it has been shown that a high-speed rail line with the specifications of the New Tokaido line could develop enough land for urban settlement beyond the 50-kilometre ring to allow the proposition to break even. The prime target for such a settlement is not a rice paddy zone but an orchard area with low rolling hills, small rich flood plains, and a varied landscape, because the drainage is better and the amenities add to the sale price.

On top of these new demands are the consequences of large allocations of time to leisure. The megalopolitan 'man-on-the-move' will travel for pleasure much more than his metropolitan equivalent today. He will do this by taking long weekends and extended vacations. At the other end of the trip there must be not just more city. There should be a resort, or a park, or a beach. Virtually every amenity in Japan will be exploited for those seeking relaxation. Therefore, the space required for a megalopolis is not restricted to a lengthened, deepened, and broadened Tokaido belt, but will encompass special-purpose colonies throughout the Japanese islands and even neighbouring countries willing to entertain tourists. Some land will be withdrawn from food production to meet these demands, although in most cases the locales most desired for recreational purposes are least suited for agriculture, forestry, or commercial fisheries.

The Tokaido megalopolis would be forced to live, like London and New York, on imports from great distance. But, even at a distance, prospects are worsening. Already the seas are being searched intensively for fish over most of the world, and reports of overfishing are becoming more prevalent. Therefore, a gloomy outlook is wholly realistic unless some quite new approach to food production, using the available resources far more efficiently, can be developed quickly enough to meet the shortages in the urbanized region.

A Way Out for Agriculture

Let it be said first, with emphasis, that in the world of emerging megalopolises it is no calamity for a population to be dependent upon international trade for its food supplies. Japan today produces about 80 per cent of its own food requirements, and the competition for space could well push this figure down to 60 per cent. The principal worry is that a number of prophets are warning that food supplies throughout the world are not increasing as rapidly as population. Nevertheless, a megalopolis draws upon many territories and can substitute the products of one for those of another when shortages appear.

The most important feature of the megalopolis, however, is its enhanced capacity to innovate, improvise, and organize. It would have the resources to solve bigger technical problems than those being resolved today, and they would be implemented more speedily. The issue of food versus living space can be recast as a technical-cum-economic problem.

Today, at any site where urban settlement and farming can use the same land, the city will win. In Japan the land controls are strongly biased in favour of agriculture, but urban uses eventually succeed in displacing rural. Urban activities at the fringe of settlement can usually afford to pay two or three times the economic rent that agriculture can. Agriculture could pay more only if it obtained more than the normal two or three crops per year.

Recently, innovations have appeared which suggest that many more crops of vegetables can be obtained from a given land surface. The method is relatively old in concept, since it is one of providing a complete nutrient solution to the roots of vegetables and small fruits grown in gravel (aquaculture or hydroponics). It has not yet succeeded because the capital costs have been too high and the labour requirements not sufficiently reduced. Most important of all, epidemics of plant viruses could not be controlled. The new technique is still capital intensive, but labour productivity is raised to urban levels, and antibiotics have now been found which control the fungi and viruses. From four to ten crops per year could be raised in the Japanese climate.

Normal distribution channels can be greatly shortened by installing such gardens within the megalopolis itself. In this way the price of bigness can be evaded, and spoilage could be cut below present metropolitan levels. Many of the part-time farmers at present on the fringe of urban development may be encouraged to convert their holdings to such facilities. With land at Yen 50,000 per tsubo ($160,000 per acre) as a typical Tokyo suburban residential value, an eight-year amortization of equipment, labour at Yen 1,200,000 per year ($3,333), and a 10 per cent return on capital before taxes, it appears that the best quality fruits and vegetables could be marketed at Yen 150–200 per kilogram. This is no bargain, but it sets a ceiling for prices which differs very little from the present level. One hectare would be sufficient to provide employment for about ten persons – the normal size for small enterprises in Tokyo. The hectare need not be contiguous but could be handled as several small plots near to each other.

There are also prospects for producing meat and fish within the boundaries of the Tokaido megalopolis as a by-product of the solution of other urban problems. A technique for treating sewage, which has just gone into full-scale operation in Concord, California, promises to be useful in densely populated regions. In this 'oxidation pond' approach, the wastes are digested by anaerobic bacteria first, and a crop of algae is allowed to grow on the overflow so as to decontaminate the water. The algae can be grown so that they have high protein content. Ordinarily, this method of treatment requires more surface than other methods available and would be ruled against in the vicinity of Tokyo, but use of the water for industrial purposes, and the conversion of the algae into food for domesticated fish (or even batteries of chickens as has been carried out in laboratories) should justify installations on or adjacent to some of the reclamation sites in Tokyo Bay. The basic engineering development work has already been completed on the sewerage treatment stage, but much more engineering study must be done on the harvest of the algae under practical conditions and its conversion into foodstuffs.

The possibility of growing algae on synthetic nutrients in open culture is much further off, but potentially significant in the 1980s and beyond. Such algae materials have nutritional properties superior to seaweed, and foodstuff properties closely resembling soya bean, groundnut meal, and wheat gluten, but they are much richer in vitamins. Professor Hiroshi Tamiya has been responsible for much recent scientific progress in the culture of unicellular algae. Thus far only a Chlorella yogurt has appeared on the market in Japan, but this is a more advanced state of technology than is to be found elsewhere in the world.

Space-Making for the New Urbanism

These new approaches to food production are highly significant because they create more room in those regions where the demand for space is the most intense. Not only are more calories of better quality food produced per unit area, but the food is produced so close to the market that considerable savings can be made in distribution. One cannot expect, however, that large cities can become wholly self-sufficient in their food production. Vegetables and fruits delight the palate and prevent scurvy, but cereals fill the stomach, and cereal yields are improving very slowly, despite advanced research on every aspect of their growth. Rice growing land at Yen 600 per tsubo ($2,000 per acre) will be very much in demand, but quite a bit of it can be preserved through various reconsiderations of land use requirements.

Large circular concrete platforms (400 metres or more in diameter) with strong resistance to wave motion promise to provide 'dry land' at a cost of Yen 300,000 per tsubo, which is comparable to prices for beach strips and apartment house sites in the city. However, depth requirements or the strong tidal currents would preclude the use of these in Tokyo Bay, though some solution like this could cope with the overcrowding at the beaches. The most important prospective use of such floating apartments and 'new towns' is that of aquatic recreation. The Inland Sea would appear to be particularly suitable as a locale for scores of floating cities.

There is quite another way in which a megalopolis may create space. Most public facilities operate for only part of a day and for only five or six days a week. Expensive transport, communications, and electrical power supply systems operate close to capacity for only twenty to forty hours per week. Calculations suggest that peak operations could be doubled or tripled if a multi-shift society were to be evolved. This possibility has often been discussed in the past (H. G. Wells built several of his 'societies of the future' around the principle), and it was sometimes attempted during periods of war emergency, but it has not been found possible to draft a schedule which plots an efficient step-by-step transition to a multi-shift urban society. With the extraordinary capacities inherent in the new computers, it seems quite likely that urban region data banks can be created which would make such transition computations feasible. Calculations suggest that, with economical use of capital equipment, as much as 20 per cent of urban space could be reassigned, allowing higher densities of settlement while reducing losses due to congestion if that were desired. Thus far the nearest approach recorded is to be found in the Yaroslavl–Mystischi corridor in Moscow where the timing of shifts in round-the-clock industries has been staggered. However, reprogramming urban movements may require considerable reconstruction as well as reorganization, so this possibility must be regarded as a very long term one in view of the scale of a megalopolis.

The Challenge for the Designer

Greater population densities, higher costs of energy, traffic congestion, air pollution, and a number of other factors make all-electric living a more important goal for Japan than for even the United States. How can the task be approached?

The market is quite a bit larger than the overall numbers of the men-on-the-move and their immediate associates imply. It contains a large share of the families of salaried men presently in the Yen 1·5 to 5 millions ($4,000 to 15,000) per year income bracket which in another decade should double according to the plans of the government. This means the market could include as much as a third of all new housing units built in the Tokaido megalopolis in the late 1970s and the 1980s.

Recognizing the fact that sewers and water supply tend to lag in rapidly developing urban areas, the design of the water utility subsystem also takes a prominent position in the final product. It is interesting to note that one direction in which western kitchen, toilet, and bath facilities are going resembles what seems to be wanted in Japan. The kitchen is equipped to handle mainly frozen and other processed foods (food-centred entertainment being outside of the home). The toilet is low and water-conserving. Hand-washing equipment may fold into the wall when not in use. Water consumption rates should never be permitted to reach western levels, because occasional droughts would then become catastrophic.

The residents will pay most attention, I expect, to the cultural functions of the dwelling. Private study areas, for both children and adults, will get highest priority. They must be separated from television and the telephone. In some instances, perhaps, parts of the wall will unfold to enclose the student without cutting off the climate control he needs.

The Avocations of the New Urbanites

A preference for motion rather than rootedness means that a large share of the extra income anticipated will go into travel and activity outside of the job. The greatest frustrations of the megalopolis, as it comes into existence, will most likely be the limited capacity for escape. Shorter weeks and longer vacations open up free time to go places, but the congestion along the way will be intimidating.

The evidence is very strong that the most popular avocation of the first megalopolitans is, and probably will remain for some time, their automobile. The auto should be considered an instrument of freedom, opening up a wide range of choices for residence, amusement, and personal services, and is therefore not necessarily evidence of a crass materialistic outlook or merely a symbol of achieved social status. However, the automobile is a space-consumer of the most insidious sort. The automotive circulation system has a rationale of its own, most clearly expressed in Los Angeles and Detroit, that leads to gigantism in public works, pollution of the air, and the bankrupting of alternative modes of movement. Since Tokyo, in particular, has insufficient space for this, it will be the task of designers to find attractive substitutes, so that autos become only a part of a general transport utility which gives better service for arriving at places where fun is to be had.

Aquatic sports will probably offer the best opportunity for the largest number to do something different from city life, because the Japanese islands are surrounded by varied seas with unusually rich detail in their coastlines. Sailing and boating will multiply many times over.

Similarly, every kind of mountain sport will be propagated. Skiing by that time will be open to the masses, and the man-on-the-move will be fishing the furthest brooks for trout and salmon planted there only a few weeks earlier from the fish culture centre, or he and his family will be riding ponies along prepared trails from one mountain *ryokan* to the next. Altogether the mountains may be expected to become more heavily populated with urbanites and those who stand by to provide services to them than they ever were by charcoal burners, subsistence farmers, and outlaws.

Sometimes the pull of these avocations becomes so strong that a residential compromise is sought. How can one live in the mountains or at the sea and still operate as a megalopolitan? Some people are willing and able to pay for convenient solutions which create 'islands' of megalopolis, geographically separated from the main body but well connected with the centres (as described earlier). The alternative is a 'second house' in the amenity area. The market in houseboats should be particularly brisk, because they can now be made unsinkable and highly typhoon-resistant.

The Networks and Service Systems

Behind the scenes, operating mostly in silence and sometimes even invisibly, are a number of networks and grids that keep the city alive. Virtually every household must be connected to the water supply, sanitary sewers, storm drains, electric power, telephone, streets, post, and radio–television signals, while many are also tied in with gas power and microwave relay beams. Comprehensive planning for cities must program the steps whereby the engineers for these networks and grids improve and expand the services.

The sophisticated systems design lying behind 'good life' in the megalopolis requires mountains of data from whose details the networks are designed. Some time in the 1970s, it is expected that computers will have achieved a memory capacity large enough to cope with the comprehensive records of metropolitan services, so that 'data banks' can be constructed which provide access to the desired information within seconds or minutes.

The data bank is the heart of a new informational network that silently and unobtrusively records transactions of the city that change physical and legal relationships. It will answer questions put to it about the present ownership of property, the kind of structure at a given address, the number of persons residing in a given area, etc. It will be immensely useful to the urban designer asked to reconstruct a given area. It is anticipated that these data banks will contain at least four basic entries: (1) names of residents with some personal records (educational achievements, vocational experience, medical background); (2) addresses of pieces of property with records of their linkages to the utility grids and other services; (3) major vehicles or pieces of mobile equipment; and (4) the services or component operations by which these are linked. Virtually all public transactions can be described with these elementary lists. Thus, a *trip* can be defined as the movement of persons in (1) from an origin to a destination in (2) in a vehicle from (3) by a route using facilities in (4).

Tokyo is so large a metropolis that computers are not yet able to store and search such fine-grained data, but new forms of memory introduced in 1966 come very close to meeting the prospective requirements. Therefore, it must be anticipated that the construction of a set of such computerized records is a design task of the 1970s.

The struggle for compatibility is a megalopolitan phenomenon. As the megalopolis becomes knit together by its increased population, some of the grids and networks of its component cities will overlap and clash. Two different water-supply systems, for example, may claim the same watershed, but more serious than anything would be an incompatibility in their data bank designs. If the megalopolis has any government distinguished from other levels of government, it will derive from the synthesis of a polycentric compatible instrument that monitors the respective networks and grids. It will need at least sufficient authority to construct and maintain the system underlying the operation of the respective (metropolitan or prefectural) data banks.

This is a new kind of urban planning which universities have so far ignored. Fortunately Japan has developed a strong computer industry and it is now placing heavy emphasis upon the elaboration of large general programs, often referred to as 'software'.

All during the period of the 1970s, the Tokaido megalopolis will experience a shortage of labour due to the dwindling size of the cohorts of population born in the 1950s and the early 1960s. This shortage will be particularly intense in the service trades, the traditional manufactures, and the more routine clerical work. Therefore, the price of service labour will increase more rapidly than that for any other kind of labour, and labour-intensive services such as urban transport will be forced to raise their rates repeatedly. Reorganizations will be frequent and thoroughgoing. As always, under such pressure, attempts will be made to substitute a flow of information for the expenditure of human effort and attention to the re-design of the service. Thus, the use of the telephone and the computer must expand and the present momentum requires that the pace in Japan be more rapid than anything experienced in Europe.

The designer, therefore, will either be put to work patching up existing urban services that have been outgrown or become obsolete, or to planning components of a larger system of urban sources which will manage the change in a number of its components. The solutions that he arrives at will determine the competitive position of Tokaido vis-à-vis the other megalopolises in the world. If that competitive position should decline, the 'engine of development' that is now producing so powerfully would falter, due to its increased internal friction.

NOTES

1. M. M. Webber, *Explorations into Urban Structure*, 1964.
2. Takeju Ogura, 'Recent Agrarian Problems in Japan', in *The Developing Economies*, Vol. IV, June 1966.

39. Cultural Growth and Urban Development: Inner Tokyo 1951–68

RICHARD L. MEIER AND IKUMI HOSHINO

How does the culture of a metropolis adjust as accelerated economic development of a region proceeds? We know already that many innovations must be adopted and quite widely disseminated in order to stimulate and sustain economic growth, and that innovation and diffusion are as much cultural phenomena as they are economic and social. But which comes first – the growth of the economically productive capital stock or the accumulation of a fund of culturally controlled behavioural patterns?

Additions to urban culture precede, and are prerequisite to, each project that results in urban economic growth. Therefore, cultural growth is one of the principal causes for the expansion of income and wealth. The process is quite straightforward: novel ideas, from whatever source, are recognized and accepted several years, sometimes decades, before income derived from them can exceed expenditure. An increment to regional income could occur only if a number of persons had been instructed in the synthesis of a novel good service and a much larger number was persuaded of its advantages. Thus, new social roles, new cultural traits, and especially new imagery in the language result from successful adoption of an innovation, while a new profitable contribution to economic growth is realized some time later.

Cultural growth may be necessary to urban economic development, but many forms of accumulation appear to be sterile. Some ideas, concepts, images, and behaviours are much more potent than others. Which of them have been associated with rapid development in recent years? What are their origins and pathways; by what channels do they enter the metropolis? What, if anything, do they displace or render extinct? How might a forecaster use this casual connection to infer future transformations of metropolitan society? How does it change planning strategy when development is the prime goal? These were the leading questions in our analysis of the nearly infinite phenomena presented by a section of Tokyo; the city that became the world's largest metropolis sometime between Ronald Dore's benchmark study[1] and our own study in 1966.

The investigation was greatly simplified by the existence of a general theory that connected urban cultural growth with economic development. It was, however, a macro-theory that had very few explicit suggestions for identifying what kinds of images are selected by urban residents during periods of sustained economic growth. The crucial case for this theory is provided by Tokyo, because it is the most dynamic metropolis in the country that has been outdistancing all other countries in the world in the rate of economic growth. Admittedly, a fully general set of empirically tested propositions can be advanced only after cross-cultural studies have been undertaken, but the prototype should suggest a number of structural and procedural conditions that expedite the conversion of cultural innovation into added income for residents. This task is assisted by the surprisingly comprehensive system of internal reports produced by each unit of Tokyo's urban government, so that many routine hypotheses suggested by field observation can ordinarily be set aside as being of insufficient magnitude to contribute significantly to the known growth rate. The richness of organized data permit some unusually deep insights regarding the mechanisms of interaction.

Urban culture is susceptible to measurement by using both stock and flow concepts. The cultural *stock* expands when the identifiable traits increase in both number and variety. We will be concerned here with a category comprising the bulk of the cultural traits, which will be designated as *images* – the patterns and forms that are endowed with meaning for at least a portion of the local population. The *flow* is indicated by the amount of cultural interaction undertaken voluntarily by members of the society per unit time. This might be gauged by the number of social transactions completed, or the volume of messages transmitted through all the communications media. A still more precise assessment would take account of the repetition and redundancy within and between the messages and so would estimate information flow between members of the society (as measured then by *habits*, so as to distinguish human communication from that which goes on between artifacts endowed with feedbacks, such as automata and instruments). Because cities have been organized and laid out so as to expedite social communication, they constitute the natural locus for measuring flow. Thus, the stock serves as a catalogue of cultural assets, while the flow represents continuous attempts to fit the traits, or images, to current opportunities for maintaining and extending social institutions which vary in size from households to governments.

Tokyo provides us with the most illuminating instance for the study of accelerated development. Japanese culture presents quite special difficulties for observers because it has always valued the transitory and the ephemeral more highly than the permanent and the invariant. It has gloried in miniaturism rather than gigantism. Despite the publication of a few grandiose engineering and architectural works, and the oft-repeated statements of regret on the part of a body of intellectuals, there is still no admissible evidence for a change in attitude. Therefore, the core of Japanese urban culture is not epitomized by climactic institutional foci, such as cathedrals, monumental terminals, or skyscraper corporate headquarters, but is elaborated on the micro-scale by the shifting mosaic of the street scene. Such an overview induced us to experiment with novel techniques for illuminating the mainstream trends in the life of the city.

The sources of the borrowed images found in the public places of the ward of Taito-ku are 80–90 per cent American. Some German images could be readily detected in the plastic toys exhibited, Swiss–French images in the horological designs, and British ones in the formal clothing. Although a few basic stylistic contributions to toys, clock-work, electronics, and clothing are Japanese in origin, this point is rarely stressed in the advertising! The images obtained from the Americans, in a number of instances, had themselves been borrowed by the Americans, either directly or through underlying concepts, well before their transmission to Japan. Due to the fusion of many alien cultures on the American continent, the channels available there for borrowing are unparalleled, but whatever images or styles (which we take to be a patterned sub-assembly of a set of images, new and old) rise from the sub-cultures to become popular in the United States are excellent nominees for adoption by Japan.

The Content of Messages and Media

We considered attempts to quantify the changes occurring in the street scene at the full ward scale, but found them to be inextricably bound up in the national mass media, leaving very little capacity for the ward to speak to itself. The highly valued ephemera pulse through a city and spill out into the prefectures with little regard for administrative boundaries. Therefore, our techniques were forced to operate at the scale set by the mass media. We were dealing with the popular culture of a primate city rather than an inner ward, so we sought efficient ways of shifting out new content in the communications media. Tokyo's productions and publications dominate the whole country; they disclose its own view of the world.

Japan is far better equipped for conducting a comprehensive analysis of changes in symbolism than any other society. The Japanese language is sufficiently different from the Indo-European group to permit ready identification of loan words; neologisms of all kinds can be quickly sorted out of printed materials.

A chronological listing of introduced newspaper terms indicates that only 30–40 per cent are complete importations, the remainder being permutations of local argots with each other or with some borrowed term. The straightforward loans are indicative of the breadth of contact and illustrate the shift from an emphasis upon reconstruction and welfare. Additions in 1950 include: 'red purge', 'teenage', 'caseworker', 'freemason', 'patrol car', 'trolley bus', 'auto race', and '"oh, mistake"'; in 1955, 'no horn zone', 'mambo', 'after-ski', 'juice stand', 'jet coaster', 'aqualung', 'swimming glove', 'key puncher', 'one dollar blouse', and 'jamboree' showed up; in 1960, 'mass leisure', 'funky', 'winkie doll', 'leisure boom', 'revival boom', 'dump car', and 'credit card' are recorded; in 1965, we see 'bunny girl', 'eroduction', 'wandervogel' ('wangel'), 'zero meter' (zone), 'racing car', 'convention', 'monkey dance', 'beauty cycle', 'sneak preview', and 'blue film'. The additions seem to be becoming less concrete and more sensual as the urban culture becomes more complex. They may also be attributed to the fact that the baby boom of the late 1940s joined the labour force just prior to 1965 and was making its influence felt.

Young men, intent upon becoming junior executives and administrators, are urged to acquire vocabularies that enable them to discuss the latest world-wide developments in technology, management methods, public administration, marketing, etc. They ply each other with questions, jokes, and jeers aimed at familiarizing all parties in this conversational game with the new images. A thorough understanding is believed to be required of them to pass examinations, impress the company interviewers, and thus qualify for the most desirable jobs. Large companies and big government both prefer professional employees with a cosmopolitan outlook.

These alien images in the messages disseminated to the public are the most immediate indicators of cultural change. Those that find niches in the cityscape are slower to appear, but more lasting. Those that get built into the mass production of artifacts are still more permanent. A study of the structure of capital investment in Japan during the postwar period showed that the cultures that originally produced the modern technology component of that investment were the same as those responsible for transmitting the influential images.

Forces Shaping the Future

Virtually all the changes wrought in the Hanazono-cho sector of Taito-ku were set in motion by exogenous forces – foreign, technological, megalopolitan, and cosmopolitan. Even the very few traditions that were honoured and preserved were supported by outsiders. The Edo tea ceremony school became a 'treasure' endowed by Metropolitan Government. A teacher of traditional Japanese singing has moved into the community. A school for karate opened some time after the peace treaty was signed. A society for the preservation of *ukiyoe* prints set up its headquarters in a well-groomed house.

Indeed, the whole area has been designated a 'scenic district' with considerable power to prevent rapid commercialization, but this is due to the proximity of the very popular modernized zoo in neighbouring Ueno Park. It can be argued that each organized attempt to preserve the traditional images was sparked by an external group that was reinforced locally.

In their search for economic opportunity the residents have been pulled away from the tight little community that was forced to take care of most of its own affairs in 1950, in much the way a village in a densely populated region had done a generation previously. Now the heads of families and the new entrants to the labour force usually find more rewarding work at a distance, thus opening up places for people coming from poorer wards, such as Arakawa-ku a few kilometres in the direction of the periphery of the central city, or for apprentices and peasant girls fresh in from the hinterland. Educated youth of the community find posts in the expanding *zaikai* organizations, the larger retailers, and the various government bureaucracies. Daily movements in and out of the ward expanded by almost a factor of three, even though the population living there had begun to decline very rapidly. Thus, the night-time population was undoubtedly more sophisticated than the much larger day-time population, even more in the ward as a whole than in the precinct.

The period 1951–66 was one in which the range of considerations open to members of the community was hugely expanded. In this short span of time we see a precinct opening up into a ward and beyond, a ward that opened to involvement in an enlarged metropolis, if not a nascent megalopolis, and a metropolis that began to deal on a businesslike basis with any place in the world and was eager to borrow ideas from any of the advanced technological societies. Local small businessmen have been watching the style-setters, wherever they may have originated, and that means the United States the majority of the time.

When Dore conducted his study of life in the ward, the traditional community associations, though formally abolished, were still operative because modern government was poorly financed and groping for efficient procedures. By 1964 the ward government had 875 employees (and by 1966 it had added two electronic computers) to handle the routines in running Taito-ku. Youth now gets the most attention, with schools obtaining the greatest slice (36 per cent) of the budget, but enough is left over to finance a number of ultra-modern play lots as well as vacation lodges (eight of them) several hours away at beaches, mountains, forests, and ski areas. The emphasis is increasingly upon the quality of education, so ward officials proudly boast that 80 per cent of the junior high graduates are able to get through the examination and be admitted to senior high school. Perhaps a third of the latter will go on to the university. This rising educational background enhances the capacity of citizens to organize and press their desires. Until now it has taken an unusual grievance, such as the abolition of a historical local name in the rationalization of addresses, to trigger a collective protest. In the future the agencies putting forward urban renewal programs in the inner wards will encounter many vocal neighbourhood associations and ad hoc groups, suffering unexpected embarrassments as a consequence. Often such groups will be backward-looking and obstructive, but the predominant youthfulness of the population and the concentration of education in the youngest components should also produce much constructive action.

Discussion and Conclusions

The most striking feature about Japanese cultural growth during a period of accelerated development is the extent to which it drew upon alien images. A selective, highly sophisticated borrowing system had been created that had overcome the barriers of distance, language structure, and levels of living. Tokyo's urban culture is now so open it often prefers foreign ideas, even when a good Japanese equivalent exists.

If, as was argued on the basis of the standard sequence of events for introducing an innovation, the cultural additions precede economic development, then some sense can be made of the selective openness of the culture. The most sensitive instrument found for measuring rate and direction of growth was the organized collection of neologisms, because it provided early indicators of changes in interest, but deductions from that source were confirmed and extended by observations of the cityscape and analyses of technology transfer. The causal connection appears to have the following steps:

1. Foreign cinema, television, magazines, and artifacts are exhibited to an urban public that values novelty.

2. Extensive foreign travel with camera in hand enables a multitude of representatives to document interesting successes overseas that might be worth borrowing.

3. A huge volume of public face-to-face interaction taking place in the varied entertainment areas sets up a continuous demand for something new to talk about.

4. Salient foreign images from the mass media, reinforced by intense discussion, stimulate fads, styles, and gimmicks, while sparking dramatic indigenous experiments aimed at regaining the initiative for the local producers.

5. The curiosity induced in the mass public creates new markets for products and services.

6. Foreign technology for meeting these demands is licensed and experiments are undertaken to adapt the technology to local conditions.

7. Institutions in both the public and private sector are enlarged to meet the new demand and are forced to advertise their appeals to members, employees, clients, and stockholders.

8. Differential growth appears in both the culture and the economy, so that the less educated sectors of society and the less accessible urban communities are left behind; this contrast creates a number of stresses, some of which only become evident when they foster disturbances of the peace.

9. An equally apparent phenomenon is the rapid rate of obsolescence, so that firms, bureaux, and households must be continually alert to the condition of their public images and set about repairing the same ('beautification') if they become anachronistic, thus releasing the powerful forces of status maintenance in a way that allows them to be used for development ends.

10. Planning of the future is then mainly aimed at maintaining the impetus of growth, and is pragmatically applied to specific locales, agencies, and functions. A number of new institutions need to be

organized to instigate such changes, but the precedents for them already exist somewhere close at hand, so that the chances for success are good.

A quick acting, wide open cultural system, sensitive to the content of public communications in the pacemaking societies of the world, seems to be one of the best instruments for overcoming serious internal bottlenecks and structural defects. The planning that accompanies it is unspectacular, but the pace of improvement in economic well-being achieved is unprecedented. Every densely populated poor country in the world today needs at least one successful imitator of Tokyo.

NOTES

1. Ronald Dore, *City Life in Japan: A Study of a Tokyo Ward*, University of California Press, 1951.

40. Lessons from the Japanese Jungle

J. M. RICHARDS

Japanese cities have become notorious for their ugliness, and it's true that the exciting modern Japanese architecture we hear so much about – to say nothing of the even more exciting ancient architecture – is hardly to be noticed, and almost impossible to find among the chaotic concatenation of buildings of every kind – shacks and sheds, flyovers, advertisements, poles and wires, with dense traffic fighting its way among them – which cities in Japan are bewilderingly composed of. This may be frustrating to the tourist in search of interesting architecture, but while engaged the other day on such a search I realized how closely the dynamic quality that Japanese cities undoubtedly possess is associated with their chaotic nature. It's a quality that our own cities seem to be denying themselves by the very means we choose to develop and improve them.

Among the town planners, the fashionable term just now is 'environment', and it's generally assumed that what is meant – what is desirable – is a *designed* environment, an architectural creation, though on a wider scale than architects traditionally operate on. Architects' and planners' training is a training in the establishment of order, and their idea of an improved city is of a place that has been subjected to some degree of overall design. But there's another, almost an opposite, way of looking at it: the city can be – to use another fashionable term – a happening, a place that derives its interest and vitality from the fact of it's *not* being consciously designed. This is what I was forcibly reminded of in Tokyo, Kyoto, and Osaka, and the question is whether the control that all cities need, to enable them to function at all and to get their social priorities right, can't somehow be combined with freedom to develop the vitality and spontaneity that this opposite approach alone seems to make possible, allowing people to participate in creating their own environment.

Popular participation in the formal processes of design would be disastrous, since this needs an architect's skill. But the Japanese city is not a design that has been done badly; it's the negation of design, an urban happening with its own special vitality. As to why this has come about in such an extreme form in Japan, I formed a personal theory that the special circumstances of Japanese land use make the city the only place where an impetuous, anarchical, instinctive life – such as everybody needs for part of the time – is possible. Outside the cities hillsides are precipitous and impenetrably wooded, so that you can't do anything but look at them. The valleys in between are intensively cultivated, so that you can't walk about in them without trampling on crops or ploughing ankle-deep through rice-paddies – they're more like somebody's garden than farmland. There are also mountains, but the least inaccessible of these are preserved as national parks; they're admirable places, but they're no longer wild in the sense of being a challenge to every kind of initiative. They're to some extent tamed and regulated. The ramble across fields and woods and moorland, which we in the West regard as the natural use of the countryside, is impossible for the Japanese, in the unorganized fashion that still provides for us an outlet for our need to explore, to go where our initiative takes us, to be free from rules and disciplines. The Japanese, consequently and instinctively, allow themselves freedom from rules and disciplines in their cities. The city has become the Japanese jungle.

And directly we accept that it's in the city that the law of the jungle prevails, the nature of Japanese cities becomes logical: their refusal to conform to a pattern, to grow according to any preconceived principles, and the visual consequences that follow. All these contribute to the sense of an environment where spontaneity is still possible, where the individual can use his own initiative and feel free of obligation to his fellow men, as free as the individuals who occupy the tidier cities of the West can feel when they go adventuring in mountains, moors, and forests.

This may at present be a peculiarly Japanese situation, but it is one that's likely soon to become ours as well. We've long been used to the idea of running wild in the country and behaving ourselves – even putting on more formal clothes – when in the city. But running wild in our countryside is a thing we find is increasingly difficult to do: less of it remains wild and there are more and more people to make it less wild still and they come in motor cars to destroy what wildness is left.

In the city, as you can see in Japan, the motor car plays the opposite role to the one it plays in our countryside. It doesn't destroy wildness, but is itself one of the wild animals in the jungle, careering about in hordes and making its presence felt noisily and alarmingly. Motor transport, instead of fighting against the natural grain of the city, as ours does, contributes a new dimension to it. The elevated expressways, the overpasses and underpasses, where road, rail, and monorail traffic weave in and out at frightening speeds, reinforce the impression of the city as one vast unpremeditated happening.

If we put it like that, and are still willing – as we should be – to regard the city as a work of art, the relation of the Japanese city to contemporary developments in art becomes evident: its relation to Pop Art, for example, which is equally concerned with images that erupt from the activities of everyday life, instead of being designed to play an artistic role. Immediacy has become an aesthetic virtue, and the Japanese urban scene that I've been describing might itself be called an example of three-dimensional Pop Art. It even owes to its sky signs and advertisements what Pop Art owes to beer-cans and strip cartoons.

What I'm concerned with is the lessons other cities can learn from the dynamic quality that has been a by-product of the anarchical growth, and the Pop Art vitality, of cities like Japan's. The lesson certainly isn't that we must revert to laisser-faire. Simply to make a city work requires several kinds of control by town planners and architects. But the qualities such professional people contribute to making it work are not sufficient to create a totally satisfactory human environment, because they don't include the qualities that arise from participation by the user, from spontaneous response to challenges of all kinds, and from the fact of conflict. Conflict, by definition, cannot be planned in advance and, in any case, the architect's and planner's instinct is to resolve it.

But conflict is an essential ingredient of the visual excitement that one misses in the self-consciously planned environment and that one values in its opposite, the Japanese jungle-city. The real difference is not between design and accident but between the idea of a city as a composition of works of architecture and the idea of a city in which architecture is only one element, and a background element at that. The dynamic quality of Japanese cities is created by layer on layer, receding in perspective, of moving objects and incidents, inextricably interwoven, each justifying its presence in the jungle by the way it involves people. The question for us is how to endow our cities with the same sense of popular participation without plunging ourselves into functional chaos – which is one of the drawbacks of the Japanese jungle – and without abdicating our responsibility, when cities are rebuilt, to give priority to social needs.

The Japanese cities don't derive their dynamic quality from the efforts of the town planner – just the reverse. Their acceptance of a degree of anarchism, their exploitation of the ephemeral and the blatantly commercial, bright lights and visual complexity and incongruity, represent a release or explosion at the very point in the procedure where we are accustomed to think control most needs to be imposed. They are thus a kind of anti-architecture that at a certain level we must bring ourselves to accept, even though to the planner it may seem to be destructive of everything he has been taught.

The paradox is that our present positive and conscientious planning only creates a negative result, whereas what comes out of an apparent negation of planning achieves something far more humanly positive. Is it not the planner's opportunity that people are beginning to recognize this?

The aim should surely be to create more places where happenings are possible, because not until the people who live in our cities can find pleasure in the gregariousness that brings cities about in the first place can we afford to despise Japanese cities and call them ugly. In the meantime we can enjoy the excitement they provide and that our cities don't, and learn at least one thing from them – a thing that applies to Britain more than to any country in the West because Britain shares with Japan the intense population pressure that threatens her whole environment. This is that, given such a pressure of population, it is in the city – where the population is gathered anyway – that individuality, and even anarchy, must be allowed the freest rein, not only in order to create cities where a full life can be lived, but as a way of stopping our countryside, which is far more vulnerable and where solitariness is still possible, from being overrun: overrun because the cities have become places where self-expression is impossible. In present-day circumstances a free-for-all in the countryside will destroy it; a free-for-all in the city, in the sense that I have defined it, could be the making of it.

41. The Pedestrian in Megalopolis: Tokyo

JAQUELINE TYRWHITT

C. A. Doxiadis uses the 'human community' as a unit of urban planning. This is a pedestrian scale unit varying in population size with
the economy of the country. Its main criteria are that it is an area that
may be penetrated but not crossed by vehicular traffic and that it
contains daily shopping needs as well as primary schools. This means
that its horizontal dimensions cannot exceed one kilometre. Doxiadis
considers such areas as the 'permanent' elements in a constantly
changing urban situation: the bricks from which a humanized megalopolis can be built up.

The idea is attractive and the use of distance rather than density
as unit of measure not only allows for a lot of flexibility but also
makes good practical sense when one is thinking about man on his
feet. A man or a woman or a child can only walk the same distance
in comfort along a street, no matter whether they arrive there from
the front door of their house or by elevator from an apartment thirty
storeys up in the air. What is this distance? Does it vary according
to age, climate, or the motive for the journey? What about car
owners? We cannot ignore the fact that every family desires to have
some independent means of transport. Perhaps the present-day car is
not the best answer to this need, but no matter how much public
transportation is improved, the desire for some personally propelled
fairly fast-moving vehicle will remain, and, if we wish to design a
'human community' − an urban unit in which the needs of man's
intimate home life are uppermost − it will continue to be necessary to
plan for the path of movement and for the storage of privately owned
vehicles without usurping the rights of the pedestrian.

A marvellous opportunity to try to find some measuring rods for
these distances presented itself in Tokyo, where the residential areas
are traditionally penetrated only by very narrow winding streets. Two

596 *Synthesis: The Example of the Tokaido Megalopolis*

small districts were chosen for study in the Suginami Ward of Tokyo. Amanuma Sanchome had 2,566 households and Kamiogi Nichome 1,925 households. Both were middle-class areas with 40 per cent apartments and 30 per cent car ownership; gross densities in both were just over 80 per hectare (about 33 per acre) and both had very stable populations. However, the two areas had one major difference: Amanuma was a maze of narrow winding streets, very few of them wider than 3 metres (10 feet) while Kamiogi had a regular grid of 4–6-metre streets (Figure 1 and Table 1).

TABLE ONE

Family Type and Dwelling Type

	Kamiogi			Amanuma		
	Houses %	Apartments %	Total %	Houses %	Apartments %	Total %
Families with children	42	12	54	61	6	67
Elderly people	8	—	8	4	1	5
Others	36	2	38	27	1	28
Total	86	14	100	92	8	100
Actual figures			(86)			(88)

A detailed land use study was plotted at 1:500 scale and a questionnaire was distributed to one household in each square of 50×50 metres. This elicited a 95 per cent response (eighty-six replies from Kamiogi and eighty-eight from Amanuma). The report was based on an analysis of this questionnaire related both to the land use study and to statistics available from an elaborate social survey of Suginami Ward made in 1966.

The two criteria for which we desired to obtain measurements were convenience and safety, and these were studied from the point of view of the woman's walk to the shops; the commuter's daily walk to the subway station; where small children play; where women gather to chat; and, finally, the point of view of the car driver.

We found that small groups of local shops only attract customers from a very small radius (150–200 metres) if there is a large shopping

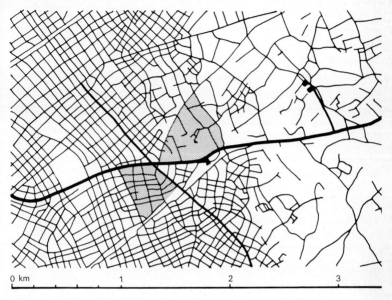

Figure 1. The two districts studied: Kamiogi Nichome (left) and
Amanuma Sanchome (right).

centre within some 700 metres. When asked about convenience of
distances, the women who lived more than 500 metres from a good
market said it was too far, but over 250–300 metres was considered
too far from local shops. Women considered their route to the shops
unsafe if they had to walk *along* traffic streets, but they did not seem
to mind crossing streets so much. As it is usually thought that crossing
a busy street represents much more of a traffic hazard than walking
beside the traffic this reply was rather surprising. However, if the
sidewalks (or pavements) are narrow and there are many pedestrians
– as was the case in Tokyo (where some shopping streets have no
sidewalks at all) it is understandable that the dangers of having to
step into the path of the traffic are much greater than occasionally
having to stop to cross a busy street (Figure 2).

The commuter responses were drawn from a very detailed questionnaire carried out by a parallel study in the same area. From this

it appeared that the commuters in Amanuma (with the narrow winding streets) try to find the shortest way to the station but commuters in Kamiogi (with the wider gridiron streets) seek out the safest route. All stated that what they chiefly desire is a clear separation from vehicular traffic: their next desire is for a very direct route without turnings or crossings. This is very understandable when one remembers that many of the commuters are half asleep when they make their way to the station early in the morning, and dead tired when they return home at night – often in the dark. Like the women shoppers, they considered walking alongside traffic more dangerous than the occasional obstacle of crossing a traffic street.

We now turn to the places where small children play. We found that only half the parents with gardens to their houses said that they were used by their small children. A quarter of all the children frequently played in the school playground and an attractive Shinto

Figure 2. Narrow shopping street without sidewalks in Amanuma Sanchome.

TABLE TWO

Complaints about Walk to Ogikubo Station

	Kamiogi Nichome %	Amanuma Sanchome %	Suginami Ward %
Safety			
No separation from car	41	26	31
No pedestrian crossings	9	1	7
Streets too narrow	—	36	22
	50	63	60
Convenience			
Too many turnings	9	19	13
Too many obstacles (street crossings)	18	3	8
Not enough street lights	9	10	11
	36	32	32
Other	14	5	8
	100	100	100

TABLE THREE

Where Children Play (Responses from 121 mothers: more than one place could be named)

	Kamiogi %	Amanuma %	Total %
In the garden of the house	63	45	53
In the street	35	45	41
In the school playground	9	37	25
In an empty lot	11	27	20
In a shrine or temple garden	11	16	14

Shrine garden drew children from as far as 300 metres. However, barren open spaces only drew children from the immediate vicinity — about 50 metres. The most popular place for all the children to play in was the street, and 60 per cent of all residents said that children were usually playing in the street outside their houses. This statement was less often made in the really quiet (and safe) streets and it can be concluded that the children of this part of Tokyo (and perhaps all children) naturally seek excitement and variety. Thus they chose the most exciting and varied places with little regard to the dangers involved (Figure 3 and Table 3).

Figure 3. Children playing in the street in Amanuma Sanchome.

And now, where do the women stop to chat? The places that were identified seemed to have very little in common until they were examined in relation to the use of near-by building. Then a pattern began to emerge and it seemed that almost every gathering place was either just near the entrance to a building where some kind of social activities were carried on (school, hospital, tea garden, shrine) or else at the approach to a shopping centre. In other words, people gathered at the threshold of their objective (Table 4).

TABLE FOUR

Gathering Places

	Kamiogi %	Amanuma %
Near local shopping centre	27	34
Near 'social building'	33	30
At crossroads or parking lot	33	17
Elsewhere	7	17
	100	100
Actual figures	(15)	(30)

Finally, let us turn to the views of the car driver before trying to piece these fragments of information together. First we must record that car ownership in this middle-class area is increasing extremely rapidly: indeed ownership jumped from 20 per cent in 1966 to 30 per cent in 1967 and another 15 per cent said that they desired to have a car. These figures were similar for house owners and apartment dwellers and it would clearly be unrealistic not to plan for 100 per cent car ownership in the not too distant future. Regulations in Tokyo require every car owner to have an off-street parking place, and the traditional picturesque entry to the Japanese house is rapidly being transformed into a garage or a car port. On the other hand, many car owners in the study area left their cars in public parking lots and these were asked to identify the lot and state whether they found the distance convenient or not. Everyone who parked within 200 metres of his home considered it quite convenient, but above this distance there were many complaints.

Two other questions that we asked were whether cars were frequently parked outside each person's house and what was the route the car drivers usually took to get on to one of the main roads around the residential district. We found a very interesting correlation between these two answers. While the even-spaced gridiron pattern of Kamiogi had sixteen exits of equal width on to the main roads, only two thirds of these were used at all frequently. The most frequently used roads were seldom less than 150 metres apart. On the other hand, day-time parking was particularly frequent on short lengths of relatively lightly travelled streets at right angles to the main roads.

Further, by far the largest single type of complaint about the neighbourhood referred to the disturbances caused by cars passing and parking before the house. There is no doubt that one of the strongest desires of residents is to face upon a quiet street, free of vehicular traffic.

A final item taken into account was the location of recorded traffic accidents. The 1966 records for the Suginami Ward showed that 60 per cent of all accidents occurred on the major roads, particularly where these coincided with shopping centres. But 40 per cent were on the residential roads. Almost all of these accidents occurred at intersections of quiet roads: places where people had come to expect very little traffic to pass, but where the road pattern did not discourage traffic. No accidents occurred at any of the relatively busy intersections in either area, where drivers knew they had to be on the alert. Similarly, no accidents occurred on any of Amanuma's narrow winding streets, where drivers were obliged to move at slow speed.

Conclusion

This study serves to give popular support to the widespread concept that residential areas should be designed as pedestrian islands, but it adds a few useful suggestions and dimensions:

1. A clearly marked pedestrian spine should lead to shopping centres, social institutions, and public transportation connections.

2. Children's play areas and adult gathering places can be located at strategic points along this spine.

3. If one planned for a continuous pedestrian system, major shopping centres could be located at something under one-kilometre intervals (say just over half a mile) with small groups of shops to service daily needs between them.

4. Outlets of service roads to the next hierarchy of the road system (often called connector roads) should not be more frequent than 200 metres and not less frequent than 400 metres (approximately a quarter of a mile) and car parking areas not more than 200 metres (preferably 100 metres) from the furthest dwelling. This gives a primary pedestrian precinct of around 500×300 metres.

Within this primary pedestrian precinct routes should never be wider than 3 metres (10 feet), except perhaps for the main pedestrian spine, and none should lead directly across the area. This is necessary in order to discourage the penetration of private cars and service vans, but still permit entry of emergency vehicles, such as fire engines or ambulances. The acceptance of this width limitation is an absolute essential if we are to safeguard the freedom of the pedestrian in the city of the future, for we must recognize that legal prohibition will never be strong enough to keep the cars out. If they can enter without too much difficulty they will enter. We must plan by design and not simply by decree.

42. Urban Poverty, Rag-Pickers, and the 'Ants' Villa' in Tokyo

KOJI TAIRA

The Occupations of the Poor

The typical living space for a poor household in Japan during the 1890s was a one-room apartment nine feet wide and twelve feet long (*ni-ken kyushaku*) in a long one-storey multiplex apartment house called *nagaya*. Except for size and density, the physical layout of the poor quarters of Japan looked very much like a cheap motor inn with its rows of one-storey, multi-room buildings in America today. The 9×12 room contained six Japanese straw mats (*tatami*), although one *tatami* equivalent of space (3×6) was allocated to the use for the vestibule, closet, and kitchen. Ordinarily, one *tatami* area would be the absolute minimum sleeping space for one person, although many poor households might have to put up with less space per capita than that.[1]

Among the activities of the poor during the Meiji period, the three least remunerative occupations were carrying, mud-handling, and rag-picking. The representative carrying jobs were rickshaw pulling and hand-carting. For this reason, the number of rickshaw pullers in an area was regarded a reasonable indicator of the degree of its poverty. The handling of mud, sand, and pebbles was an activity associated with the construction industry. Finally, rag-picking was the activity of scavenging in the streets. It is clearly the least preferred form of gainful employment, and many of the poor would rather beg or steal than pick rags. All the data, private and public, indicate that the earnings from rag-picking were far below those from other activities the poor were capable of. Rag-picking is on the borderline between employment and vagrancy.

Closely related to, but somewhat better off than the rag-picker, is the rag-buyer who buys waste materials from households. The capital with which the rag-buyer acquires waste materials is advanced to him on a daily basis by a rag-dealer (*shikiriya*) who stores, classifies, and disposes of the materials obtained from rag-buyers and rag-pickers. Both rag-buyers and rag-pickers are highly dependent upon the rag-dealer, who provides them with shelter for a nominal rent in the shanties improvised in his junkyard. The people to whom rag-dealers sell their collections are called 'processors' (*kakō gyōsha*), who are specialized by category of material and who, after proper treatment of the materials bought from the rag-dealers, pass them on to factories and plants. Rag-pickers, rag-buyers, rag-dealers, and processors among them constitute an industry which the Japanese call 'regenerated resources industry' (*saisei shigen gyo*).[2] Some call it *shigen saisei gyo* – 'resource regeneration industry', which, though a mere reshuffling of terms, conveys the sense of a dynamic process that characterizes this industry. It is also the preferred expression because of its favourable implication for the rag-picker as an agent of resource regeneration. One who regenerates resources may eventually regenerate himself.

Table 1 shows the size of the 'resource regeneration industry' in Tokyo and its change over time. Rag-picking and rag-buying as poverty-linked occupations have demonstrated a remarkable staying power. The 'resource regeneration industry' expanded remarkably during the early postwar years, reaching its peak in terms of employment in 1952. The table indicates that, except for 1940, rag-buyers have always been more numerous than rag-pickers. When employment in this industry was increasing during the early postwar years, the number of pickers increased more slowly than the number of buyers. Since 1952, pickers have been decreasing faster than buyers. This is understandable, because rag-buying is somewhat more respectable than rag-picking. It may be noted that the number of rag-dealers has increased in recent years. Why this has occurred is somewhat enigmatic, but it may well have been due to the increase in the productivity of rag-pickers and rag-buyers associated with more efficient methods of junk collection. At the centres of junk trade today, we often see bicycle-pulled carts with pneumatic tyres on their wheels, small three-wheeled motor vehicles, and, in more favourable cases, trucks of varying sizes. When we recall that the rag-picker's sole means of production during the Meiji period were a bamboo basket

TABLE ONE

Employment in the 'Resource Regeneration Industry' in Tokyo, Selected Years (Number of Persons)

Year	Pickers	Buyers	Dealers	Processors
1896[a]	788	6,153	n.a.	n.a.
1940[b]	7,000	2,000	260	370
1947[c]	5,800	7,900	n.a.	n.a.
1952	7,300	11,800	n.a.	n.a.
1954	6,800	10,500	854	608
1960	4,800	7,200	940	1,100
1965	1,700	5,800	972	1,074

n.a. – not available.

[a] Kunijiro Tashiro, ed., *Nihon shakai fukushi no kisoteki kenkyū* [Basic Studies on Social Welfare in Japan] (Tokyo: Doshinsha, 1965), p. 92.

[b] Metropolitan Government of Tokyo, *Saisei shigen gyōkai no enkakau* [A Short History of the Regenerated Resources Industry] (mimeographed, undated), p. 5.

[c] Data for this and ensuing years were supplied to the author from the worksheets in the Sanitation Bureau of the metropolitan government of Tokyo.

and a long stick, we notice that the general progress of the economy and technology has touched even the lowest boundary of gainful employment, such as rag-picking.

'Ants' Villa' in Tokyo, a Rag-Pickers' Community

'Ants' Villa' is a community of fifty households located on Tract No. 8 of the reclaimed land at the waterfront of Tokyo Bay belonging to the administrative district of Koto-ku. The economic activity of the community consists in recovering value from all kinds of junk – cans, glass, paper, rags, rubber, scrap metals, straw, wood, etc. Everyday life is organized on a thoroughly communal basis, beginning and ending with a group prayer in the community chapel, which is a constituent of the Catholic archdiocese of Tokyo. The work process is highly rationalized; junk is collected in large quantities from major business concerns in the central area of Tokyo, transported to the community workshops in several trucks, sorted out by teams of worker-residents, packed by machines, and delivered to the commercial processors of these materials for further rounds of industrial use. The organization of work in the community compares favourably with any efficient small-scale firm in Tokyo. The compound of the community is spacious (16,700 square metres). In addition to the chapel, workshops, and equipment just mentioned, there are four residential structures meeting reasonable standards, a house for children's recreation, a guest house, a community restaurant where the residents take their regular meals, and a store of daily necessities with adjacent facilities for between-meal snacks. The community is clean, quiet, and prosperous. Its standard of living is above the social minimum in every sense.

Fifteen years ago, however, Ants' Villa was a totally different place. Not only was its location different, but it was 'sub-minimum' in every sense, verging in fact upon the underworld of vagrants and criminals. The history of Ants' Villa at its present location dates back to June 1960, prior to which it was located at a corner of the Sumida Park on the right bank of the Sumida River. Ants' Villa leased its present site from the metropolitan government of Tokyo for Yen 15,000,000, payable in instalments over five years. Ants' Villa accepted these terms in 1958, when they seemed extraordinarily stiff with reference to the financial capability of ordinary workers. The annual instalment, which amounted to Yen 3,000,000, was 10 per cent of the annual earnings of a hundred able-bodied workers working full time at the monthly rate of Yen 25,000. During 1955–8, however, the average monthly earnings of the regular employees in Japanese manufacturing were less than Yen 20,000.[3] Moreover, the taming of the wild land, which was a refuse disposal area for Tokyo, required a considerable initial investment, to be borne entirely by Ants' Villa. All of this meant that Ants' Villa had to work many times as hard and as ingeniously as regular workers, and to formulate and implement a resettlement plan with the care and efficiency of a first-class business enterprise.[4]

Ants' Villa surmounted these obstacles, despite the fact that its members were rag-pickers, whom one would not ordinarily expect to have regular work habits, sustained efforts, foresight, planning, saving, investment, or other qualities indispensable to an efficient enterprise.

Ants' Villa was organized as a rag-pickers' cooperative by Motomu Ozawa when he took charge of fifteen unemployed rag-pickers dismissed by a retiring rag-dealer in 1950. Ozawa, who was born in 1895, was a successful businessman before the war and was ruined by being caught in the disorders following Japan's defeat. In organizing the rag-pickers' cooperative, Ozawa was assisted by Toru Matsui. Matsui was born in 1910 and directed the Taiwan Theatrical Association during the Second World War, returning to Japan in 1946. Before he joined the rag-pickers of Ants' Villa he had taken on a variety of jobs, including junk collection in the military compounds of the Allied Forces, land reclamation in a mountain region, and promotion of a movement for world government. The constitution, bye-laws and formal organizational structure of Ants' Villa were Matsui's artifacts.[5]

Ozawa's practical leadership and Matsui's intellectual counsel would perhaps have maintained Ants' Villa as a rag-pickers' cooperative. But an efficient cooperative was still a far cry from being an effective community. But an additional stroke of luck was in store for Ants' Villa. Early in 1950, the person who was to become the spiritual catalyst for the community development of Ants' Villa moved into the near-by area of Asakusa. She was Miss Satoko Kitahara, a young lady twenty years of age. She graduated from a pharmaceutical college in Tokyo in the spring of 1949 and then pursued religious study which led to her conversion to Catholicism. When Miss Kitahara visited Ants' Villa in December 1950, it was the first real contact with poverty she had ever experienced.[6]

In May 1951, Miss Kitahara decided to pick rags in the streets. From May to December 1951, when illness forced her to rest, she rose regularly at five in the morning, tramped in the streets picking rags, disposed of her collection in Ants' Villa accounting section early in the afternoon, made her rounds to visit the aged, sick, and infants in the Villa, dispensing medicine where necessary, and taught children at her home in the evening until 10 p.m. She also organized community recreation activities for children, with adult participation. These events and activities, executed with Miss Kitahara's delightful ingenuity, ushered into Ants' Villa those essential elements of community life: solidarity, identity, planning, expectation, and general warmth of feeling among people. Miss Kitahara took up her permanent residence within Ants' Villa in 1952 and stayed there until she succumbed to critical complications arising from tuberculosis in 1958.

The psychological breakthrough of its residents and the development of Ants' Villa as a genuine community with a sense of purpose and solidarity made possible the next step in its history. Although not illegal, Ants' Villa was squatting on a public park. There was no question about the desirability of restoring its site to public use. What Ants' Villa wanted to avoid was a purposeless eviction accompanied by a dispersion of its members. The metropolitan government had so far shown no interest in the question of community relocation. Ants' Villa patiently negotiated with the metropolitan government, emphasizing that it would be poor social policy to destroy a community which had demonstrated its moral integrity and economic efficiency. In January 1958, the metropolitan government finally yielded to the request of Ants' Villa, though at the price outlined at the beginning of this section.

Conclusion

A dynamic socio-economic system is full of shifts and changes. Individuals and institutions must accommodate themselves to the requirements of the dynamic system with ingenuity, flexibility, and speed. Where there are shifts and changes, there are lags and gaps. Urban insular poverty is a gap between the individuals' or households' resources and the cost of housing of adequate standards. Behind this is the lag between the individuals' or households' employment capability and the changes in occupational structure of a dynamic economy.

Our review of the historical experience of Ants' Villa indicates several policy areas for minimizing the social cost of a dynamic urban industrialism:

1. A vigorous housing and urban policy far in advance of urban growth.

2. Efficient institutions of help and remedy to counteract the dislocations arising from 'acts of God'.

3. An economic policy to stabilize general economic conditions and the employment market in particular.

4. A social policy to neutralize the effects of age, sickness, and family size.

5. What might be called a 'psycho-cultural policy' to regenerate and strengthen the personality, outlook, and will to live of the hard-core poor.

We would like to emphasize the last policy area, for it is novel and tends to be overlooked in practice. Nations and cities have often acquired substantial experience in the other policy areas. But the 'psycho-cultural' policy has only begun to receive some attention in recent years. The professions required for an effective policy of this type come under various new titles: for example, 'animateur', 'encourager', 'non-professional social worker'.[7] Governmental, philanthropic, and religious organizations need to maximize the effectiveness of on-going welfare projects by a conscious reorientation of the required means and methods along this line. A new outlook is also needed on the part of the society at large towards the maximum generation of what Sorokin calls 'love energy' in order to ensure the success of psycho-cultural policies.[8]

NOTES

1. R. P. Dore, *City Life in Japan*, Berkeley, University of California Press, 1958, Ch. 4.

2. Tokyo Metropolis, Sanitation Bureau, *Saisei shigen gyōkai no enkakau* (A Short History of the Regenerated Resources Industry).

3. Japanese Government, Economic Planning Agency, *Keizai yoran* (Economic Abstract), Tokyo, 1961, p. 232.

4. See *Ekistics* 38, December 1958, pp. 297–302.

5. Matsui's writings include *Ari no machi kiseki* (The Miracle of the Ants' Villa), Tokyo, Kokudosha, 1953; *Binbo tsuiho – Ari no machi no keizaigaku* (Conquest of Poverty: Economics of the Ants' Villa), Tokyo, Sankei shinsho, 1956; and 'Ari no machi no kuraku' (Trials and Triumphs

of the Ants' Villa), a series of four articles in the Sunday editions of the *Yomiuri shimbun* (Tokyo), starting on 13 November 1966.

6. For a detailed description and interpretation of Miss Kitahara's life and work, see Toru Matsui, *Ari no machi no mariya – Kitahara Satoko* (Satoko Kitahara, Mary of the Ants' Villa), Tokyo, Chiseisha, 1958, and Shunjusha, 1963.

7. Peter Marris and Martin Rein, *Dilemma of Social Reform: Poverty and Community Action in the United States*, New York, Atherton Press, 1967; William W. Biddle and Loureide J. Biddle, *Encouraging Community Development*, New York, Holt, Rinehart & Winston, 1967.

8. Pitirim A. Sorokin, *The Ways and Power of Love*, Boston, Beacon Press, 1954; Pitirim A. Sorokin (ed.), *Forms and Techniques of Altruistic and Spiritual Growth: A Symposium*, Boston, Beacon Press, 1954.

43. Approaches to the Twenty-First Century: A Development Policy for the Tokyo Metropolitan Region

MASAO YAMADA

The basic idea of the Capital Region Development Law in 1956 was to meet the increasing problems of excessive urban growth and the resultant inadequacy of public services by a regional planning approach. A broadly defined 'Capital Region', with a radius of approximately 100 kilometres from Tokyo Central Station, was established for planning purposes. The region was divided into three concentric rings; the Inner Urban Area, the Green Belt Area, and the Peripheral Area (Figure 1). A number of industrial satellite towns have been planned in the peripheral area to absorb industry and population which would otherwise be attracted to Tokyo and population which would otherwise come up to Tokyo or which might be decentralized from the central city. A Green Belt Area was envisioned at the outskirts of the built-up area in order to prevent the further sprawl of the inner built-up area. This regional plan for the metropolis was worked out after a study of the regional planning pattern which was adopted for London on the basis of the Greater London Plan, 1944. To supplement the basic law for bringing about an orderly development of the capital region as a whole, the Law for the Construction of Satellite Towns and the Law for Controlling Industry and Other Activities within the Inner Urban Area were enacted.

Nearly ten years have passed since the Capital Region Development Law was put into force. However, in view of its limited effectiveness in controlling the overgrowth of Tokyo, opinions have been growing demanding the rethinking of the adequacy of applying a static method to an 'exploding' city like Tokyo, which has grown parallel with the development of the Japanese economy, and this has been developing at a formidable rate for the past decade. Thus, a

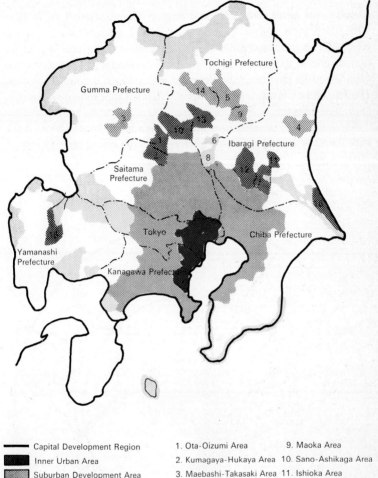

Figure 1. Capital Region Development Plan, 1965.

Capital Development Region
Inner Urban Area
Suburban Development Area
Peripheral Development Area
Recreation and Sightseeing District
Wide Urban Development Area
Satellite Town

1. Ota-Oizumi Area
2. Kumagaya-Hukaya Area
3. Maebashi-Takasaki Area
4. Mito-Katuta Area
5. Utonomiya Area
6. Oyama-Mamada Area
7. Tuchiura-Ami Area
8. Hurukawa-Sōwa Area
9. Maoka Area
10. Sano-Ashikaga Area
11. Ishioka Area
12. Tukuba Area
13. Tochigi Area
14. Kanuma Area
15. Kōhu Area
16. Kashima Area

revision was made to the Capital Region Development Law in June 1965, based on a new idea of development pattern of the Capital Region. The proposed green belt of concentric ring shape was abandoned, and in its stead a comprehensive development pattern for the capital and its environs (50-kilometre area), which is composed of the existing Inner Urban Area and a newly defined suburban development area, was adopted.

This suburban development area surrounds the Inner Urban Area, with its outer boundary 50 kilometres from the city centre (Figures 2,

Figure 2. Number of population increase per year, 1950–55.

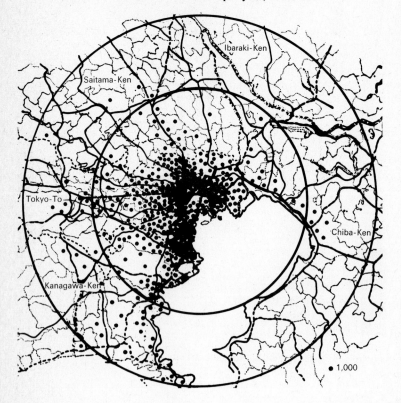

3, and 4). The purpose of this plan is to induce industry and population to locate at suitable places in this area without permitting unplanned sprawl of the built-up area, and at the same time to bring about planned distribution of suburban settlements with abundant parks and open spaces. Therefore, the satellite town development areas have now been included in the suburban development area and each has become a focus of a multi-focal structure within the 50-kilometre boundary. On the other hand, the policy of building satellite towns was changed from building a number of small-scale towns to

Figure 3. Number of population increase per year, 1955–60.

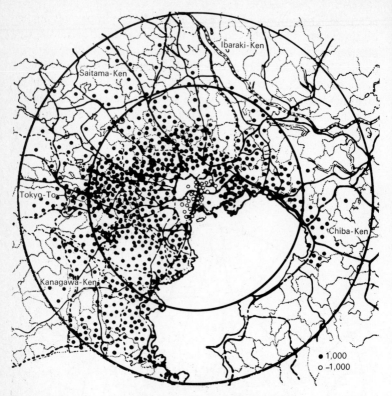

Figure 4. Number of population increase per year, 1960–65.

fostering a small number of pivotal provincial towns in the area beyond the 50-kilometre boundary. With the revision of the Capital Region Development Law, the Satellite Towns Development Law was also revised to become the Law Concerning the Development of the Suburban Development Area and the City Development Area.

The fundamental items which are required for pushing forward a rational plan for the 50-kilometre area are as follows:

1. The proposed green belt in the shape of a concentric ring should be abolished and, in its stead, a comprehensive planning pattern should be established for the 50-kilometre area as a whole, with the

existing proposed green belt, industrial satellite towns, and the Inner Area combined together. Planned redevelopment within the 15-kilometre area and planned development in the 15–50-kilometre area should be pushed forward in organic relationship with each other.

2. To reorganize the 50-kilometre area into a more efficient urban structure, it is necessary to reorganize the urban structure from the existing single-focus structure into a multi-focal structure. To achieve this purpose, it is necessary to push forward urban redevelopment schemes centring around the city centre and sub-centre districts, to induce planned development of industry and housing in the surrounding areas, and to develop a number of auxiliary sub-centres, like distribution centres and others, along the arterial routes of transportation.

A number of the measures mentioned below would be effective for bringing about a multi-focal urban structure.

Firstly, an efficient network of transportation, especially a rational relocation of road transportation facilities must be established. However, these inter-city highways run merely in radial directions out into the outer fringe of the ward area. These inter-city highways would mean little unless they have links with one another by having junctions somewhere around the Outer Ring Expressway (Figure 5). However, the Outer Ring Expressway is not required under the urban structure as it exists at the present moment, because most of the traffic flow on the inter-city highways has stronger directional inclination towards the city centre than in foreign countries. Although the economic value of the Outer Ring would be low, it should be useful to bring about a reorganization of the urban structure of Tokyo by locating sub-centres and auxiliary sub-centres along it, and by extending the existing urban expressways to it, thereby ensuring mutual links between the main city centre, sub-centres, and auxiliary sub-centres. This would not only facilitate a shift to a multi-foci urban structure, but also increase the effect of investment in the Outer Ring Road.

Secondly, as can be seen from the tendency of industrial firms and business offices to move, momentum has been mounting for launching redevelopment schemes on a large scale. According to a survey, it is estimated that the vacated premises of the industrial plants with desire to move from the Inner Urban Area to its surrounding area, amount to 3·9 per cent square kilometres. The Tokyo Metropolitan Government spent three billion yen (8·3 million dollars) in 1965–6 on the purchase of these vacated premises, but the applications from business firms which desire to move have amounted to twenty times as much as the funds which are available for this purpose, annually. It is neces-

Figure 5. Tokyo freeways, 1967.

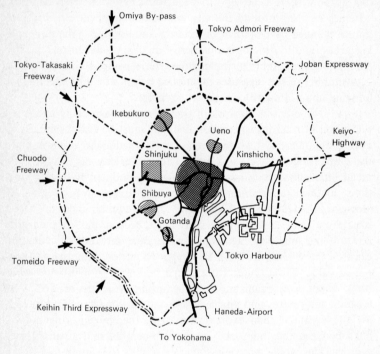

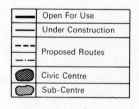

▬▬▬	Open For Use
▭▭▭	Under Construction
- - - -	Proposed Routes
-·-·-	
⬤	Civic Centre
▨	Sub-Centre

sary for the Central or the Tokyo Metropolitan Government to acquire these vacated premises for the use of urban development, not to leave their re-use to the discretion of the individual business concerns. Needless to say, an abundant amount of low rates and long-term funds are desirable to achieve this purpose. Acquisition of vacated premises is a last chance for pushing forward urban redevelopment schemes under the existing economic and social system.

Another method which is left unused for improving the land policy is the coordination of the proprietorship and the use of land by way of town planning measures. Only if this coordination is done will unplanned housing (in search of low price of land) and unplanned location of multi-storey buildings (due to sky-rocketing prices of land in the built-up area) disappear. Similar difficulties have been experienced in cities in foreign countries in coordinating various kinds of rights in connection with the redevelopment of the existing built-up area by way of multi-storey buildings, or the more efficient utilization of space. City ordinances or bye-laws, such as they have had for the purpose of urban redevelopment, do not exist in Japan.

The greatest headache for planners in Japan is the exorbitant price of land which has been boosting at an unreasonable rate compared with other commodity prices, and it is hardly expected that any national legislation to arrest the rising price of land will be made in the near future. In the new Urban Redevelopment Law to be enacted in Japan, it states that subsidies should be given to persons able to effect redevelopment schemes in coordination with those recommended by the City Planning Council, and local authorities are able to effect redevelopment schemes without purchasing the land. Thus, the twin objects of urban redevelopment, or the joint construction of multi-storey buildings and provision of dwelling units in large number, are achieved, and the fatal defects of present land policy and housing policy in the built-up area improved greatly. Urban redevelopment in built-up Tokyo means elimination and improvement of the numerous narrow roads and lanes which are one of the features of the urban structure of Tokyo, as well as alleviation of burdens upon various public facilities such as roads, parking garages, etc., by the integration of blocks, joint construction and multi-storeying of buildings, and other projects. If the upper floors of the multi-storeyed buildings in the built-up area are used for dwellings, the urban structure will become compact, as a result of residences being located near the places of work, thus solving some of the housing and land problems and reducing the economic investments for railways and roads for commuter transport.

The Future of Tokyo

In February 1966, the Tokyo Comprehensive Development Council submitted to the Governor a written recommendation of what Tokyo should be like in twenty years' time and the measures to be taken to orientate the future growth of Tokyo in that direction. It is a reply to the 'terms of reference' of the targets and master plan for the redevelopment of Tokyo which was referred to the council. The recommendation is based upon an assumption of what Japan as a whole and the Tokyo region will be like in the twenty-first century and sets forth the targets to be achieved in ten and twenty years' time respectively, which are designed eventually for constructing Tokyo as one of the international economic centres in the true meaning of the term. The gist of the recommendation is as follows:

What Tokyo should be in the future must be sought in the light of what Japan as a whole and urban areas in the country will be and should be in the future. The factors which are and will be at work affecting the future course Japan will take would include some factors which would be beyond our prediction . . .

As confirmed by the results of the 1965 national census, the urbanization which has been proceeding in Japan for the past decade is still going on at a formidable rate. Our projection is that the urban population in Japan will increase to 80,000,000 persons in twenty years' time from now and it will reach nearly 100,000,000 persons at the beginning of the twenty-first century. This means that the great majority of the Japanese people will live in urban areas.

According to a projection of the economic growth and population increase of Japan as a whole, the population increase in Japan, the Capital Region and the 50-kilometre radius area will reach its zenith some time between 1985 and 2000 and the nation-wide population total is estimated at 120,000,000 persons around that time. The urban population of 100,000,000 which is anticipated to reach that level would occupy as much as 80 per cent of the nation-wide total. The population around that time is estimated at 40,000,000 persons within the Capital Region and at somewhere between 28 and 30 million persons within the 50-kilometre radius area respectively (Figures 2, 3, 4).

The recommendation proceeds to anticipate the formation, as an eventual result of the rapid urbanization in Japan, of a 'megalopolis' which stretches from the Kanto Region to Northern Kyushu at the beginning of the twenty-first century. The functional area of Tokyo will be enlarged remarkably, due to technical renovation in transportation and communications, and Tokyo will play an increasingly important role as the centre of the megalopolis, an international urban centre and as the brain and information centre of the Japanese economy. It is anticipated that in the process of attaining that stage, the structure of the Japanese economy will become stabilized gradually and the pace of change will also stabilize through gradual steps. It is therefore anticipated that the present rate of increase in day-time population in the cores of the national capital and other large cities will stagnate and will take a stabilized course. Then, the target of constructing an attractive Tokyo through the improvement of environmental conditions for ensuring the amenity and the modernization of the people's livelihood in urban areas will become the realistic demand of the people.

Based upon the above-mentioned assumptions, the recommendation sets forth several targets of plans which must be achieved in the immediate and near future. As the planning target in connection with the redevelopment of the economic functions of Tokyo, the recommendation puts special emphasis on the increased efficiency and strengthening of the central managerial function of Tokyo as the generating power of the Japanese economy. In other words, while efforts should be made for purifying the C.B.D. (central business district) functions by helping concentrate the central managerial functions which are deemed necessary for national market and international market activities, the planned deconcentration of other economic functions should be considered on a regional basis.

As a target connected with the regional structure of industry in the capital city, the recommendation mentions the decentralization and localization of manufacturing departments and a part of distribution departments. Namely, the manufacturing (production) department which is concentrated excessively within the built-up Tokyo should be relocated in the surrounding districts in such a way as to make them contribute to the economic growth of the city cores once again and thereby to establish a rational structure of industry in the Tokyo region as a whole.

As seen clearly in the recommendation, the growth of a city should go together with its economic growth. Viewed from the position of Tokyo as the centre of the Japanese economy, a future plan for Tokyo should not be confined to a mere plan for getting rid of 'large city problems' and must be a plan which can achieve the task of strengthening the functions of Tokyo as the core of the Japanese economy, which will go on growing in the future. How to strengthen the functions of Tokyo is a national task which would greatly affect the future of Japan as a whole.

Tokyo Expressway

For the purpose of making smooth the traffic flow between the city centre and sub-centre districts, eight routes (standard width of four lanes, 16·5 metres, total length of 71·6 kilometres) were decided at the City Planning Council in 1959. The designers of the Tokyo expressway set the standard speed of automobiles at 60 kilometres per hour (36 miles per hour) and planned a total of ninety-one rampway accesses (Figure 5). The structure is mainly in viaduct form and only occasionally open-cut or underground. As an average automobile trip in this area is approximately 7 kilometres, an appreciable amount of automobile traffic can be absorbed from the ground level roads on to the expressways, owing to the large number of rampways.

A network of expressways has now been proposed and agreed with nine routes and a total length of 92·4 kilometres, and a total length of 58·7 kilometres is now under construction.

Arterial Roads

The arterial roads network has a pattern of ring and radial forms combined (Figure 6). It is expected that the present increasing demand for traffic facilities will reach its summit some twenty or thirty years from now and it is hoped that all proposals will have been finished by that time. The improvements of the existing arterial roads and construction of urban expressways, which have been effected energetically over the past decade, contribute much to the alleviation of the traffic congestion in the city centre and sub-centre districts. However, in the meantime, traffic congestion on the roads has moved out to the zones between 10 and 15 kilometres from the centre.

The physical structure of the urban area of Tokyo is featured by fragmented blocks and numerous traffic intersections. Therefore, from the standpoint of traffic engineering, the most important point in road improvement in Tokyo is how to bring about grade separation at traffic intersections rather than the mere widening of roads. The point is how to obtain the maximum traffic capacity at a minimum cost. To take an example, along the city centre part of the Showa-dori boulevard, a driver can now pass under five major intersections at grade within a distance of 2·8 kilometres. The Ring Road No. 7, with a standard width of 25 metres and total length of 56·5 kilometres, has a plan of continuous grade separation at sixty-seven traffic intersections.

Parking Facilities

In accordance with the Parking Facilities Law which was enacted in 1957, the Tokyo Metropolitan Government launched a drive for constructing public parking facilities with the revenues from parking meters. At the same time, developers of buildings of certain specified size (floor space) in the city centre or sub-centre districts were required to attach a specified size of parking facilities to the building to get a planning permission for that building. After that, the obligation to attach parking facilities was extended to the commercial district in the whole of the Inner Urban Area.

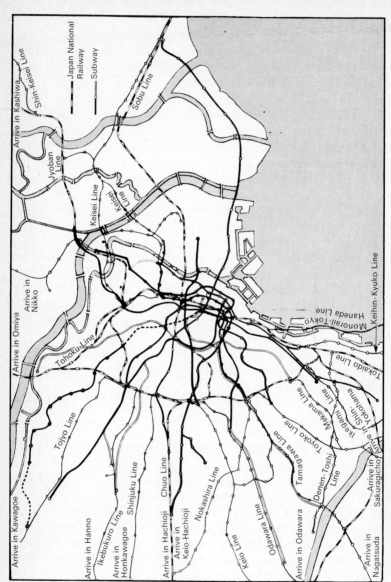

Figure 6. Network of rapid transit lines in and around Tokyo, 1967.

Rapid Transit Subways

Until the Tokyo Metropolitan Government commenced the construction of subway Route No. 1 in 1958, the Teito Rapid Transit Authority had been the sole authority constructing the operating subway network in Tokyo.

The proposed network of subways in Tokyo is ten routes with a total length of 267·7 kilometres, out of which a total of 76·5 kilometres is now in operation (Figure 6).

Locational Pattern of Housing

Dwelling houses constructed by both private and public money have been spreading in a centrifugal pattern in search of low-priced land, resulting in disorderly settlements which are scattered around within the 50-kilometre radius area (see Figure 1 on p. 613). These dwelling units have been provided with little consideration given to city planning either on local or regional levels, or to the convenience of the users. As a result, apart from problems involved within the individual housing estates, viewed from a regional planning point of view, imbalance has been brought about between demand and the supply of public facilities, such as roads, transport, water supply, drainage, collection and disposal of refuse, and compulsory education facilities. This overtaxes the minor local authorities financially and, regionally speaking, it lengthens commuting distances and increases the congestion of one-way passenger traffic during rush hours. The present one-way congestion in passenger transport has forced the transport enterprises to launch an investment for increasing carrying capacities. The provision of collective housing with emphasis laid on the increase in the number of units tends to be a main cause of a vicious circle, in which the searching for low-priced land for houses again causes the boosting of land prices, unless rising prices of land are halted by a firm land policy.

In order efficiently to solve these related problems (which come from the rising price of land, the lack of land policy, and the defectiveness of housing policy), from the viewpoint of city planning it is necessary to take legislative measures which require local authorities to estimate housing demands and to make a plan for the supply of land and housing, as a part of city planning. At the same time the provision of multi-storey buildings, the adjustment of streets and blocks, and the rational utilization of land in the Inner Urban Area around the city centre must be assured, as well as the planned supply of housing.

44. A Case for Satellite Cities of 300,000 in Japan

R. KAKUMOTO

In the Tokyo–Yokohama Region (Figure 1), with its area of 1,255 square kilometres, as many as 15,680,000 people live. Some of the commuters to Tokyo's central business district (C.B.D.) travel distances of up to 70 kilometres, but most come from within the radius of 50 kilometres from the C.B.D. and the greater number of them originate from within 30 kilometres.

Even though no accurate figure is available about the commuters entering the C.B.D. by all means of transport, it is estimated that some 1,200,000 are commuting by rail, i.e. 750,000 (62·5 per cent) by J.N.R. (Japanese National Railways) and 450,000 (37·5 per cent) by subway.

Longer Commuting Distance and the Speeding-up of Trains

Two measures have been suggested to solve the shortage of both houses and transport facilities. One is that we should have no more houses in central areas, and the other is that we must disperse our working places and residences to the Outer Ring of the Metropolitan Area or even outside that.

The first measure is strongly supported by some people in spite of the existing high-density situation in built-up areas. In reality, however, population is decreasing in a fairly wide sphere in and around the C.B.D.

The second measure is similar to the New Towns of the United Kingdom, and more than ten satellite industrial cities have been planned, and some of them already built.

Building of new factories or expansion of existing factories in built-up areas has been forbidden since 1959. Thus, there is a tendency among industrialists to move their factories to an outside area and sell the land they own in the C.B.D., taking advantage of the inflated land prices there. However, we must recognize that building new satellite industrial cities is not effective in bringing about a dispersion of business offices.

In attempting to disperse working places, the problem is with offices. In round figures, employment in the C.B.D. in 1955 was 500,000 persons in Tokyo, 1,000,000 in London, and more than

Figure 1. Built-up areas within 50 kilometres of Tokyo, 1967.

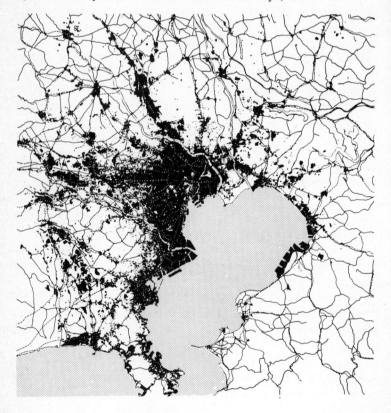

2,000,000 in New York. The figure for Tokyo was then too small for the capital city of a country with a national population of 100,000,000. It was therefore quite natural that the numbers rose to 1,000,000 in 1965. At this stage of expansion, it was just as useless to try to restrain the growing of the C.B.D. as to stop the growth of a boy.

Initially, houses were built in small units of several hundreds or thousands around all the existing railways stops, but this resulted in making the railways overcrowded. Moreover, there were so few houses in any one unit, that it was difficult to supply them with adequate public facilities. It has proved necessary to build houses in much larger groups to provide good living conditions. But it is impossible to find available space for this along the existing railway lines.

As a result, an entirely new project has been worked out, to build residential cities to accommodate 300,000 or 400,000 people, and to connect these cities with the C.B.D. by new railways.

As an example, the railway to Den-en-toshi (residential city) was opened in 1965, and the city is under construction. And land purchase for the Minami-tama New Town started in 1966 (Figure 2).

These cities are both situated 30–40 kilometres from the C.B.D. It should be noted that there is practically no land left within this area that is cheap enough for the ordinary salaried class people to procure. Physically, too, there is hardly any left for construction of a city measuring 30 square kilometres in size.

Proposal

There is a very small difference in the construction cost of building a railway for a maximum speed of 100 kilometres per hour, or of 200 kilometres per hour, if no level crossings are allowed. The same applies to the operating costs.

On the New Tokaido line, trains cover a distance of 76·7 kilometres in forty-one minutes on one section, and 107·2 kilometres in forty-four minutes on another section.

Supposing that the distance between a residential city and the

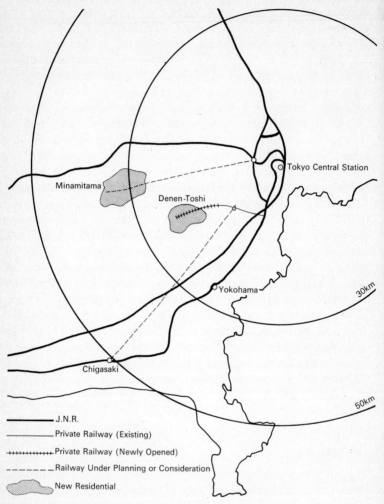

Figure 2. Railway construction and new residential cities.

C.B.D. is 70 kilometres, and that trains run non-stop at speeds of up to 200 kilometres per hour, as on the New Tokaido line, the distance between these two points could be covered in only thirty minutes.

The construction cost of such a railway and the passenger fares may be calculated hypothetically as follows:

Let us assume that this railway would be constructed by a shield construction method some 50 metres under the ground in passing through the final 10–15 kilometres of the built-up area. The cost would be about 2,000 million yen per kilometre. This cost would be lower than in the case of present subway construction, as there would be no need to build stations in the intermediate underground section of this railway. The elevated part (15–20 kilometres) to be built in the suburban area would cost 1,000 million yen per kilometre, and the embankment section (40 kilometres in length) 800 million yen per kilometre. The total construction cost, including electrical facilities and rolling stock, may be estimated at about 100,000 million yen.

Assuming that each train will consist of sixteen coaches, which is technically feasible, that each train will be equipped with 1,700 seats, and that trains will be operated at three-minute intervals, the transport capacity of the new railway can be estimated at 34,000 passengers per hour.

A new residential city to be served by such a railway should house about 300,000 people. It is assumed that one in four, i.e. 75,000 people, will be workers, of which 80 per cent or 60,000 will commute to the C.B.D. This railway is capable of carrying this number of commuters in less than two hours.

This assumes that the city is organized in a circle around the railroad station with a radius of 3·3 kilometres. This means it will take an hour to walk on foot from the circumference, and, assuming all commuters travel by bus, and that about sixty people be carried on one bus, 500 buses will be enough to transport 30,000 people to the station in one hour.

The scale of 300,000 population is much larger than the other new urban satellite cities already built around the world. England has built new towns of 50,000–80,000, and Stockholm's one city of 100,000 includes a number of suburbs. Even Senri New Town near Osaka has only a final target of 150,000. But, as the area of Japan is very small, a scale of 300,000 can be considered almost inevitable, and Tama New Town and the New Garden City near Tokyo are already planned to about this scale.

A city of about 300,000 can provide independent cultural facilities, amusement facilities, health facilities, and good quality higher education.

However, if the total construction cost were to be borne by a single 300,000-person city, the financial burden on each citizen would be too much, and at the same time, the commuting fare per person per trip would inevitably become 190 yen, or 8,000 yen per person per month. Therefore, something needs to be done to alleviate these burdens.

As the travelling time would only be thirty minutes, the carrying capacity of trains could be increased by adopting a less spacious seating arrangement, such as can be seen in J.N.R.'s regular commuter trains, and allowing some 25 per cent for additional standing passengers. The carrying capacity could thus be doubled. If two

Figure 3. Diagram of twin cities, each of 300,000 population.

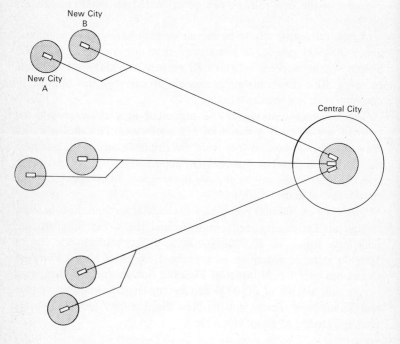

cities, each with 300,000 inhabitants, instead of only one, were to be served by this railway, as shown in Figure 3, the fare per trip per person could be reduced to 95 yen, or 4,000 yen per month of commuting. This amount would not be unreasonably high for the ordinary working-class people.

Then, what would a city of 600,000 be like? Considered only from the transportation point of view, it would be much better than linking two cities of 300,000. But a city of 600,000 must be on a much larger scale. Its radius will be 4·4 kilometres, and it will no longer be a residential city, but a metropolitan city, with central congestion, air pollution, and a railroad problem. From this wider point of view, it seems that two cities of 300,000 are greatly preferable.

Raising railway construction funds is no easy task. However, we must not ignore the fact that the value of land will rise tremendously (tens of times in some cases) once a railway service is commenced, and that landowners will make a huge profit on account of this.

This kind of profit is a form of unearned increment caused by public action. If it were to be returned by the landowners to a central fund, construction of railways would become easier and social equity could thereby be realized at the same time. The Conference on Commodity Price Problems (an advisory organ for the Minister of Economic Planning) reported to the Minister on 31 May 1966:

Deliberation of comprehensive policies is an urgent matter for the problem of land prices. Your Conference considers that so long as an increase of land prices is admitted to be the result of public investment by transportation industries and others, the profit caused by the resultant development, which takes the form of an increase of land prices, should be returned to the subject of public investment (transportation industries and others) which is the creator of that profit, and that, if the profit were to be returned to its creator, a rise of land prices by speculation would be restrained and this system would be effective in the stabilization of land prices.

Now, therefore, your Conference will request:

1. That the Government should make immediate study of a system whereby sale of land in any special districts is required to be made only through the medium of a public organ, after generalizing the system of land utilization, and further:

2. That the Government should revise the existing tax system or the

system to levy the share from the beneficiaries, and thereby make it possible to return the profit caused by development to the subject of public investment such as transportation industries and others.

At present, the price of land in Tokyo within thirty minutes (10–15 kilometres radius) of the C.B.D. is well over 100,000 yen per *tsubo*. In this fact lies the definite advantage of the plan at issue. It will be far more economical, even including the cost of new railway construction, to develop a residential area at 60–70 kilometres from the C.B.D. By this plan, land can be offered to people at 30,000 yen per *tsubo* – an amount within the reach of an average citizen – allowing them to commute to the C.B.D. conveniently.

The Land Price Control Measure, referred to above, involves a revision in the method for determining the prices of land as specified by the current Land Expropriation Law. The current law provides that the prices of land for expropriation shall be those in effect 'at the time the expropriation permission is granted'. It is deemed necessary, however, that this principle should be modified, as is the case in many countries of the world, to 'the prices in effect prior to the granting of this permission', i.e. prices that are not affected by knowledge that a project is in need of the land in question. If these developments could be accomplished, the residents both of suburban and city areas would be provided with better environmental amenities than at present.

45. Images of the Future Urban Environment

KENZO TANGE

Although it would be meaningless, even if it were possible, to draw the ultimate picture of the Japanese Archipelago, I believe that the country will advance towards a higher level of organic composition. In this connection, it seems to me that a necessary condition to the maintenance of organic life is the establishment of a rapid, smooth, and well-balanced system of links among and between areas of various sizes: the city blocks, the urban districts, the regional districts. I do not only mean the physical area, but the organizations that exist within these districts and the functions which these organizations perform. I am thinking of both physical movement coupling and informational coupling, but I am primarily interested in the informational coupling, since it seems to me that in contemporary Japanese civilization its control mechanism has only just begun to form.

By control mechanism, I do not mean an organization of the elite in a small number functioning as the administrative nucleus. What I have in mind is a large and growing organization of brain power, joined by dynamic informational links, dedicated to the advance of Japanese civilization and to cultural creation, and flourishing in an atmosphere of freedom and constant evolution. I conceive of the city of contemporary times as a physical expression of such an organization. As such, I think the city must be endowed with freedom, with diversity, with mobility, and with choice of contact.

Present official thinking favours the satellite system pattern, in which each great urban region would have a nuclear city of, say, 10,000,000, surrounded by satellite cities with populations ranging from 500,000 to 1,000,000 (it has not been too long since satellite cities were conceived of in terms of 50,000 or 60,000 inhabitants). If urban regions of this type were actually to exist, information links between the city and the satellites and between satellite and satellite would have to assume the complicated crisscross pattern that one might see in a cut diamond – a pattern which in terms of nervous systems, is to be observed only in the most primitive organisms. This would prevent the development of high-level informational coupling, and would lead to a division of the country into distinct sectors, each centred, both physically and politically, around a metropolis-type nucleus (Figure 1). The whole concept is opposed to the development of the nation as a single highly developed organism.

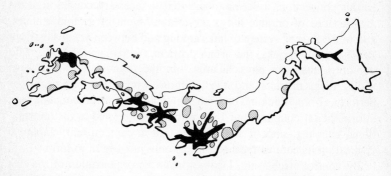

Figure 1. The Japanese archipelago, seen from the metropolis concept.

It seems to me that if the present competition between the Tokyo and Osaka regions continues, there is little question but that the bulk of the newcomers will aim at Tokyo. If this happens, there will develop a hierarchy of satellite cities in the vicinity of the capital forming a super-metropolis of 60,000,000–70,000,000 people. This would mean a fantastic centripetal force pressing in the centre of the system, and it is difficult to imagine a spatial structure that would enable Tokyo to stand up under this pressure.

I formerly published a suggested program entitled 'Plan for Tokyo, 1960'.[1] The basic idea of that plan was to convert the city's present structure, which is closed and centripetal, into a linear structure, which would be open and susceptible to any amount of expansion. I proposed, in other words, to replace the present civic centre of the city with a civic axis which could be lengthened at either end as necessary.

As one possible pattern for this type of reconstruction, I prepared a model in which the civic axis began at the present centre of town and stretched out across Tokyo Bay. The idea behind the plan was a repudiation of the present system of centripetal satellite cities radiating out over the whole Kanto plain. Obviously, even if the central part of the city assumed an open, linear form, there would be little improvement so long as this was surrounded by a much larger circular structure of centre-seeking satellites. It was essential that the axis break through this confinement into open territory, and I suggested expansion across the bay as a possible line of development.

It would appear, however, that in the natural course of development, the lines of connection along the Tokyo–Nagoya–Osaka strip are gradually breaking through administrative divisions and overcoming the traditional atmosphere of competition that has divided the three great cities. I have therefore come to believe that the strengthening of links along the Tokaido strip could become vital in the conversion of the Japanese nation as a whole into a higher organic entity.

The opening of a throughway between Osaka and Nagoya has greatly strengthened the connection between those two cities. In the near future there are to be two more vastly important high-speed highways: one running down the coast from Tokyo to Nagoya and connecting with the Osaka–Nagoya highway, and the other running down through central Honshu from Tokyo to Kyoto and Osaka. These roads will certainly create still stronger bonds between the three cities.

The present Osaka–Nagoya highway has four lanes and a daily capacity of 30,000 cars in each direction. The coastal Tokyo–Nagoya highway is to have six lanes with a daily capacity of from 40,000 to 50,000 cars in each direction. Allowing two persons to each vehicle, this highway will make possible a feedback of 60,000–100,000 persons between Tokyo and Osaka daily. Adding for bus transportation and subtracting for truck transport, it seems likely that about this number of people will actually be moving between the two cities each day – each of them forming a part of a great informational coupling.

Even more epoch-making is the new railway trunk line between Tokyo and Osaka, which was opened in 1964. The old railway line along the Tokaido carried 150 trains daily each way, with a capacity of about 1,000 persons each. This made possible a flow of about 150,000 persons between Tokyo and Osaka every day. The new line had only thirty trains daily at the beginning, but this was increased to fifty in October 1965, and it is probable that the number will increase to 100 within a few years. This will add 100,000 persons going each way from Tokyo to Osaka per day.

When the Tokyo–Nagoya highway is completed, it will take from five to six hours by car to make the trip from Tokyo to Osaka. At present, trains on the new trunk line require three hours for the journey, but it is thought that within a few years the time will be reduced to two and a half hours. Such speeds will mean a tremendously high rate of exchange of personnel between the two cities. In effect, the Tokyo–Osaka strip is already on the verge of becoming a Tokaido megalopolis in which people can commute from one end to the other in a single day.

I foresee a growth of the sort indicated in Figure 2, which contains two great parallel lines of force, one running from Mito through Tokyo, Nagoya, Nara, and Osaka to Tokushima (Tokaido), and the other running from Utsunomiya through Tokyo, Nagoya, Kyoto, and

Figure 2. The Japanese archipelago, seen from the megalopolis concept.

Osaka to Okayama (Central highway and Nagoya–Osaka highway).

The two lines will form the major structure of the Tokaido mega-lopolis and at the large centres, Tokyo and Osaka, and the corridor cities, Nagoya, Toyohashi, Hamamatsu, and Shizuoka-Shimizu, some branch lines will stretch out towards the sea-coast. This whole structure reminds us of a spine and its ribs.

This general plan is very different from the metropolis concept charted in Figure 1. Instead of a number of circles, each of which is directed towards its own centre, there would be a long belt with forces of flow moving back and forth along its length. The great centres at Tokyo, Nagoya, and Osaka would not disappear, but their mutual interrelationship would be more important than their independent features. There would doubtless be other smaller centres along the axis, but the axis itself would link all the centres, large and small, into a single organic entity. This is the vital feature of the plan.

We may consider the various architectural works as the leaves, and the transportation and communications facilities as the trunk of a great urban tree. The trunk might be called the infra-structure, and the leaves, the element structure.

Until the dawn of modern times, there was not anything in cities except streets and buildings, and the buildings were lined up along the streets. When railroads came into being, everybody realized that it was senseless to have houses built along the railroad tracks, and stations were erected at important points. There developed a new urban relationship between the station and near-by architectural clusters. When people began to drive about the streets in automobiles, however, no one seems to have noticed at first what an unnatural situation the new vehicles created. It took quite a long time for people to see that without parking space, it would be impossible to preserve the connection between streets and buildings, and it was not until the appearance of throughways that we discovered the impossibility of building houses along roads. Now, however, we have come to see the need for an ordered progression from buildings to parking space to low-speed highway to high-speed highway.

Furthermore, parking spaces have been introduced into buildings and even the public roads themselves are finding their way into buildings. In large-scale structures, the elevators have taken on the characteristics of public roads, albeit vertical ones. There has arisen a need for a direct link between, say, the twentieth floor of one building and the twentieth floor of the next building over, with the result that there are signs of the development of three-dimensional traffic grids in the air. People are seriously discussing the erection of spatial cities. All of this signifies that we are faced with the necessity of working out completely new means of linking the infra-structure with the element structure.

Man has a tendency to cling to the ground, but there are limits to the compactness that can be achieved when man actually lives on the ground, and anyway natural ground tends to hinder, rather than promote, the construction of the facilities needed in contemporary buildings. Planners, therefore, have developed the concept of man-made ground, and we are in the process of creating methods whereby such land, replete with 'topographical' variety, can serve as an infra-structure within or upon which people can construct high-density element structures.

NOTES

1. Kenzo Tange, 'Plan of Tokyo, 1960', *The Japan Architect*, April 1961, pp. 8–38; *Ekistics* 69, pp. 9–19.

Index